CARL.

THE ILLUSTRATED ENCYCLOPEDIA OF
HOW ANIMALS LIVE

THE ILLUSTRATED ENCYCLOPEDIA OF

HOW ANIMALS LIVE

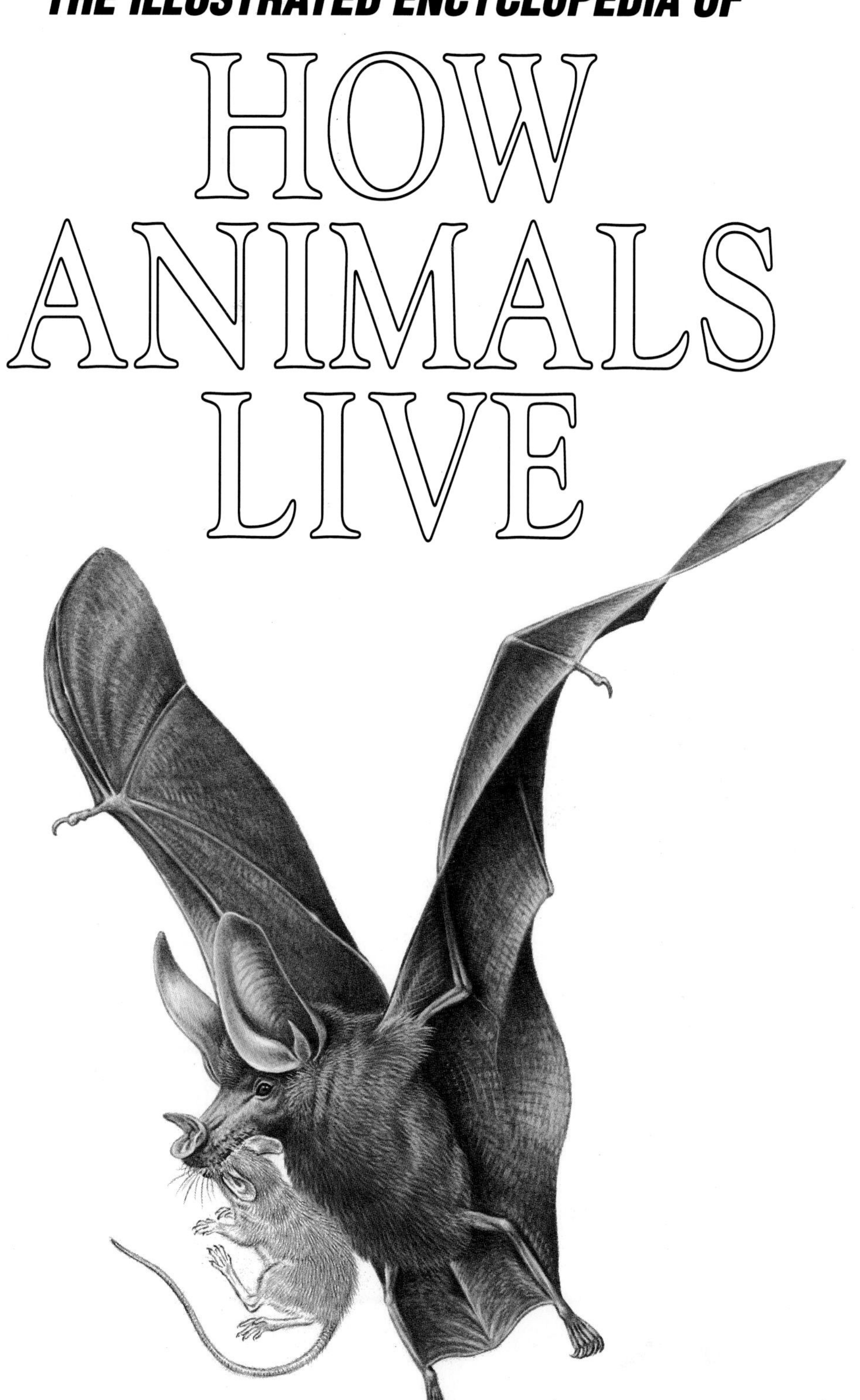

ANDROMEDA

THE ILLUSTRATED ENCYCLOPEDIA
OF HOW ANIMALS LIVE

Consultant Editor: Andrew Branson
Managing Editor: Lionel Bender
Art Editor: Ben White
Designers: Malcolm Smythe, Ben White
Text Editors: David Burn, Angela Royston, John Stidworthy
Production: Clive Sparling

Media conversion and typesetting:
Peter MacDonald and Partners and Brian Blackmore

Planned and produced by:
Andromeda Oxford Ltd
11–15 The Vineyard, Abingdon,
Oxfordshire OX14 3PX

ISBN 1 871869 13 7

Published in Great Britain by
Andromeda Oxford Ltd
This edition specially produced for
Selectabook Ltd

Origination by Alpha Reprographics Ltd, England

Printed in Hong Kong by Dai Nippon Ltd

Authors:
Dougal Dixon
Robin Kerrod
John Stidworthy

CONTENTS

INTRODUCTION

The planet Earth, with its equitable atmosphere and varied land- and seascapes, is unique in the Solar System in supporting a vast array of life forms. All are dependent directly or indirectly on the ability of plants to convert the sun's rays into energy which they can use for growth. The complex web of interrelationships between animals and plants and between animals themselves means that we are all reliant upon each other. For this reason, it is important for us to understand and appreciate the biology of other animals: ultimately our well-being and survival is inextricably bound up with theirs.

Animals range from microscopic creatures to gigantic whales, from slow-moving slugs to acrobatic monkeys and from flower-like sea-anemones to high-flying aerial swifts. Defining an animal is more difficult than it might seem. They cannot generate their own energy – unlike plants – but need to take in nutrients containing energy. In general, animals are living organisms that breathe, move about, feed and breed to produce more of their kind. But there are many exceptions. Adult bryozoans (moss animals) do not move about – they are stuck to a rock or piece of seaweed. Mayflies, when they reach adulthood, have no mouths and do not feed, surviving for a few short hours simply to breed.

Classification

In order to describe the animal kingdom it is important to be able to group similar types of animal together. Over the past three centuries, scientists have devised a way of classifying animals which is generally accepted through the world. The basic unit that is used is called the species. For example, all tigers in the world belong to a single species – the tiger. Tigers vary in size and colour from region to region but they are all able to breed together and produce fertile offspring. Whilst different species of animal can interbreed, their offspring would be infertile.

Similar species are put together in larger groups. These are known as genera (singular: genus). Lions, tigers, leopards and jaguars are put together in one genus. The common name for this genus is the 'big cats', the scientific name is *Panthera*. This, together with the specific name for the tiger, *tigris*, provides the full scientific name for the tiger – *Panthera tigris*. Genera, in turn, are grouped together into a larger unit known as a family which are then grouped together to form orders. Orders are combined into classes and finally into phyla. Therefore the tiger *Panthera tigris* belongs to the family Felidae, Order Carnivora, Class Mammalia, Subphylum Vertebrata, Phylum Chordata. This scientific grouping of animals means that scientists from any part of the world can tell which animal is being discussed.

Common names can cause confusion. For example, an Australian talking about a robin may be referring to the Scarlet Robin, *Petroica multicolor* (a member of a family related to flycatchers). In North America the robin is a member of the thrush family, *Turdus migratorius*, and in Britain the robin is also a member of the thrush family but is the smaller *Erithacus rubecula*. They all have a red breast, however they all are very different species of birds.

How Many Animal Species?

We do not know how many kinds of animals there are. So far, almost one and a half million animal species have been named. New ones are discovered regularly – particularly in tropical forests and remote mountain ranges. Currently it is thought that there are about a million species of insect in the world, but recent techniques such as 'fogging', where scientists spray insecticide into the rain forest canopy and collect the fallen insects, have meant that some people now think that we could have underestimated the number of insect species by as much as ten times. There are about 9,000 species of birds, 4,000 species of mammals, and 37,000 species of molluscs (the phylum that includes snails, slugs and oysters). Some phyla are very small. There are only about 260 species of lampshells, or brachiopods, which are ancient sea-dwelling creatures rather like clams.

The Illustrated Encyclopedia of How Animals Live is divided into three main themes. The first looks at the biology of the animal kingdom. Within this, there are sections on the constituents of an animal cell and how the cells are arranged into tissues and organs. Another section deals in turn with the main body functions and organ systems of animals, explaining what they do and how they work. It discusses the senses used by animals. You can discover, for example, how certain types of spider use vibrations to detect their mate. There is also a section on how different animal species reproduce and grow.

The second theme of the encyclopedia is on animal behaviour. This part includes sections on finding food and feeding, living in groups, aggression and defence, migration, courtship and how animals communicate to one another. The song of a male bird, for example, can be interpreted in a number of diffent ways depending on who hears it. There are also sections on instinct, intelligence and learning, animals as builders and natural rhythms such as hibernation.

In the 20th century, the study of animal behaviour has expanded into an important branch of biology. This type of study is known as ethology. Some of the work in ethology has given an insight into human behaviour. We can see that although we are very complex animals and can do things other animals cannot, such as play chess, some aspects of our behaviour are directly comparable to those seen in our wild ancestors. The use of lip and face muscles to express feelings is a good example of this.

The third theme of the encyclopedia is on ecology – the study of living organisms in relation to their surroundings. This part of the encyclopedia includes sections on the world distribution of different habitats and the types of animal and plant communities that live within them. This ranges from the wildlife of land habitats, (forests and deserts, grasslands and tundra) to aquatic habitats, including rivers, lakes, wetlands and oceans. The encyclopedia finishes with a look at the wildlife of the new urban environments.

Ecologists – people who study ecology – examine the natural world at a number of different levels. For example, they study whole populations of a single species, individuals of several species, communities of living organisms and large ecosystems that cover vast areas of continents and oceans. It is often only by understanding the complex nature of the relationships between all the various elements that the whole system can be understood. For example, some tropical rain forest trees rely on the foraging of fruit bats for pollination. If the bats – which may roost some distance away – were wiped out, a vital link in the forest cycle would be lost and the whole ecosystem could die. Often even subtle changes to one part of a system can have devastating consequences elsewhere. The Large Blue butterfly has become extinct in many places, not because of being collected by humans but because the grassy slopes where it used to fly are no longer grazed as intensively. This has meant that the grasses have become more rank. They are now therefore unsuitable for a species of ant vital to the survival of the Large Blue butterfly's caterpillars.

Each article throughout the encyclopedia is devoted to a specific aspect of the subject and starts with a short scene-setting story that highlights one or two of the topics described. The main text then continues with details of the most interesting aspects, illustrating the discussion with specific examples. This encyclopedia explores the world of the animal kingdom, looking at the biology, behaviour and ecology of the astonishing variety of animals that populate the Earth from the lowliest single-celled protozoa to the mighty herds of mammals that roam the African plains. Illustrated with beautiful photographs and stunning diagrams, *The Illustrated Encyclopedia of How Animals Live* introduces the reader to the exciting and colourful world of animals in their habitats.

CELLS, TISSUES, ORGANS

A scientist looks down her microscope. She is studying how a sea urchin egg develops. As time goes on the single egg divides. Now it consists of two blobs joined together. Soon it is four, then eight, as it keeps dividing. Soon it is difficult to count how many blobs, or cells, it has divided into. The whole adult animal is made up of millions of these cells.

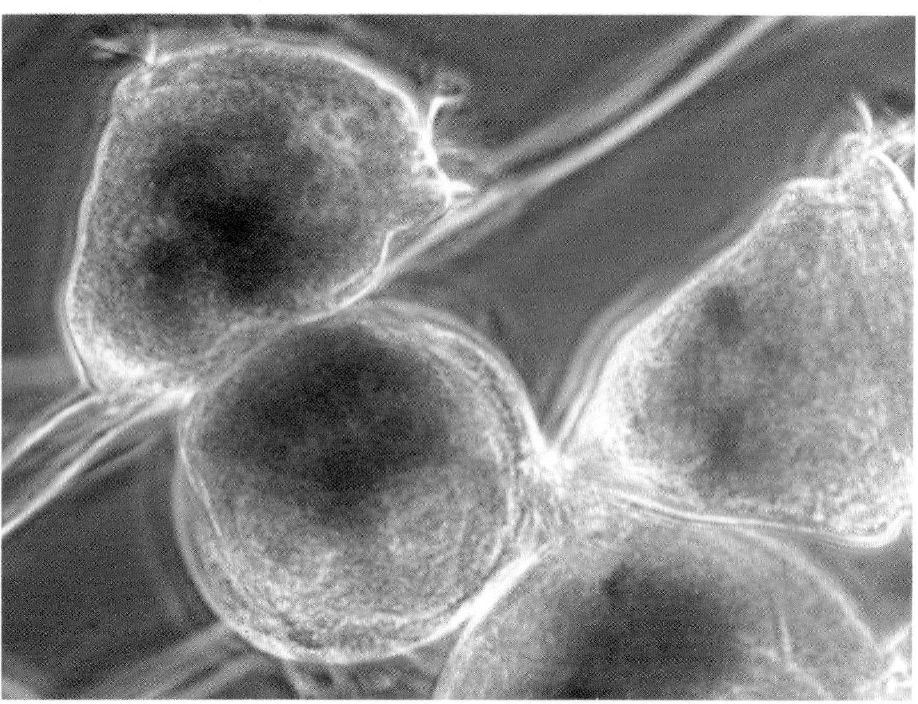

Cells are the basic building blocks of animals. (They also make up plants, fungi and other living things.) The simplest of animals, protozoans, each consist of only one cell.

Larger animals are built from many millions of cells. A human being, for example, consists of around 10 million million cells. These cells are not all the same. There are many different kinds that do different jobs. Nerve cells carry nerve signals. Muscle cells are long and thin, but they can shorten to help an animal move. Red blood cells carry oxygen in the blood. There are about 200 main kinds of cells in an animal such as a human.

THE SIZES OF CELLS

Apart from a few exceptions, cells are very small. The largest single-celled animals, protozoans, are about 2mm long, and the smallest about 1μm (one-thousandth of one millimetre) across. Microscopes are needed to study them in detail.

A typical cell in any multi-celled animal is 10 to 20μm across. Bigger animals have more cells than smaller ones. It is as though nature uses bricks of the same size, whether building a small house or a giant skyscraper.

A few highly specialized single cells are much larger, such as birds' eggs. Others are much smaller, for example the doughnut-shaped red blood cell which is only 7μm across and 2μm deep at its thickest.

INSIDE A CELL

The typical animal cell is surrounded by a thin, flexible "skin" called the cell membrane. Inside, a system of microtubules and microfilaments forms the cytoskeleton – the cell's internal "scaffolding". The cytoskeleton gives the cell its basic shape and helps it to change shape as it moves. It controls and channels the movements of all chemicals and substances inside the body of the cell.

There are also several recognizable structures inside a typical cell. These are known as organelles. Each of these does a specific job, as shown opposite. The nucleus contains the genetic instructions for building and maintaining the cell – and indeed, for building and running the whole animal (see page 76). A few very specialized cells, such as red blood cells, do not have a nucleus.

BREAKDOWN AND BUILD-UP

Cells need energy to live. Animals obtain their energy from the food they eat. This is either from plants or other animals. Chemicals in the food are

▲Animals like this amoeba carry out all life's functions in a single cell. They usually live in water, since they have no thick, protective cell wall like a plant cell, and so would soon dry out in air.

▼Animals such as these gemsbok, in Namibia, are made from billions of cells. Tiny contractions of the millions of muscle cells propel the whole animal at speeds of more than 50kph.

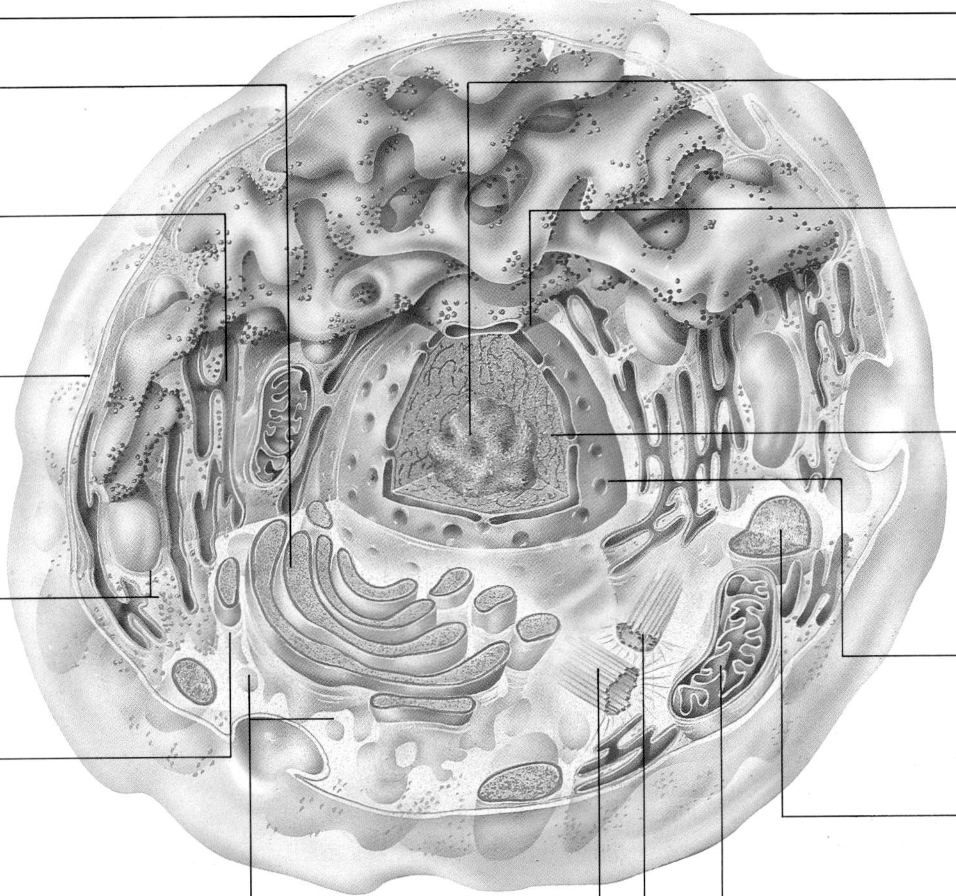

Golgi apparatus
Endoplasmic reticulum
Cell membrane
Ribosomes
Cytoplasm
Small vacuoles
Centrioles
Nucleolus
Nuclear envelope
Chromatin
Nucleus
Lysosome
Mitochondrion

Structure of a cell

This general diagram of an animal cell shows that it is not a mass of jelly, but has a complicated internal structure. Various organelles can be seen within. The main one is the nucleus, the control centre of the cell, which also houses the genetic information. It is surrounded by its nuclear envelope. Another, larger membrane surrounds the whole cell and forms its "skin". These membranes are not total barriers, but partial ones. They allow certain substances to pass through, such as nutrients on their way in, and wastes on their way out. The thin, clear fluid between the organelles is known as cytoplasm.

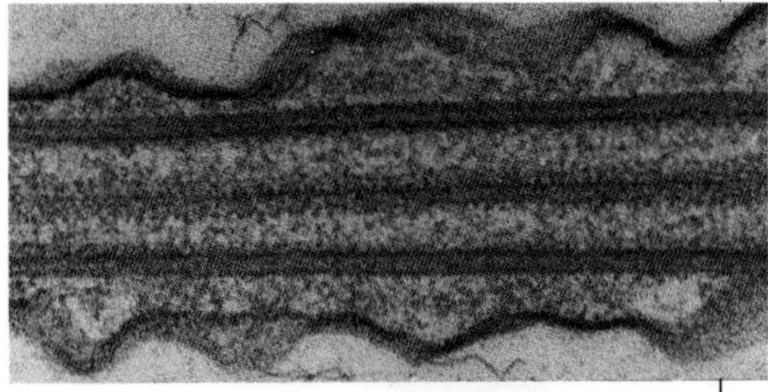
4

1
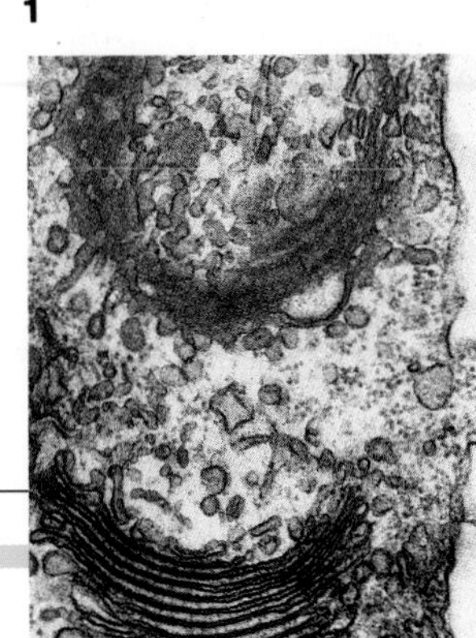
2
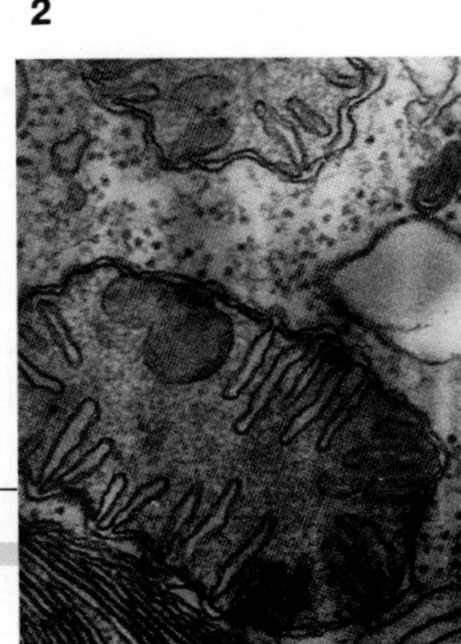
3
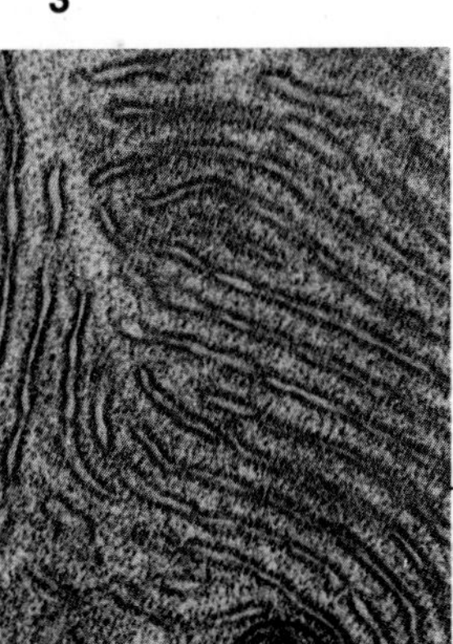

◄▲Organelles under the powerful electron microscope. Golgi bodies **(1)** make secretions such as mucus and digestive juices. Mitochondria **(2)**, the cell's "powerhouses", generate chemical energy from nutrients. Endoplasmic reticulum **(3)** makes proteins. Microtubules **(4)** form the cell's skeleton.

Cells and tissues

▲▼Nerve cells, or neurons, are long and thin, with many fine branches. They carry the tiny electrical signals that form nerve messages. The myelin sheath speeds the signals on their way along the main "wire", the axon. The photograph shows a network of mouse neurons.

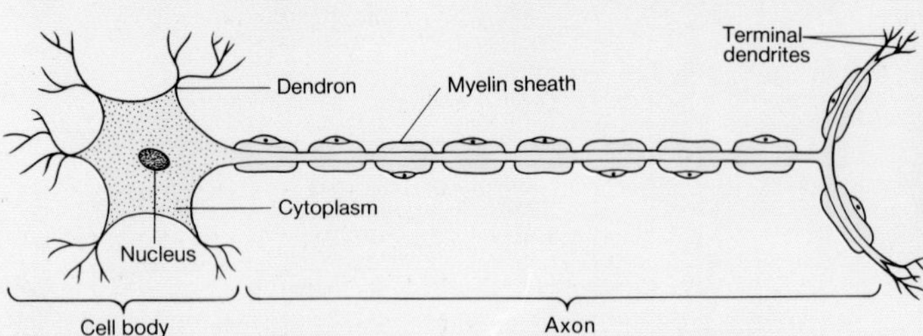

▼There are various forms of connective tissue, such as bone and cartilage. The photograph (below left) shows the circular pattern of human bone under the microscope. The diagram shows areolar tissue, a connective tissue made of cells and elastic fibres.

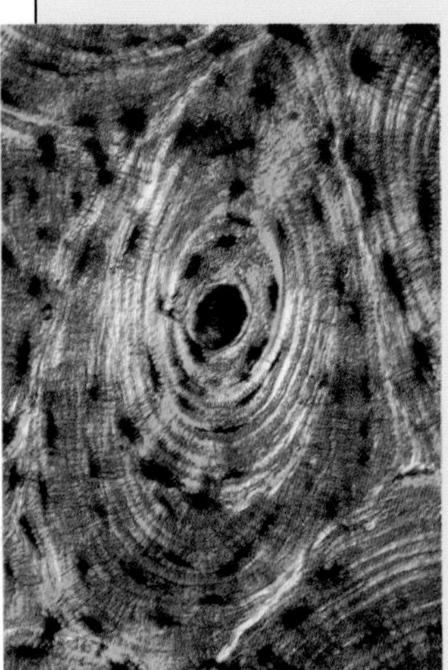

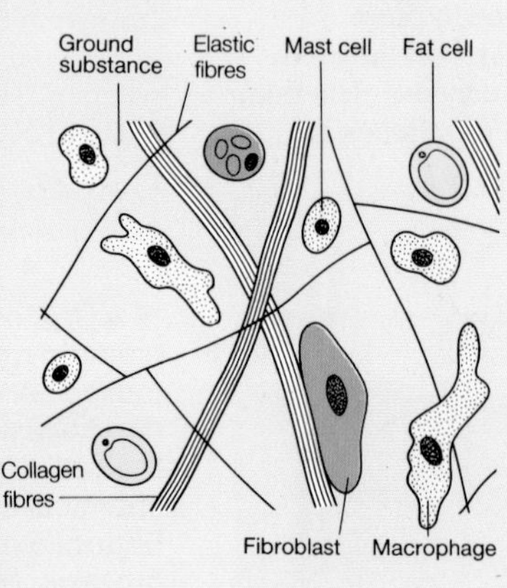

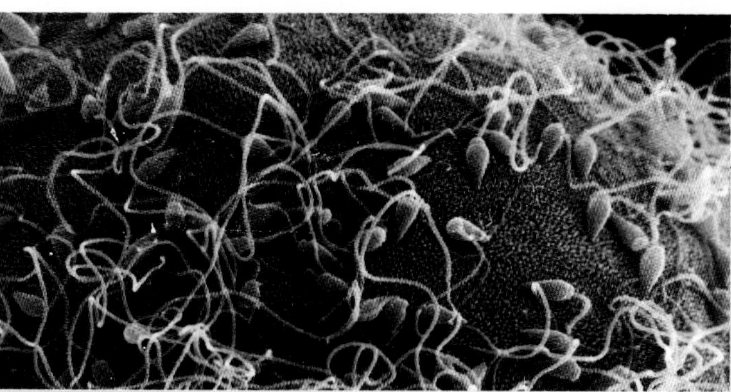

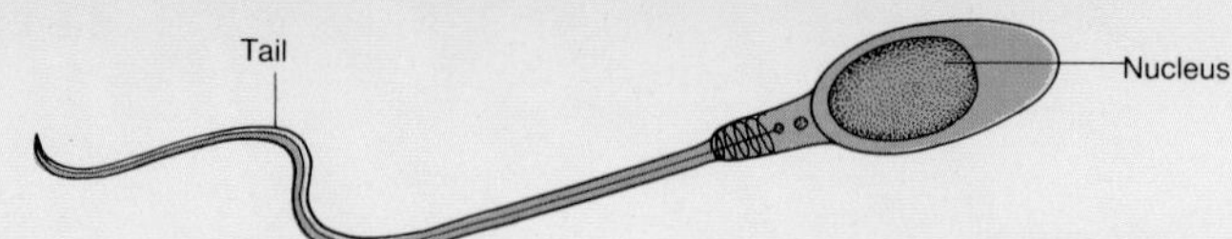

▲Sperm cells are the reproductive cells from the male organs. They are shaped like tadpoles, and the tail lashes to make the sperm swim towards the female egg. The photograph (top) shows swarms of sperm cells from a sea urchin surrounding an egg.

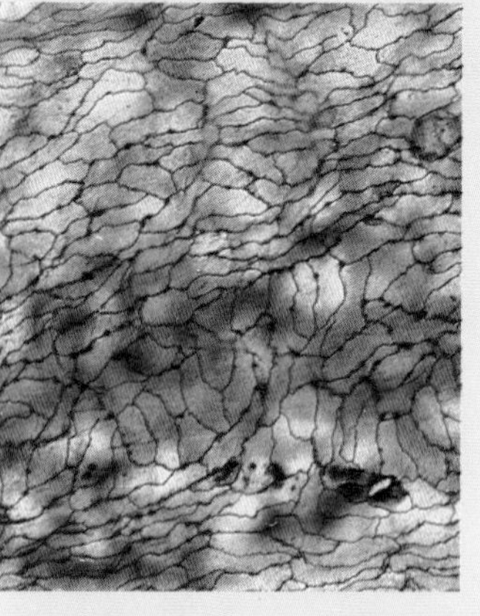

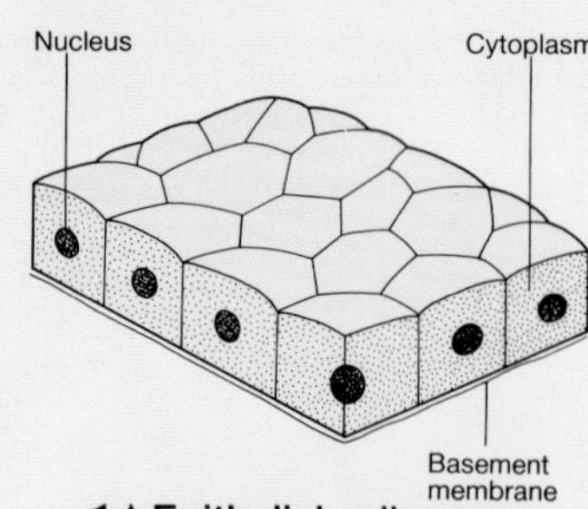

◀▲Epithelial cells cover many body parts, on both the outside and inside. They fit together like crazy-paving (left) or a brick wall (above).

▼Blood is a type of tissue, although it is in the form of a liquid. It contains several different kinds of blood cells. The red cells carry oxygen. The various types of white cells help to fight disease. The photograph (bottom) shows two white cells surrounded by red cells.

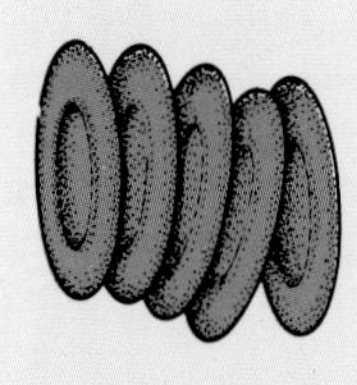

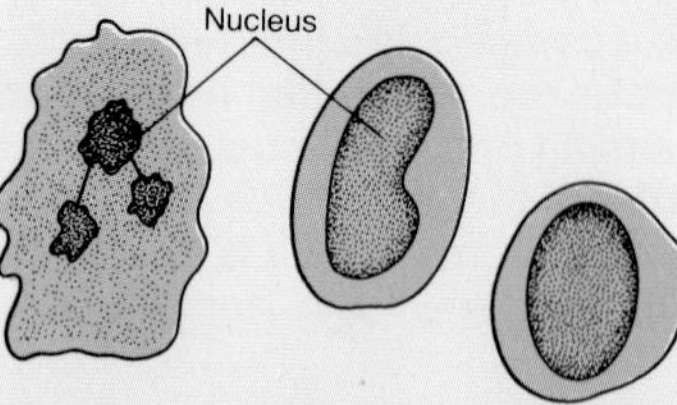

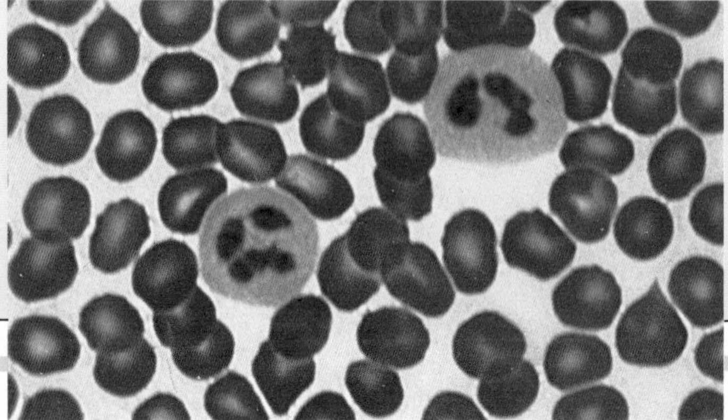

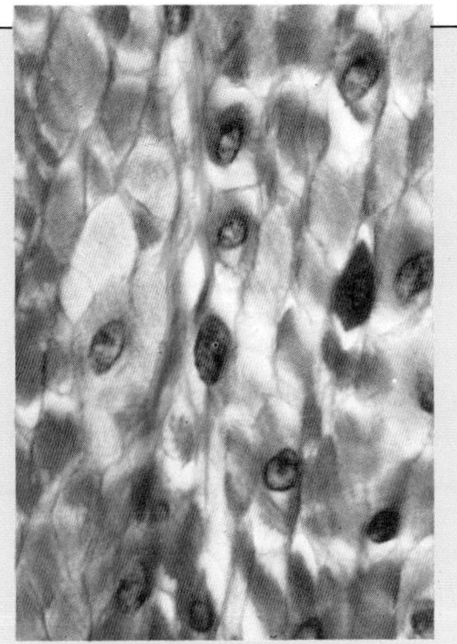

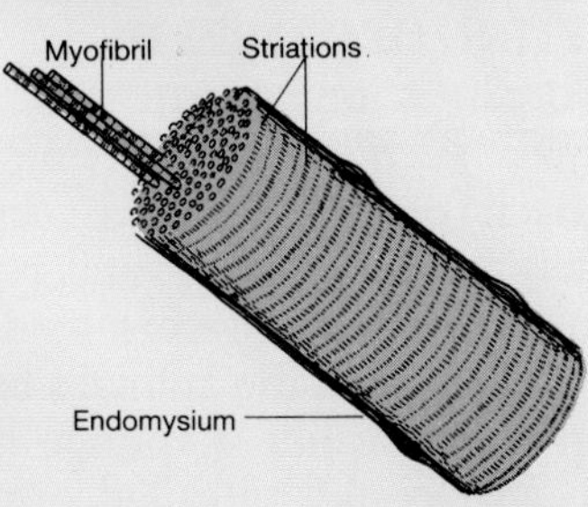

▲Muscle cells are bundled together in their thousands to make muscle fibres. The photograph (top) is of muscle cells from a cat's intestine.

broken down to release their energy. They also provide raw materials for building new cells and replacing old or worn-out parts. These changes occur as hundreds of chemical reactions that take place inside cells. These reactions are collectively known as the metabolism.

LIFE AND DEATH

Few cells live for long. A worm's intestinal cell lasts for a few days. A red blood cell has a life of about 3 months. A human bone cell might live for 25 years. In most animals, certain cells are specialized to multiply and form new cells, which replace the old, worn-out or damaged ones. A human skin cell lives for only about a month. It is formed in the multiplying group of cells at the base of the outer skin layer. It gradually passes outwards, becomes hardened and dies. It reaches the skin's surface, and is worn away. The rate of cell multiplication matches the rate of cell loss, so new cells are "born" at the right rate to replace those that "die".

A few cells, such as certain nerve cells, cannot multiply once the animal is fully developed, although they may be repaired if they are damaged.

JOINING FORCES

Similar cells are grouped together into tissues. For example, many long, thin muscle cells lie side by side to form muscle tissue. Many nerve cells, with their networks of branching "wires", are linked together into nerve tissue.

A tissue is specialized to carry out one or more functions. Epithelial tissue acts as a covering for many body parts, both inside and outside the animal. In a complex creature, such as a giraffe, it lines the inside of the mouth and throat, the airways down the windpipe and lungs, and the inside of the stomach, intestines and other digestive parts. It is usually made of cells that multiply at a fast rate, so replacing those cells which are rubbed off or die on the surface.

SUPER-CELLS

Muscle tissue is specialized to contract, or get shorter. The giant molecules inside it move past each other like ratchets, making the cells shorter. In fact muscle is slightly more complicated because its "cells" are actually "super-cells", formed from many individual cells joined together into one larger unit, with many nuclei.

PACKING TISSUES

A relatively simple type of multi-celled animal, such as a jellyfish, consists of only a few types of tissue. A more complicated animal has dozens of tissue types, including several kinds of connective tissues. These are the body's "packaging materials". They surround, support, separate and protect other parts. Their cells are not usually packed tightly together but

◀The ostrich's egg, before it starts to develop into a chick, is the largest example of a single cell. It weighs over 1.5kg and is 20cm long. Most of this is food stored as yolk, to feed the growing baby bird.

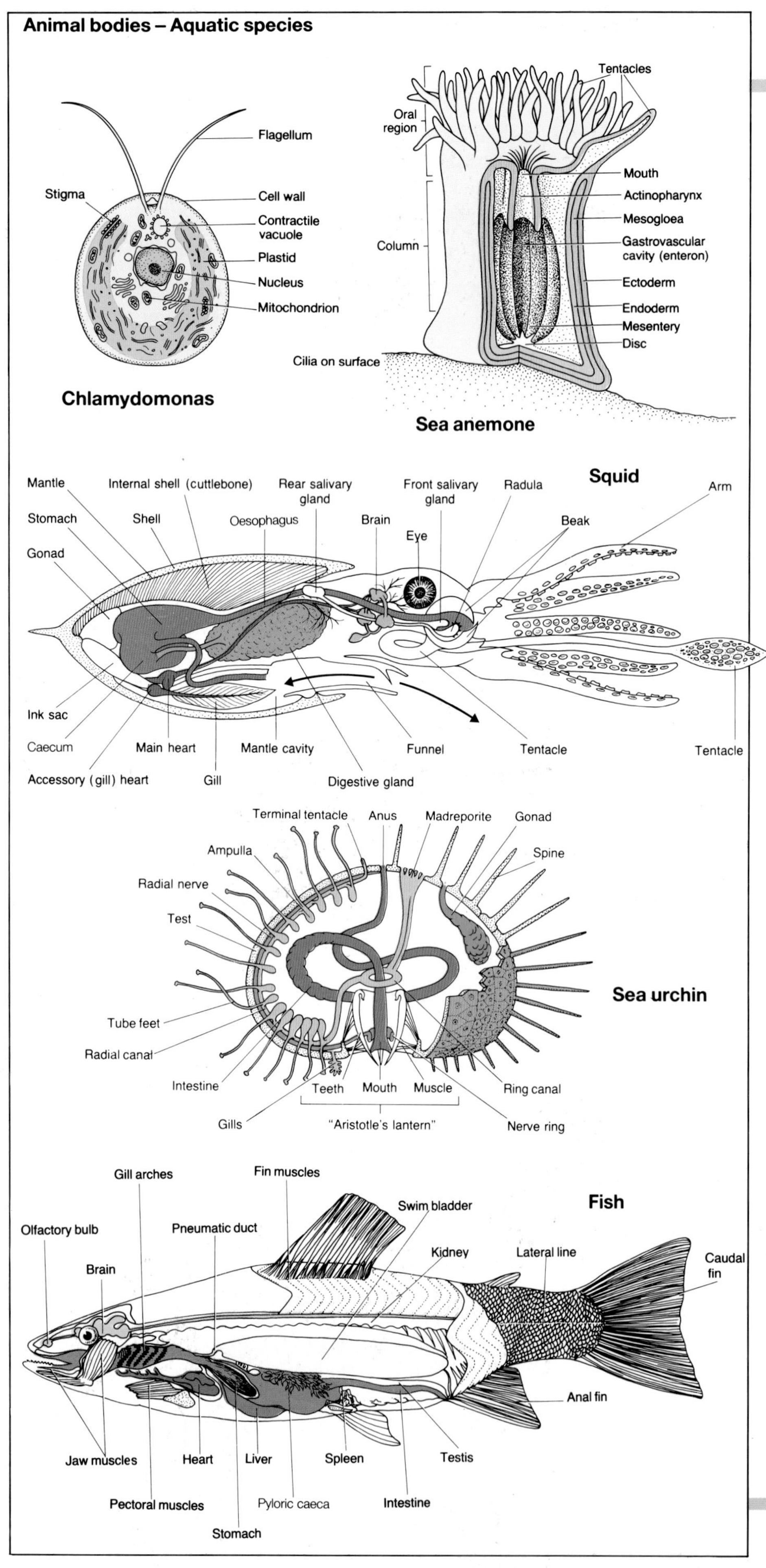

scattered about, embedded in a "background" substance known as the ground-tissue or matrix.

The different kinds of connective tissue have different types of cells and matrices. In areolar connective tissue there is a tangle of slender fibres with various cells dotted about. In adipose connective tissue some of the cells are swollen with blobs of fat. In fibrous connective tissue the fibres are much more numerous and arranged as bundles or sheets. Two other types of connective tissue are the bone and cartilage of the skeleton.

GETTING ORGANIZED

An organ is one main "part" of an animal, such as the brain, heart, stomach or kidney. Each organ is usually made up of several types of tissue that work together to do one important job in the animal's body. A simple animal like a sponge has no parts that could be called organs. A complicated animal such as a fish or bird has many organs.

The brain is the organ that controls and coordinates the whole body. The heart is a muscular organ that pumps blood. The stomach is a digestive organ that pulps food and dissolves it with powerful chemicals. The kidneys are filtering organs that remove waste substances from blood.

The same tissues can occur in different organs. For instance, the brain is chiefly nerve tissue, but also contains blood vessels and connective tissue. A muscle is mainly muscle tissue but it is also has blood vessels and controlling nerves, as well as connective tissue.

ALL SYSTEMS GO

The more complicated animals have organs that are linked together into

◄These diagrams show the main internal parts of different water animals. Chlamydomonas (top left) is a single cell. All the others are multi-celled and some have many different organs.

systems. A system is a group of organs that works together, to carry out one of the main functions of a "living thing" – for example its breathing, feeding, breeding, or excretion.

The circulatory system of a human is one example. It consists of the heart as the pump, the large blood vessels known as arteries and veins, the smaller blood vessels called capillaries, and the blood which flows continuously around the system.

Another example is the digestive system. Its organs vary from one kind of animal to another. In mammals such as ourselves it consists of a mouth for taking in food, a stomach for mashing it up and digesting it, a small intestine for the job of absorbing nutrients, and a large intestine for dealing with the left-over wastes.

Not all organs of a system are found near to each other in the body, or even joined to each other in an obvious way, as in the digestive system. In fact the circulatory system, and others such as the hormonal system and the nervous system, are spread throughout the body.

WHOLE ANIMALS

The first part of this encyclopedia looks at the way in which the vast variety of animals carry out the essentials of life. In small and simple creatures such as amoebas, everything goes on within a single cell. In large and complex creatures such as fish, frogs and mammals, there are hundreds of tissues, organized into many organs, which are grouped into a few main systems. There are many ways in which an animal's body can be organized. Each phylum is different. But the end result is the same: a fully functioning animal.

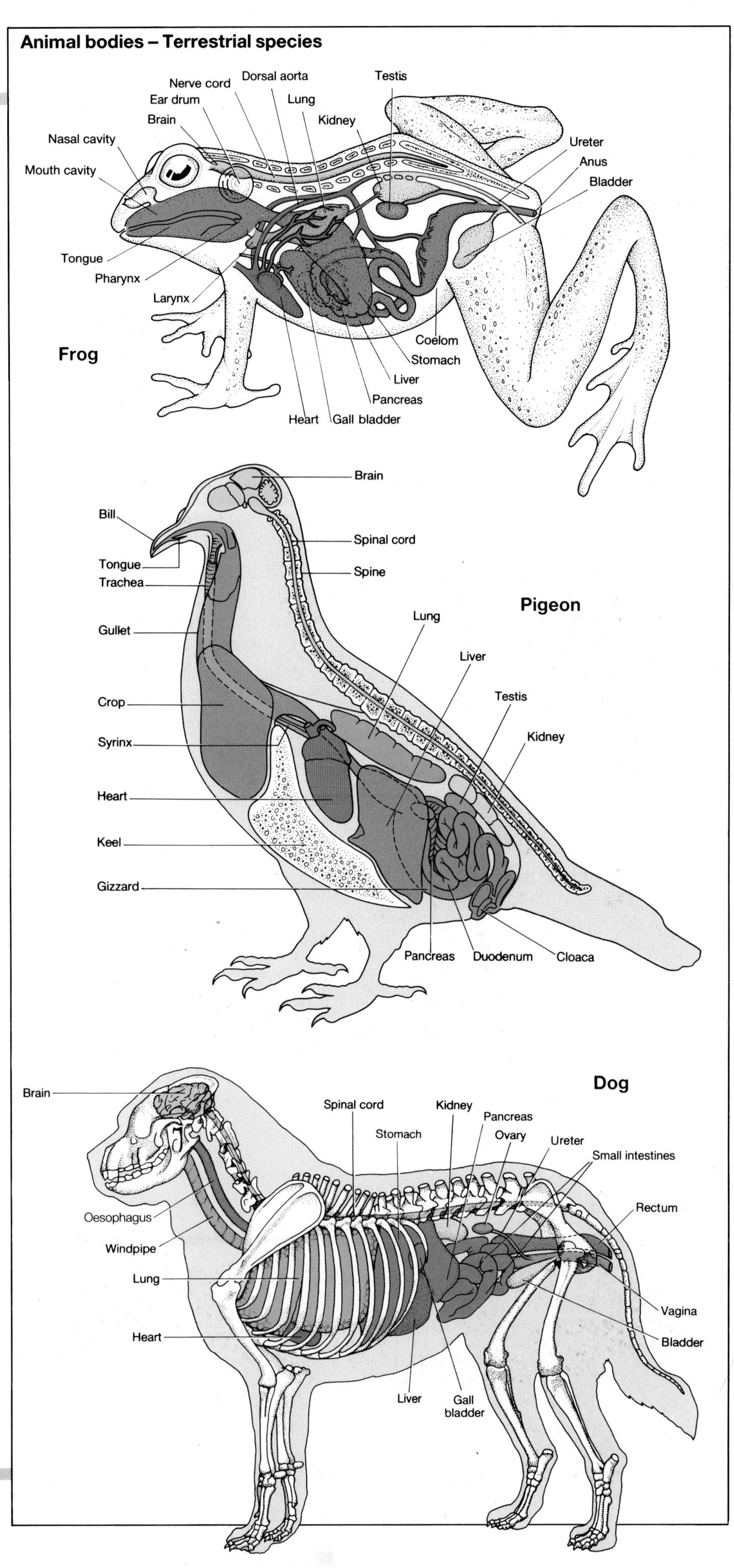

►The main internal organs of land-dwellers. Each has a heart to pump blood, lungs for breathing, and a skeleton made of bones. The digestive organs differ: a bird has a large crop to store food.

RESPIRATION

Hunting in the ocean depths, a hungry young Sperm whale comes upon its deadly enemy, a Giant squid. The two animals grapple, and the squid squirms as the whale tries in vain to seize it in sharp-toothed jaws. Soon the whale realizes its mistake, but the squid now holds it with powerful suckered arms. The whale begins to gasp – it needs air. But the squid hangs on, and the whale drowns.

Humans and many other animals take breathing for granted. We do not have to think about it. The movements of breathing happen automatically, even when we sleep. But what is breathing for, and how does it take place?

BODY CHEMISTRY

The chemical reactions inside an animal's body rely on a constant supply of energy. This energy is contained in food (page 22). But once inside the body, the food must be changed into a suitable form to power the various chemical reactions.

The usual way of doing this is to combine the energy-containing food with oxygen, in a series of chemical stages known as metabolic respiration. During the sequence, energy is transferred onwards to other chemical reactions and used. At the end there are leftover waste products such as carbon dioxide and water, which contain little or no energy.

Chemical reactions are happening all the time in a living thing. So a constant supply of oxygen is required. Oxygen as a gas makes up one-fifth of the air, and it is also dissolved in water. Extracting oxygen from air or water is therefore a vital part of staying alive.

SMALL AND SIMPLE

Oxygen does not stay still. It is always spreading around, "seeping" from places where it is concentrated to places where its levels are lower. This process is called diffusion.

The inside of a small and simple organism such as an amoeba has low oxygen levels, since it is always using up oxygen in respiration. Therefore new supplies of oxygen tend to pass into the amoeba's body from the water around it, through its very thin "skin". Diffusion is a slow process, but the amoeba's oxygen needs are very small, and its body is also very small. Diffusion is fast enough to keep pace.

As the oxygen near to the amoeba is used up, so more oxygen diffuses towards it from the surrounding water. The waste products from the amoeba, such as carbon dioxide, travel in the opposite direction. As their levels build up inside its body, they diffuse out through its skin.

PROBLEMS OF BEING BIG

The inside of a larger animal is also continually using up oxygen. But size brings several problems. One is that a bigger creature usually has a thick, protective covering, such as a fish's scales or a mammal's furry skin. Oxygen cannot pass easily through these coverings.

Another problem is that parts of a big animal are some distance from its outside. Oxygen would take too long to diffuse over such a distance. Also, larger animals use up more oxygen than tiny ones. As they do so, the air or water around them becomes oxygen-poor and "stale". Diffusion cannot work fast enough to bring in more oxygen from the surroundings and make the air or water oxygen-rich and "fresh" again.

BIGGER MEANS LESS

A small organism like an amoeba has a relatively large surface area ("skin" area) compared to the volume of its body. So there is plenty of surface through which oxygen can enter. Bigger animals have less surface area

▲Some air-breathing animals in water
Some animals breathe air, yet spend much or all of their time under water: King penguin (*Aptenodytes patagonicus*) **(1)**, the larva of a mosquito (*Culex* species) **(2)** and a damselfly (*Coenagrion* species) **(3)**, Yellow-bellied sea snake (*Pelamis platurus*) **(4)**, and Blue whale (*Balaenoptera musculus*) **(5)**.

►The European grayling. Just behind its eyes lie the bony opercula, the gill covers. Water enters the mouth, passes over the gills – where gas exchange takes place – then leaves via the gill slits.

▲Mudskippers spend much time in air. They hold water in their gill chambers, and regularly renew this from nearby pools. They also absorb oxygen from air through the mouth and throat lining.

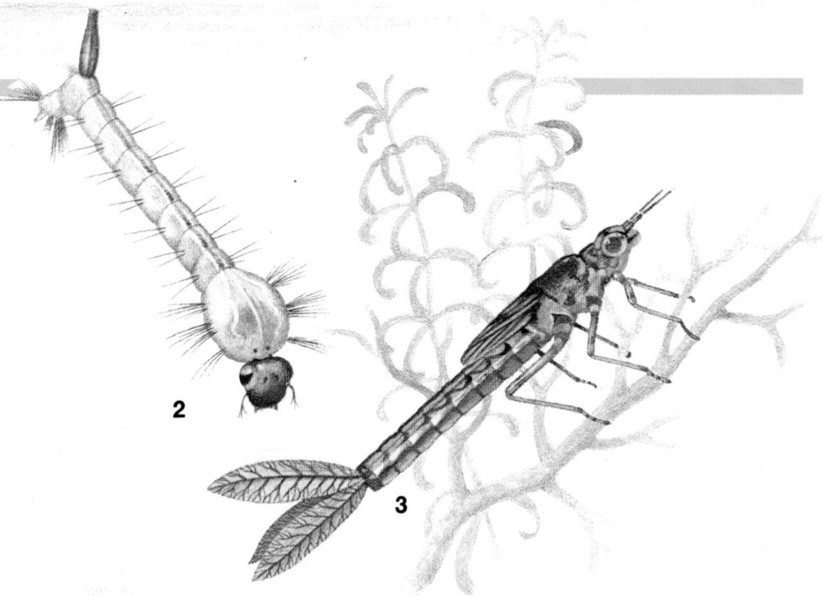

2

3

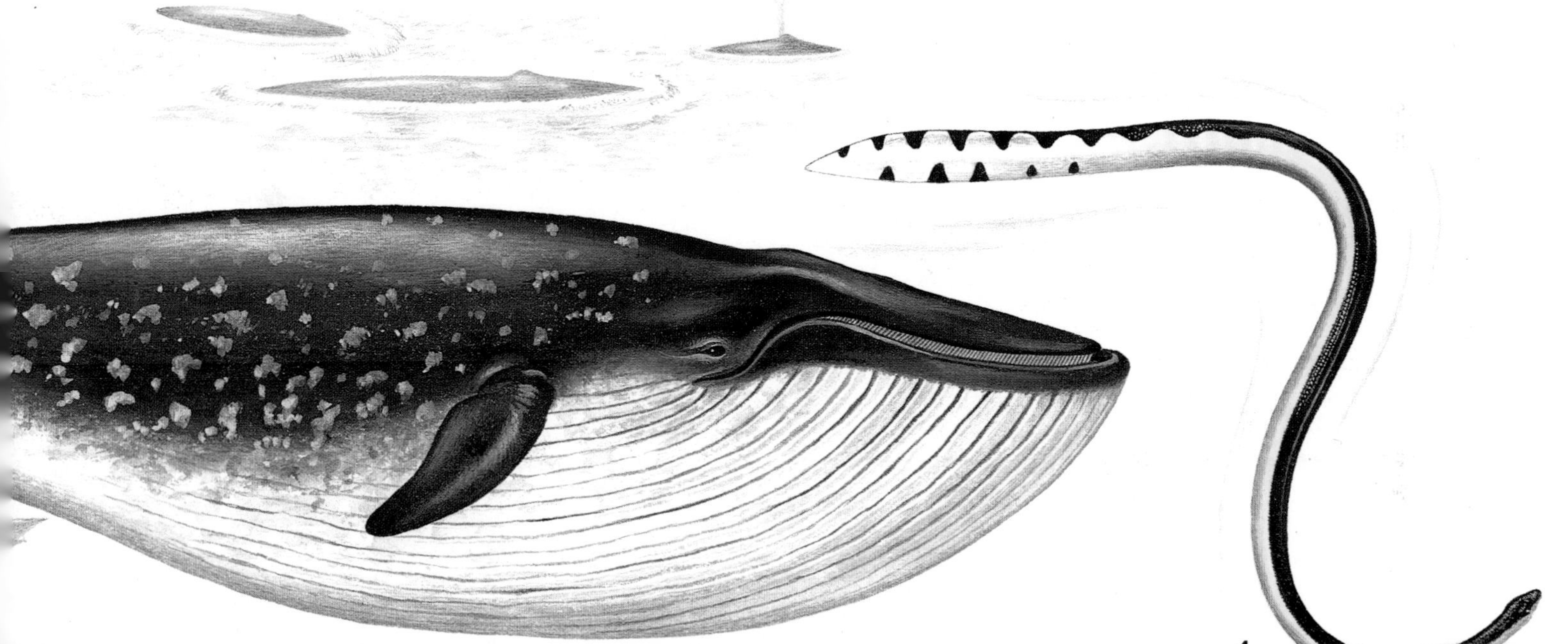

5

4

compared to their volume. Although their oxygen needs increase with size, the ability to absorb oxygen through that surface falls in proportion to their bulk.

GILLS AND LUNGS

For these reasons, larger animals have developed many different ways of getting the oxygen they need. Two examples are gills, which absorb oxygen dissolved in water, and lungs, which take in oxygen from the air. Inside the body, the oxygen is distributed by a circulatory system such as the blood network (see page 26). In order to replace stale, oxygen-poor air with a fresh supply, mammals such as ourselves, and birds and reptiles carry out the movements we call "breathing". Old air is blown out of the lungs, and new air is sucked in.

◀A Water spider in its "diving bell". It brings small air bubbles from the water surface trapped in its body hairs to add to its underwater store of air.

In bigger animals, as in the amoeba, waste carbon dioxide travels in the opposite direction, from the body out into the surroundings. Getting rid of carbon dioxide is just as important as obtaining oxygen, since if the carbon dioxide level builds up in the body, it acts as a poison. This is why the entire process is known as respiratory gas exchange – in effect, swopping carbon dioxide for oxygen.

FROM FLATWORMS TO FISH

Many small water-living animals are like the amoeba. They can absorb sufficient oxygen from the water, without the need for specialized body parts. Calculations show that most animals up to about 1mm in diameter can take in sufficient oxygen by diffusion alone. If larger, they need specialized parts for gas exchange.

Even so, some animals larger than 1mm still rely on simple diffusion. They usually have a body which is a series of thin, folded sheets or narrow fingers, as in sea anemones, or they have a very flat, leaf-like shape, as in flatworms. Then no part of the body is more than about 1mm from the surrounding water.

Most bigger water-dwellers have gills of some kind. These are outward expansions of the body surface with blood vessels just underneath. They vary in shape from simple cylinders or flaps, as in worms and starfish, to the

Obtaining oxygen

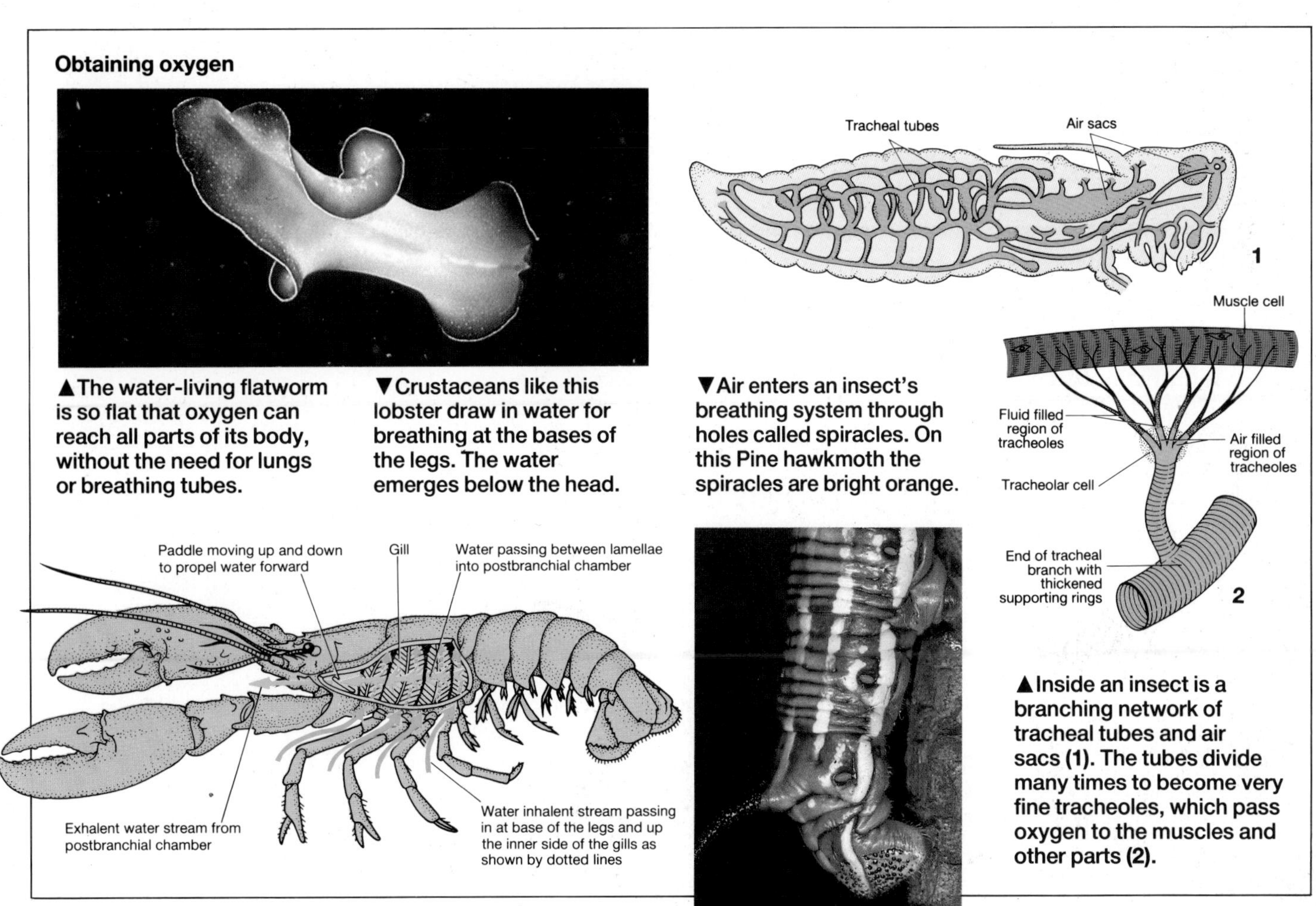

▲The water-living flatworm is so flat that oxygen can reach all parts of its body, without the need for lungs or breathing tubes.

▼Crustaceans like this lobster draw in water for breathing at the bases of the legs. The water emerges below the head.

▼Air enters an insect's breathing system through holes called spiracles. On this Pine hawkmoth the spiracles are bright orange.

▲Inside an insect is a branching network of tracheal tubes and air sacs (1). The tubes divide many times to become very fine tracheoles, which pass oxygen to the muscles and other parts (2).

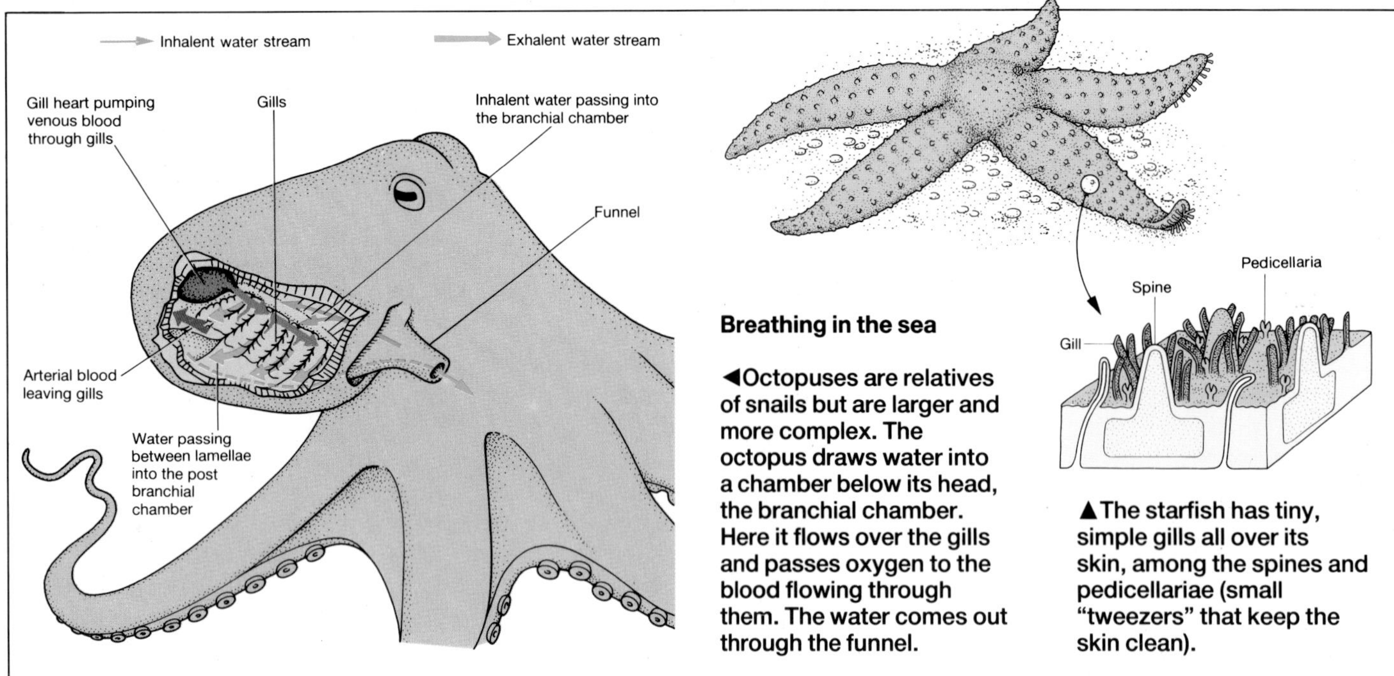

Breathing in the sea

◀Octopuses are relatives of snails but are larger and more complex. The octopus draws water into a chamber below its head, the branchial chamber. Here it flows over the gills and passes oxygen to the blood flowing through them. The water comes out through the funnel.

▲The starfish has tiny, simple gills all over its skin, among the spines and pedicellariae (small "tweezers" that keep the skin clean).

complicated feathery gills found in crabs, fish and some molluscs.

BREATHING UNDER WATER

Delicate, feathery gills, packed with fine blood vessels, are likely to get damaged unless they are well protected. In little animals such as the young tadpole, this is not too hazardous. The gills are fluffy-looking tufts on either side of the head, but they are very small, and they soon shrink away as the tadpole's lungs develop for breathing air.

Bigger creatures have more of a problem. In the octopus, the gills are safe inside the main space in the body, known as the mantle cavity. In most fish, they are under a hard, bony flap known as the operculum on the side of the "neck". In a crab, they are along the sides of the body, under the hard outer shell.

However, enclosing and protecting the gills means that water can no longer flow freely past them. So these types of animals have pumping systems that force a flow of fresh, oxygen-rich water past their gills. Water is a dense, "syrupy" substance compared to air. It would be difficult for a water-dweller to take in and then squirt out water, in the way that land animals breathe air in and out. Usually the water flows in through one opening, passes over the gills, and leaves the body through a separate opening.

The pumping equipment varies between the main groups of animals. In molluscs like the octopus, it is the pulsating muscular walls of the chamber housing the gills. Crustaceans such as the lobster have beating, paddle-like structures. Fish use rhythmic expansion and contraction of the mouth and gill chambers. Swimming forwards also causes water to pass over the fish's gills.

LIVING ON LAND

Most bigger land-dwellers have lungs of some kind. These are infoldings of the body surface with blood vessels just under their lining. In their simple form, as in land snails, they are hollow chambers with walls that are not folded. In more complex versions the lung has folds or tunnels or finely branched tubes, to increase the surface area for absorbing oxygen.

Insects do not have proper lungs. They are small enough to rely on a form of diffusion. Oxygen diffuses into the air in a network of tiny tubes within their bodies. The tubes branch and reach every body part. However, this system is one of the reasons why most insects are small. The oxygen

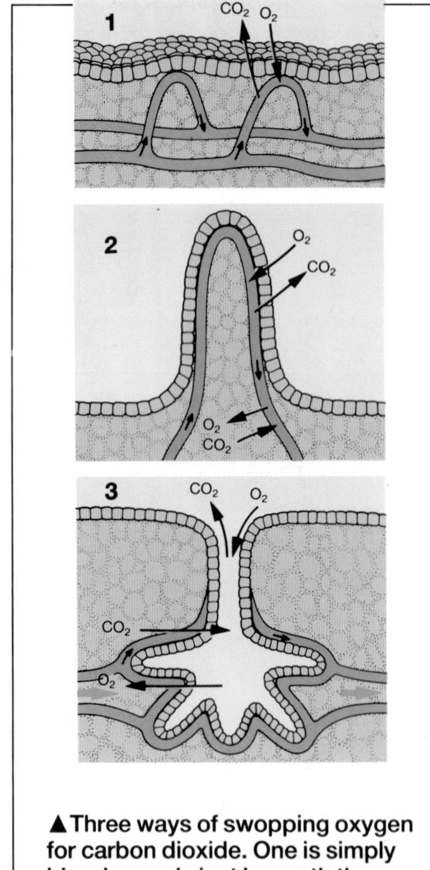

▲Three ways of swopping oxygen for carbon dioxide. One is simply blood vessels just beneath the skin (1). The second has finger-like projections from the surface with blood vessels inside (2), as in fish gills. The third is a hole leading to a chamber with blood vessels just under its lining (3), forming a lung.

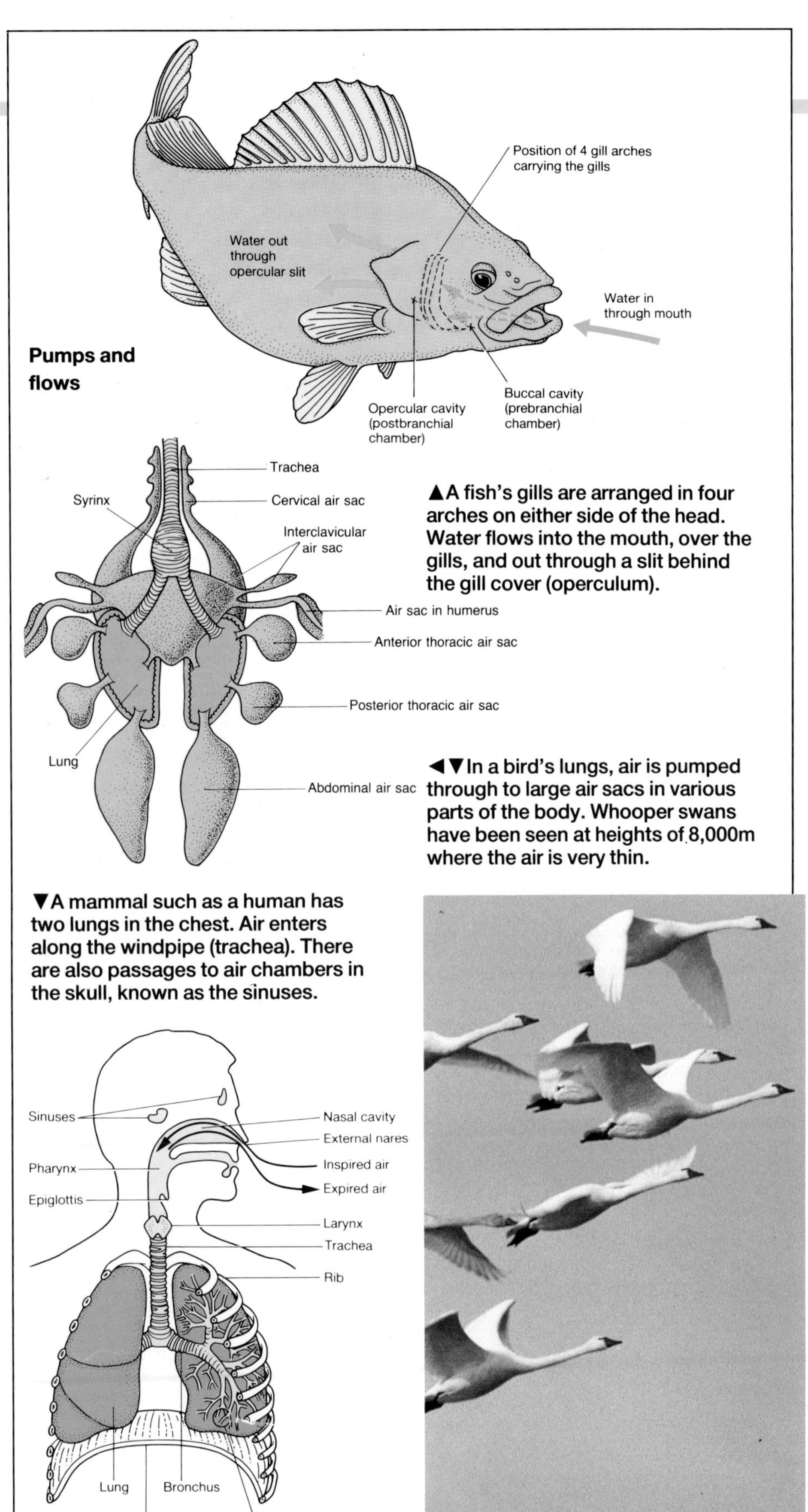

▲A fish's gills are arranged in four arches on either side of the head. Water flows into the mouth, over the gills, and out through a slit behind the gill cover (operculum).

◄▼In a bird's lungs, air is pumped through to large air sacs in various parts of the body. Whooper swans have been seen at heights of 8,000m where the air is very thin.

▼A mammal such as a human has two lungs in the chest. Air enters along the windpipe (trachea). There are also passages to air chambers in the skull, known as the sinuses.

can diffuse only a matter of millimetres. The biggest insects, such as the Goliath beetle, are at the size limit for its efficiency. However, the insect's body movements help to squeeze stale air out and suck fresh air back into the tubes.

THE BREATH OF LIFE

All the vertebrate land animals (those with backbones) have a pumping system to move air in and out of the lungs. Amphibians use the floor of the mouth and throat as a pump. Its up and down movement is a familiar sight in many frogs. The nostrils and the throat open and close in time with the pump, to force air into the lungs or allow it to escape.

Reptiles such as lizards, and all mammals – including ourselves – use the chest as a pump. The chest is moved by muscles attached to the ribs and backbone. Mammals also have a diaphragm, a dome-shaped muscle in the floor of the chest. It pulls down the bases of the lungs to increase their volume when breathing in. Inside the spongy lung tissue there are millions of minute air spaces called alveoli, which increase the surface area of the lung many times. Spread out flat, the inner surface of a human lung would cover an area the size of a tennis court.

BREATHING WHEN AIRBORNE

Bird lungs are different from those of other air-breathing vertebrates. They are solid and through them run many parallel tubes called parabronchi. Holes in the walls of these tubes open into very fine air tubes that are surrounded by equally fine blood vessels, giving a great area for absorbing oxygen. Air is moved through the lungs by altering the volume of several thin-walled air sacs in other parts of the bird's body. This system is so efficient at obtaining oxygen that flocks of curlews have been seen in the rarefied air at 10,000m, higher than the summit of Mount Everest.

FEEDING, DIGESTION

A chameleon sits perfectly still on a branch in an African forest. A fly buzzes past and lands about 20cm away. The lizard's eyes slowly swivel, and – snap, the fly is gone. A wildlife film-maker captures the moment on high-speed film. Only when the film is slowed down on playback, can she see the chameleon's long tongue flick out, grab the fly on its sticky tip, and whisk it into the mouth.

Any machine needs fuel to drive it. The animal body is a kind of machine, and its fuel is food. Food provides the energy for powering the chemical reactions of life, and the nutrients for body development, growth, maintenance and repair.

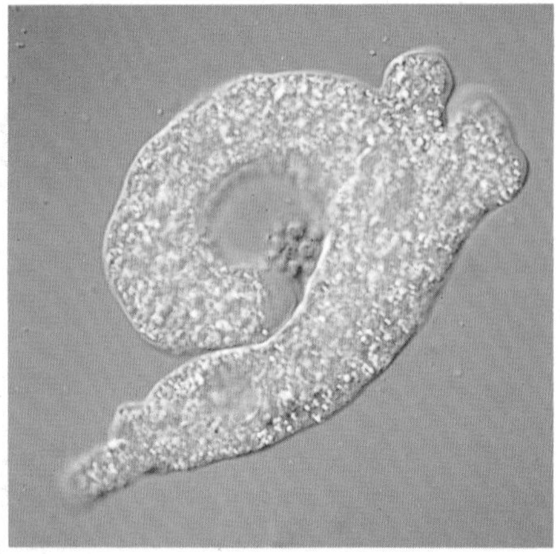

▲▼The Giant amoeba, seen here under the microscope, has a simple feeding method. It simply flows jelly-like arms around the food, in this case a small group of green algae (simple plants), and takes it into its body. This process, known as phagocytosis, is shown step by step in the diagram below.

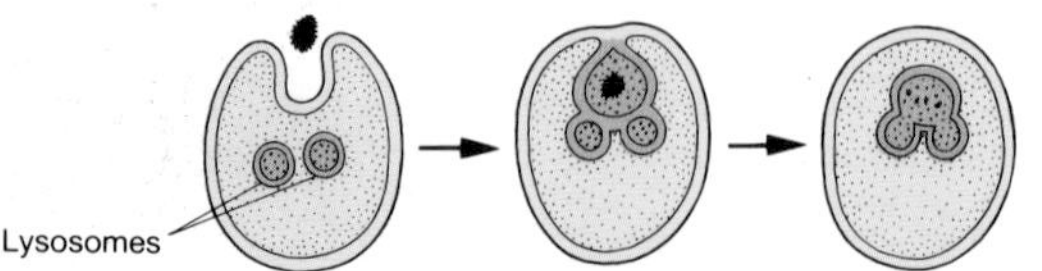

Plants make their own food. They use the energy in sunlight to build complex body tissues from carbon dioxide, water and other simple substances. Animals do the opposite. They take their food into the body. We call this feeding. Then they break the food down into smaller and simpler substances. This process is known as digestion. Finally the substances are absorbed into the body, converted and used for energy or to build new body tissue.

Animals therefore rely on plants for food, directly or indirectly. Some animals, the herbivores, eat plants directly. Others, the carnivores, eat animals. Still others are scavengers, feeding on the dying and dead remains of living things.

SIEVING AND SUCKING

Not all food comes in convenient bite-sized lumps. In the waters of most lakes and seas the main food source is the phytoplankton. This consists of microscopic plants, many of them single-celled. This food is best obtained by filtering or sieving the water. Many water-dwelling animals are filter-feeders. They include such

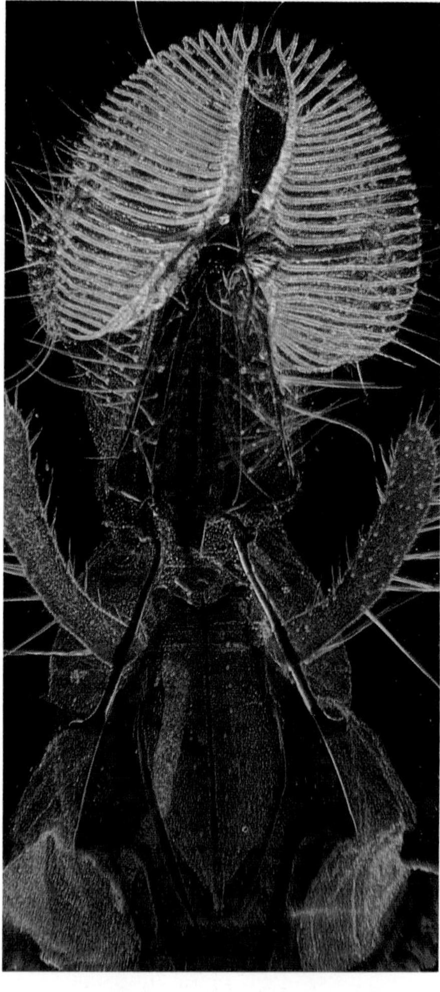

▲Digestion does not always take place inside the body. This magnified photograph shows a housefly's sponge-like mouthparts. The fly pours digestive juices on to its food. These turn it into a "soup". The fly then mops up the soup and sucks it into the body.

▼The "fan" of the fanworm is used for feeding. Each feathery tentacle filters small bits of food floating in the water and passes them down to the worm's body, which is in a tube part-buried in the mud. If danger threatens, the fan is pulled into the tube.

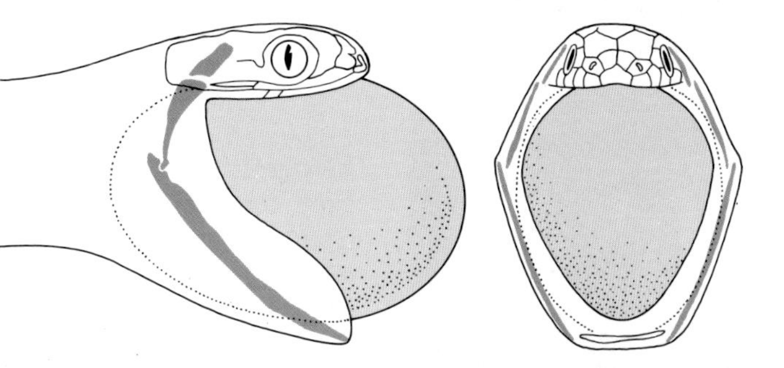

▲►The African egg-eating snake can swallow an egg more than four times as wide as its head. The bones in its jaws hinge and slide apart to allow the snake to open its mouth so wide. The egg is broken by bones in its throat, and the snake spits out the eggshell.

shellfish as mussels, worms such as fanworms, and also the tiny water fleas and similar creatures that occur in their millions and form the animal part of the plankton.

Animal blood and body fluids, and plant sap and nectar, are food for creatures that suck or pump fluids into their digestive system. Leeches suck the blood of larger animals. Mosquitoes, aphids and similar insects have piercing mouthparts like hollow needles. A butterfly's mouth is a hollow straw for sucking up nectar.

TOUGH TO EAT – OR TO CATCH

On land, many plants grow to a large size, and so herbivores have little trouble in finding them. But plant food such as bark or old leaves is tough, stringy, and hard to eat. Many herbivores have chewing mouthparts or wide, flat teeth, and they spend much time grinding and crushing their food before they swallow it. Because their food is so tough it wears down the teeth. Some herbivorous mammals have teeth that grow continuously from the roots, for example rats and mice. Others, elephants for instance, have teeth that are replaced in sequence throughout the animal's lifetime as they wear out.

Carnivores have to catch their food. They usually have powerful senses to detect prey, and also sharp teeth and claws to seize it, kill it and tear it into pieces that can be swallowed. However, there are many variations. The Giant anteater has no teeth. It licks up termites and ants with its sticky 60cm-long tongue, and grinds this meal with horny plates in the roof of its mouth and in its muscular stomach.

FEEDING TIMES

Plants tend to be less nutritious than meat, and are more difficult to digest. On average, herbivores have to spend more time feeding than carnivores, and they eat more. A snail spends most of each night rasping at plant leaves with its file-like tongue, the radula. In contrast, a snake that captures a large meal may not feed again for many weeks.

WHAT IS IN FOOD?

In many animals, the mouthparts or teeth help to chew and mash lumpy food into a pulp. This is the physical part of digestion. But chemically, the bulk of most foods is made up of giant molecules that animals cannot use directly. These giant molecules are split into smaller ones during digestion. This job is done by digestive enzymes. These enzymes are powerful juices that break the chemical bonds within the molecules and allow them to fall apart.

▲The elephant is a "fermentation tank on legs". Its leafy food consists of plant cells with thick, tough walls of cellulose (shown inset). Mammals cannot make digestive enzymes that break down cellulose. But the elephant's stomach contains microscopic bacteria which have enzymes that digest cellulose.

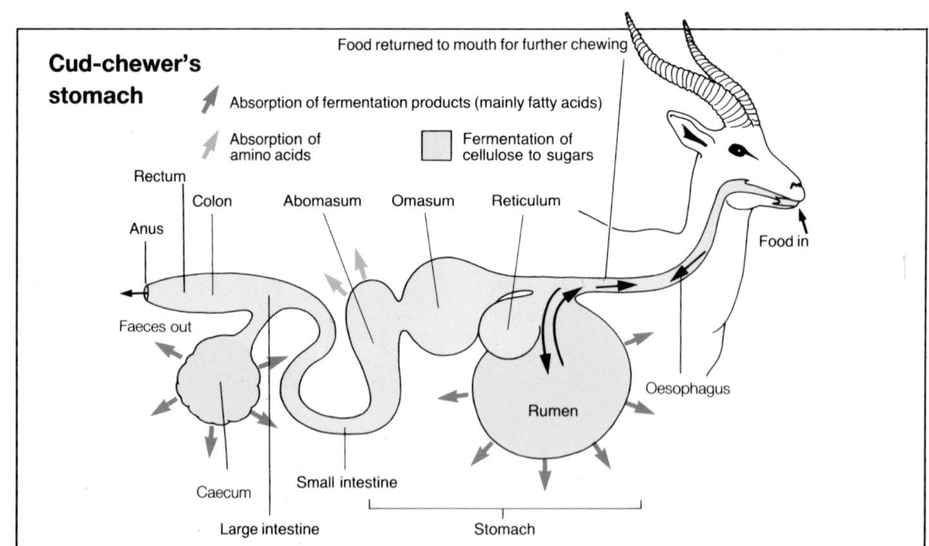

►The parts of a ruminant mammal's digestive system. Ruminants include cattle, sheep, goats, antelopes, deer and giraffes. The stomach has four main chambers. Food is swallowed into the largest chamber, the rumen, and partly broken down. Later, it is brought back into the mouth and chewed again – "chewing the cud". After the second swallow it passes to the other three chambers and on to the small intestine.

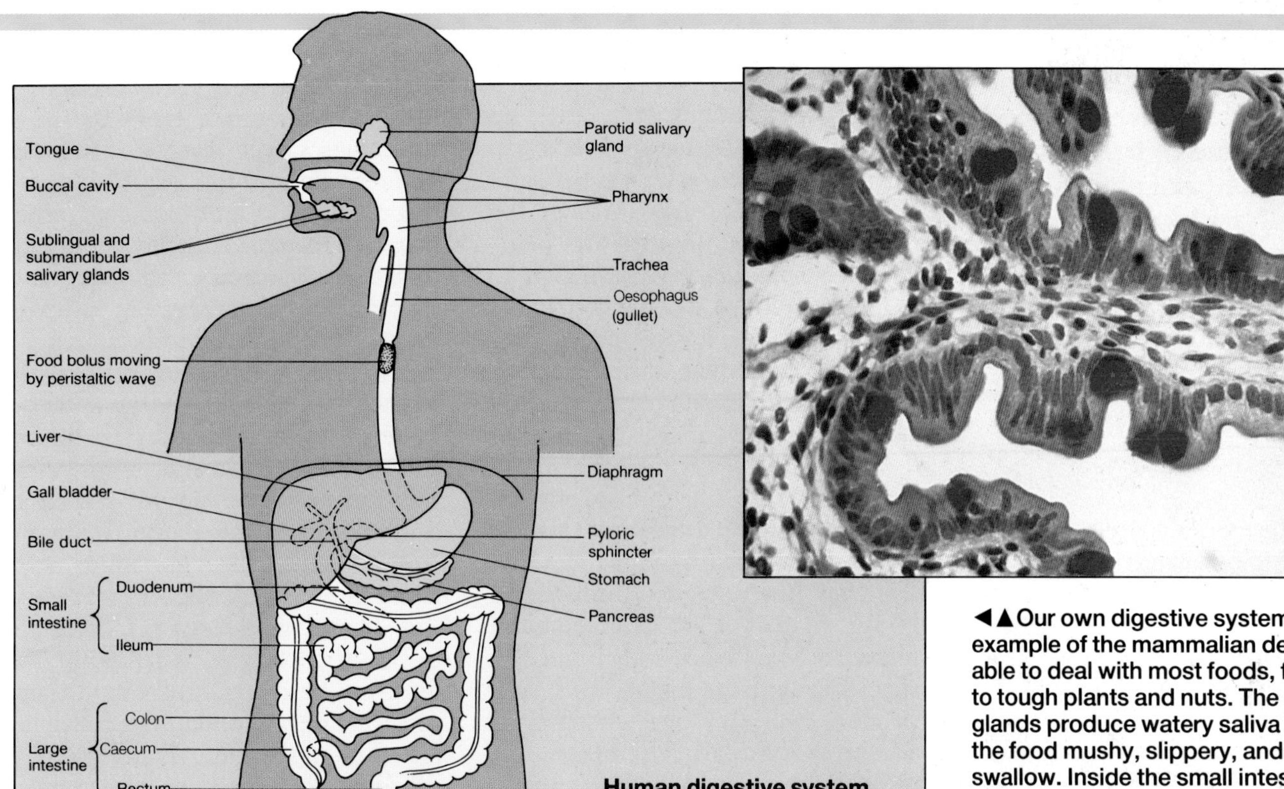

◄▲Our own digestive system is a good example of the mammalian design. It is able to deal with most foods, from meat to tough plants and nuts. The salivary glands produce watery saliva that makes the food mushy, slippery, and easy to swallow. Inside the small intestine, the lining has many small finger-like folds called villi (magnified in the photograph above). These greatly increase the surface area for absorbing food.

In their food and feeding methods, animals are extremely varied. Herbivores, carnivores, fluid-suckers and filter-feeders take in very different kinds of food. But at the level of cells and body chemicals, they are much less varied. So we find that much the same types of digestive enzymes are present throughout the whole of the Animal Kingdom.

BASIC NEEDS

The basic nutrient needs of different animals are also very similar. They require energy sources. They all need proteins (in meat and some plant materials), lipids (in fatty and oily foods), and carbohydrates (starches, sugars and cellulose). They also need small amounts of other substances, such as minerals.

Animals have three main types of enzymes to deal with these nutrients. Carbohydrases split carbohydrates into simpler sugars. Peptidases split proteins into amino acids, and the enzymes called esterases split lipids into fatty acids and glycerol.

ESSENTIAL EXTRAS

Animal enzymes are themselves proteins, but they often have several other chemical substances built into them, which are essential for their working. These extra substances include vitamins and minerals.

For example, in humans, the vitamin folic acid is essential for healthy blood. If it is lacking in food, then the person will become pale, breathless, tired and weak. This condition is known as anaemia. A lack of the mineral iron can also be a cause of anaemia. Many animals have similar needs for vitamins and minerals.

THE THROUGH-TUBE

The digestive system of an anemone is just a simple bag inside the animal's "stalk". Food is taken into the mouth, digested, and any leftovers are then pushed out of the mouth.

Most other animals have a tube-based digestive system. Food enters the mouth, is digested and absorbed as it moves through the tube. Leftovers and wastes pass out of the other end, the anus. Many worms have this design, where the tube is fairly simple and straight.

In more complex animals, parts of the digestive tube become specialized, and the tube itself is folded and coiled within the body. After the mouth there may be a crop to store food, a gizzard that grinds it up, and a stomach which pulverizes it and bathes it with digestive juices. Then comes the small intestine, which absorbs some of the nutrients. The large intestine absorbs further nutrients, water and minerals. The final part of the system is the rectum. It stores the wastes, called faeces, until they are expelled from the body.

CIRCULATION, HEART, BLOOD

In the cold north of Canada, a Snowshoe hare noses for food among patches of frozen snow. As it moves near a clump of bushes, a lynx bursts from the undergrowth and rushes at the hare. But the hare is too quick, and dashes away at great speed. The lynx gives chase for a time, but soon it has to stop, panting heavily and with its heart pounding in its chest.

The processes of life require many substances to be moved from one part of the body to another. Oxygen must be brought to the tissues for respiration. Carbon dioxide is taken away. Nutrients from food must be carried from the digestive system to other parts of the body. There they are stored, or used for their energy value, or else built into new body tissues. If the distances are sufficiently small, up to about 1mm, these movements can happen by diffusion (page 16). Substances simply spread through the body, from areas where they are being produced and their levels are high, to parts where they are being used up.

For example, a flatworm is only about 1 to 2mm thick, although it may be several centimetres long. No part of its body is more than 1mm from the outside. Oxygen can diffuse in and carbon dioxide can diffuse out fast enough to supply the animal's needs. Also, the flatworm's gut has many fine branches that spread through its body. No part is far from digested nutrients. So flatworms do not need a special system for transporting substances such as food or oxygen around the body. The same is true for many of the smaller kinds of animal.

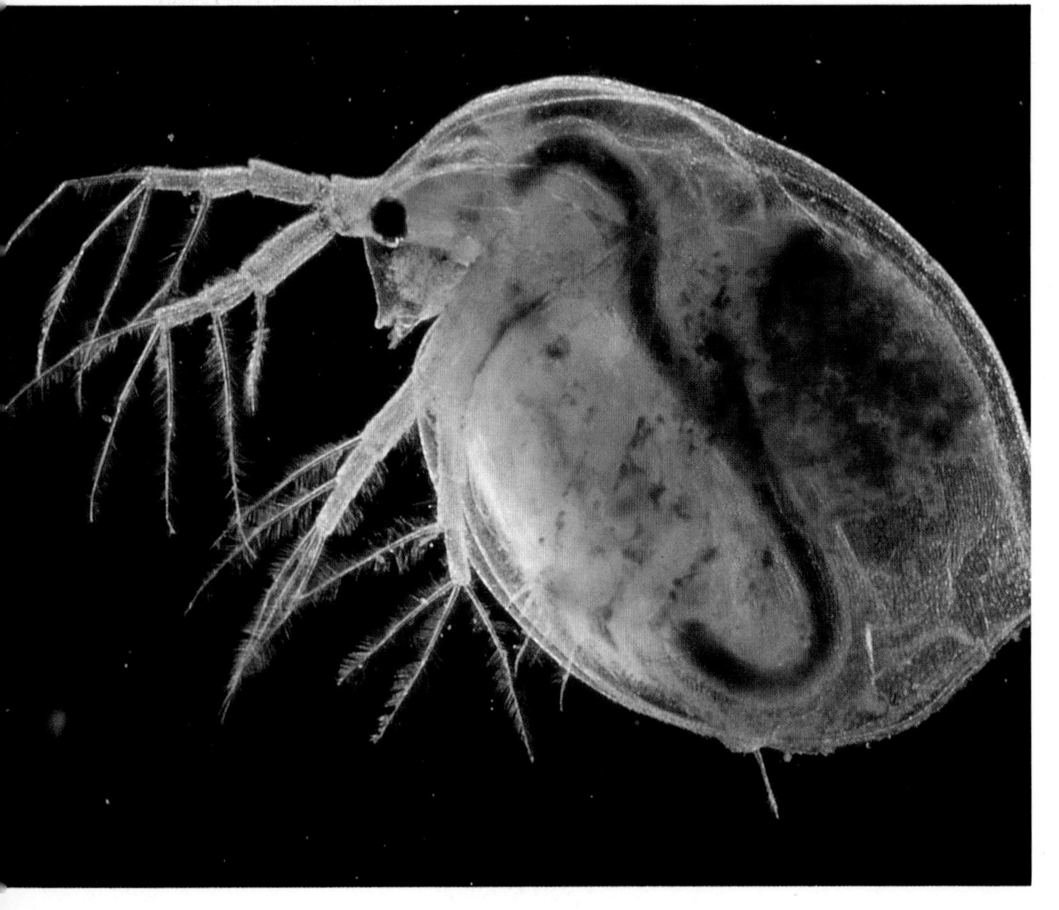

◀The beating heart of the Water flea, *Daphnia*, helps to circulate the "blood" that fills its body. The heart shows through the transparent body. Unlike most crustacean blood, *Daphnia*'s contain the red pigment haemoglobin.

LONG-DISTANCE TRANSPORT

Most larger animals need to move substances over longer distances. Their bodies are too big for oxygen, carbon dioxide, nutrients and other materials to spread quickly enough by diffusion. So many animals have evolved a circulatory system based on a special fluid – the blood.

The circulatory system is a branching network of tubes known as blood vessels, in which blood goes round and round (circulates).

Blood is a "carrier liquid". It collects nutrients from the digestive system and conveys them to other body parts. Some nutrients are processed and altered in the liver. Others are stored, for example as fat. Some are used for body-building, growth and repair. Energy-containing nutrients are taken to the muscles and used for movement.

In many groups of animals, oxygen is also carried in the blood, from the lungs or gills to the body tissues.

In addition, blood is part of the waste-disposal system. It collects carbon dioxide and wastes from the tissues and takes them to certain organs, such as the kidneys, where they can be eliminated from the animal's body through the urine.

THE HEART OF THE SYSTEM

Blood is pumped around the system by a length of blood vessel which has become thickened, more muscular, and specialized for squeezing. This is the heart. Most animals have one heart. But complex molluscs such as the squid and octopus have three hearts each, and in some kinds of worms, for example earthworms, individuals have five or more pairs. The simplest kind of heart is a tube

▲A red blood cell flowing through the smallest of blood vessels, a capillary looks like this under the microscope. In the narrowest capillaries, the tiny red blood cells have to move along in single file, pressed against the capillary walls.

with muscular walls, that pushes blood along by wave-like contractions of the muscles, called peristalsis. Sea squirts (bag-like animals that filter sea water for food) have this type of heart. It can pump blood in either direction. A sea squirt pumps its blood one way for a few minutes, then reverses the direction of pumping and the direction of flow of the blood.

The hearts of other animals pump blood in one direction only. There are non-return valves in the heart, and sometimes in the main blood vessels. These allow blood to pass through one way, but shut to prevent it flowing in reverse.

HOW MANY CHAMBERS?

The hearts of the molluscs (snails, shellfish and their relatives) have two main chambers. These are the atrium, (also called the auricle) and the ventricle. The atrium has thinner, slacker walls than those of the much more muscular ventricle.

Blood returns from the body parts along blood vessels to the atrium. This contracts to squeeze blood into the ventricle. The thick-walled ventricle then contracts more powerfully to push the blood out into the blood vessels again. Amphibians and reptiles have hearts which have two atria. Blood from both these flows into a single ventricle. This pumps blood to the body and lungs. Birds and mammals have two atria and two ventricles, as part of their double-circulation, explained below.

THE BEAT GOES ON

The heart pumps rhythmically, alternately contracting its muscular walls to push blood out, and then relaxing them as it refills. Each of these cycles of contraction and relaxation is called a heartbeat.

Heartbeats do not happen at a constant speed in all animals. In general, smaller animals have faster heart rates. At rest, a shrew's heart pumps at more than 200 beats per minute. A human heart rate is around 60 to 70 per minute, and an elephant's about 25 per minute.

The warm-blooded birds and mammals have faster heart rates than cold-blooded creatures such as reptiles, because their bodies use up energy faster in making heat.

Heart rate changes according to the activity of the animal. Muscles that are working hard need greater supplies of

►Being so tall brings problems for the circulation. The giraffe's heart pumps very strongly to force blood up to its head, 5m above the ground. When it bends to drink, special valves in the neck veins reduce the blood pressure.

oxygen and energy, so blood flow to them must be increased. The human heart, which is about the size of a clenched fist, pumps some 5 litres of blood each minute when the person is resting. After strenuous exercise it beats much faster and more powerfully, and pumps up to eight times as much blood per minute.

DIVIDING AND DIVIDING

There are three main kinds of blood vessels in the circulatory system: arteries, veins and capillaries. Arteries carry blood away from the heart. Veins bring it back. Capillaries are the smallest and thinnest blood vessels. They link the arteries and veins.

In the arteries, blood is at relatively high pressure as it spurts out of the heart with each beat. In veins, the pressure is much less and the blood oozes along slowly. This is why arteries need thicker walls than veins.

The larger arteries of vertebrates (fish, amphibians, reptiles, birds and mammals) have a substance called elastin in their walls. It is a protein with rubber-like properties. It lets the artery swell with each heartbeat, and then makes it shrink again by elastic recoil. This helps to smooth out the movement of blood, changing any sudden surges into a more even flow.

In many animals the arteries form a branching network, dividing many times and becoming smaller each time. They spread out to all body parts, getting narrower and narrower until they become capillaries.

THE GREAT EXCHANGE

Capillaries are only a fraction of a millimetre across, and their walls are just one cell thick. The blood inside them is only a very small distance from the surrounding tissues.

At this microscopic level, diffusion works efficiently. In the lungs or gills, oxygen from the air or water diffuses through the lining and across the capillary wall into the blood. In the

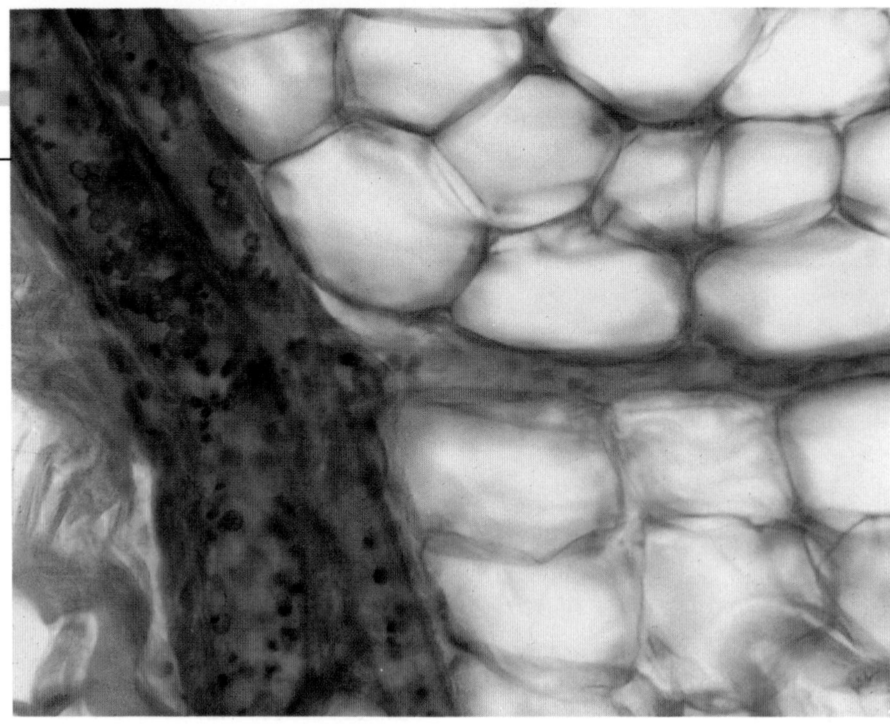

▲Arteries divide into finer and finer vessels as they carry blood into the organs and tissues of the body. The smallest vessels visible here are capillaries running into an area of connective tissue.

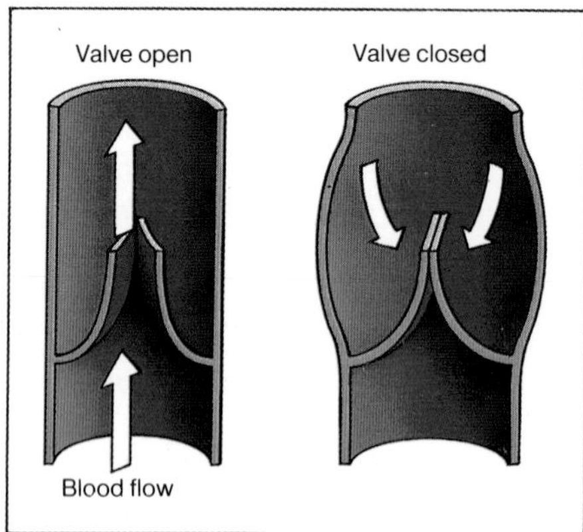

Blood vessels
►Non-return valves in the circulatory system make sure that blood travels in one direction. Blood going the wrong way makes the valve flaps bulge and seal together.

▼The three main types of blood vessels. Veins (1) carry blood back to the heart. They have a middle layer of muscle and fibres, and a tough outer covering. Arteries (2) take blood away from the heart. The thick, muscular middle layer withstands surges in blood pressure with each heartbeat. Capillaries (3) are small and thin-walled.

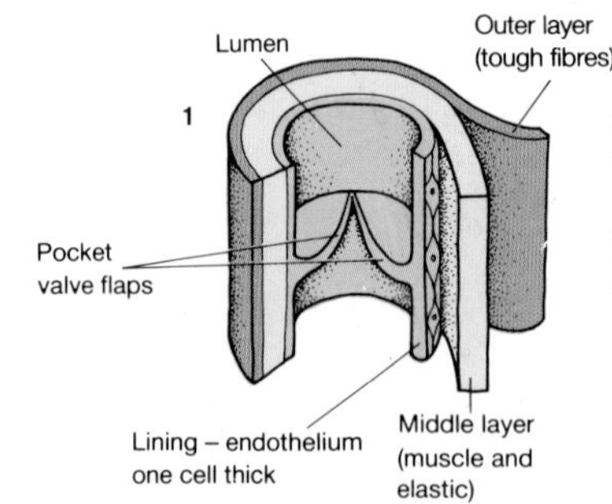

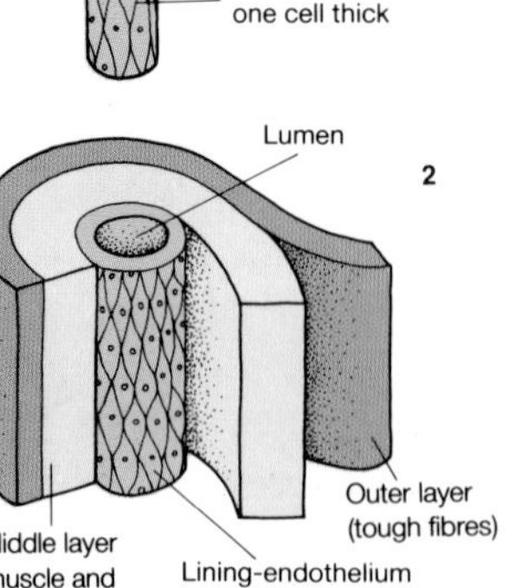

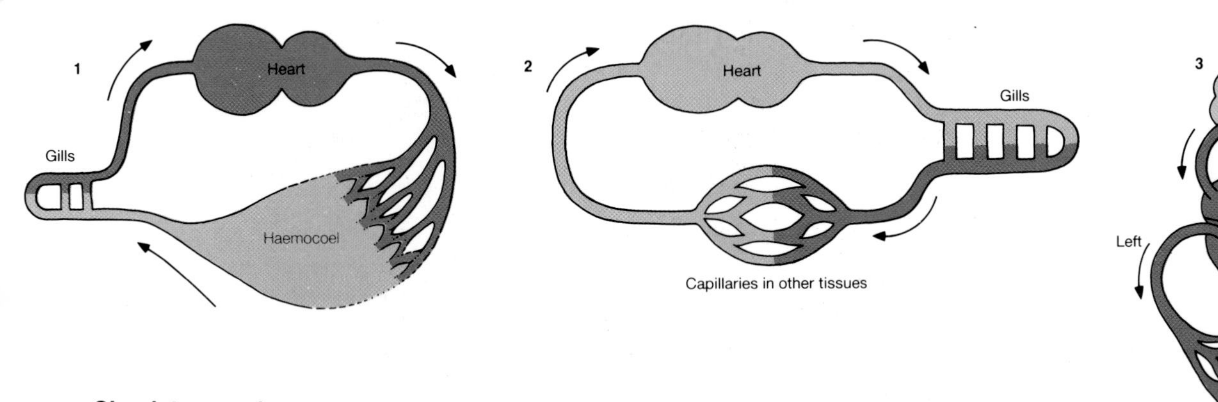

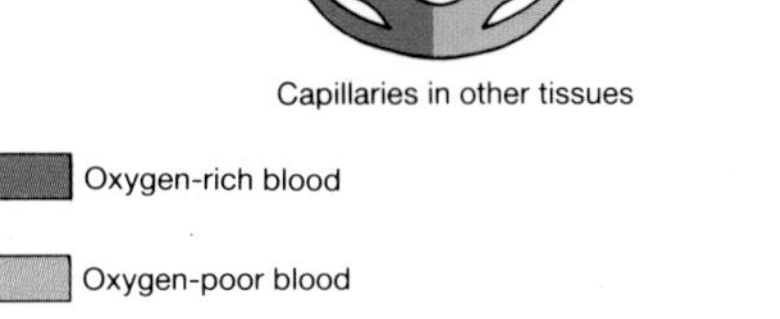

Circulatory systems
Types of blood circulation. In crustaceans (such as crabs) and molluscs (such as squid) **(1)**, blood flows from body tissues into the general body cavity, the haemocoel, and then to the heart through the gills. In fishes **(2)**, the blood passes from the heart to the gills, and then on to other body tissues. In birds and mammals **(3)** the heart is two-sided and there is a double circulation. One side sends blood to the lungs and one to the other body parts.

HEART AND BLOOD CIRCULATORY SYSTEMS

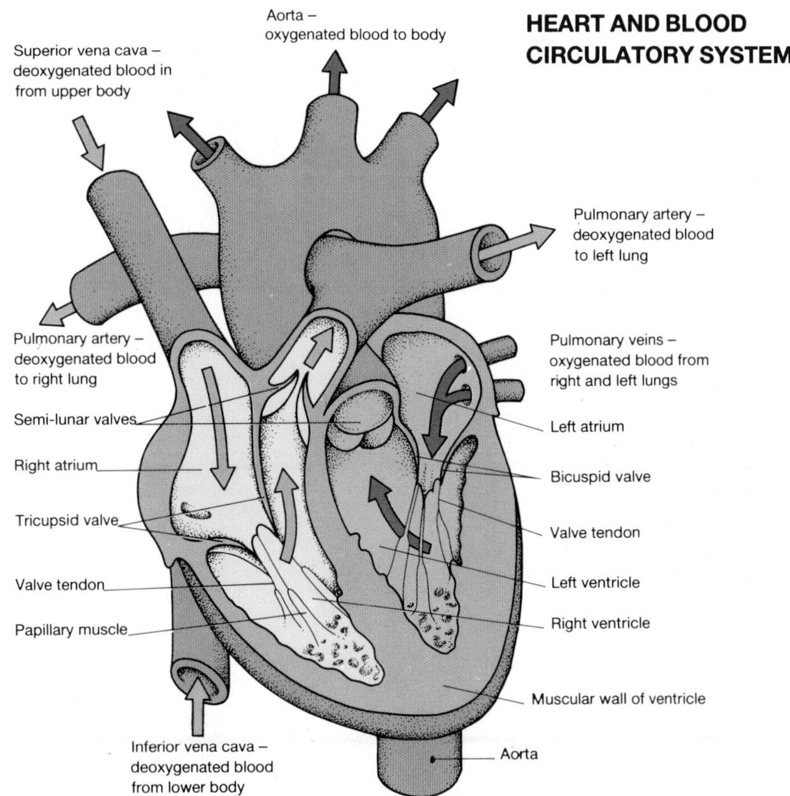

The heart
▲The heart of a mammal, such as a human. It is basically a muscular pump, with two main chambers on each side, an upper atrium and a lower ventricle. The right side (on the left, facing you in the diagram) receives blood from body parts and pumps it to the lungs for fresh oxygen along the pulmonary arteries. The oxygen-rich blood returns to the left side along pulmonary veins.

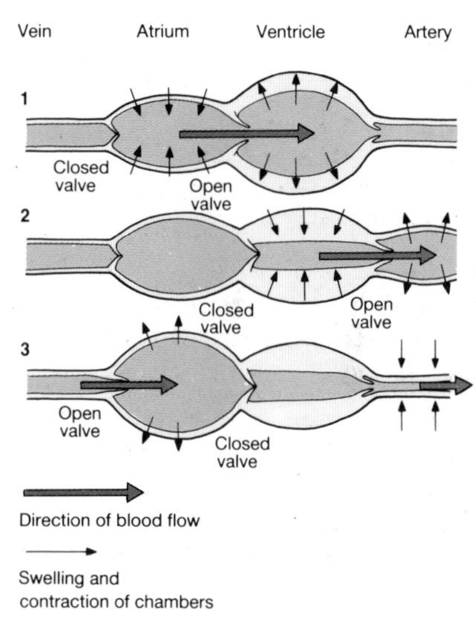

▲The atrium and ventricle work together to pump blood. The atrium contracts **(1)**, filling the ventricle through the open valve between them. Blood is prevented from going back into the vein by the closed valve on the left. The ventricle's strong muscular walls contract and squeeze blood out into the artery **(2)**, which bulges under the pressure. The valve in the centre is now closed, and the one on the right opens. The artery's elastic wall returns to its normal size **(3)**, and the atrium refills from the vein.

digestive system, nutrients diffuse from inside the intestine through its thin lining into the blood.

In the body tissues, oxygen and nutrients diffuse from the blood through the capillary walls and out to the tissues beyond. Carbon dioxide and other wastes diffuse the opposite way, from the tissues into the blood, and are carried off.

Capillaries join together to form larger and larger vessels, eventually becoming veins. The network of veins collects blood from all over the body and brings it back to the heart.

VARIATIONS ON A THEME

Not all animals have the full circulatory system of arteries, capillaries and veins. In some arthropods – such as crabs, lobsters, other crustaceans and spiders – the arteries do not end in capillaries. They open into a blood-filled cavity, the haemocoel, which is the main body cavity of these animals.

Gastropod molluscs (such as snails) and bivalve molluscs (such as mussels and oysters) also have this system. The blood oozes through the haemocoel and is channelled into the gills before

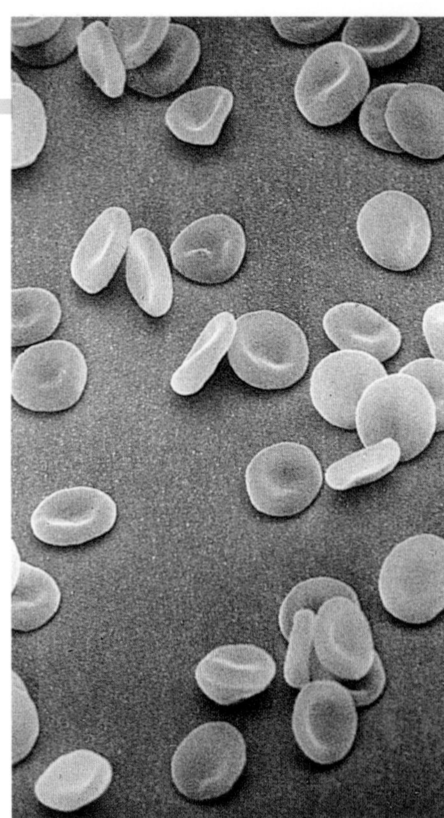

►Under an electron microscope, red blood cells are revealed as tiny discs with a dimple in each side. (The microscope takes only black-and-white photographs). A human body makes two million new red cells every second.

▼One function of the blood is to clot, to seal breaks and wounds. A series of chemical reactions, started by damage to a blood vessel, forms the string-like substance fibrin. Blood cells are caught in the fibrin net and form a clot.

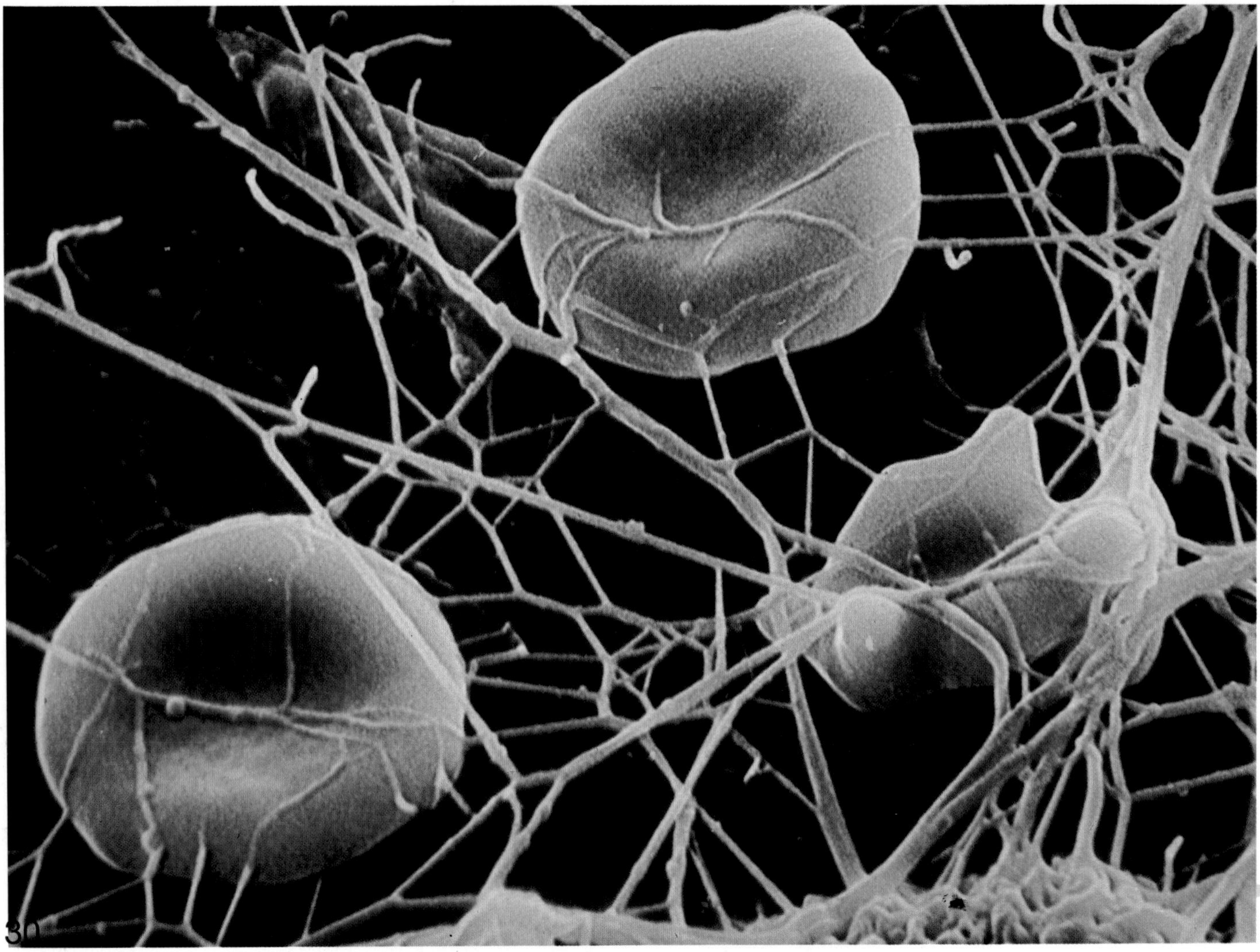

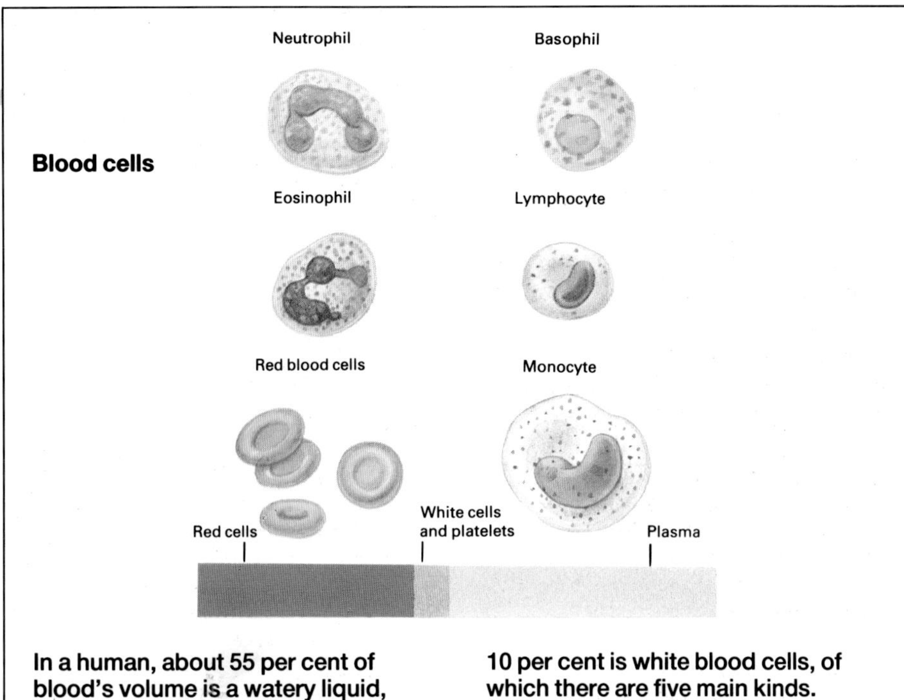

In a human, about 55 per cent of blood's volume is a watery liquid, plasma. Floating in the plasma are red blood cells, which make up 35 per cent of the volume. The remaining 10 per cent is white blood cells, of which there are five main kinds. Neutrophils and lymphocytes are the most numerous, and they help the body to fight infection by germs.

travelling back to the heart. In insects, the blood circulation simply passes through the heart to the haemocoel and back to the heart. Oxygen travels to the tissues along air-filled tubes, tracheae (page 19), so the blood is not involved in carrying it.

Mammals and birds have a two-sided heart and a double circulation. Blood leaving the right side goes to the lungs, where it takes up oxygen and gets rid of carbon dioxide. It comes back to the left side and is driven out on a second journey, to all the body tissues except the lungs. It then returns to the right side of the heart, and the cycle begins again.

WHY IS OUR BLOOD RED?

Many of the substances that blood carries, such as nutrients and the waste urea, are dissolved in it. It is also carrying some dissolved oxygen. However, in many groups of animals, the bulk of the oxygen is carried in chemical combination with other substances, the blood pigments.

Vertebrates have the blood pigment haemoglobin, which is red in colour, and it is this which makes blood red. Haemoglobin is contained in small doughnut-shaped cells, red blood cells, which float in the blood. In every human red blood cell there are about 270 million haemoglobin molecules, and there are five million red cells in a tiny drop of blood.

Crustaceans and molluscs have a similar blood pigment, haemocyanin, that helps to carry oxygen. But this pigment is light blue.

BLOOD'S OTHER ROLES

Blood is not simply a fetcher and carrier of nutrients. It has many other roles in the body. The white blood cells are part of the immune system which defends the body against invading germs. White cells either "eat" the invaders, or make substances called antibodies that kill or disable them.

Another type of blood cell, the platelet, is involved in the process of blood clotting. This seals cuts and leaks in the body. In warm-blooded animals, blood spreads out heat from the hotter, more active organs such as the muscles and heart, to warm the cooler parts. The continual movement of blood is therefore vital to life.

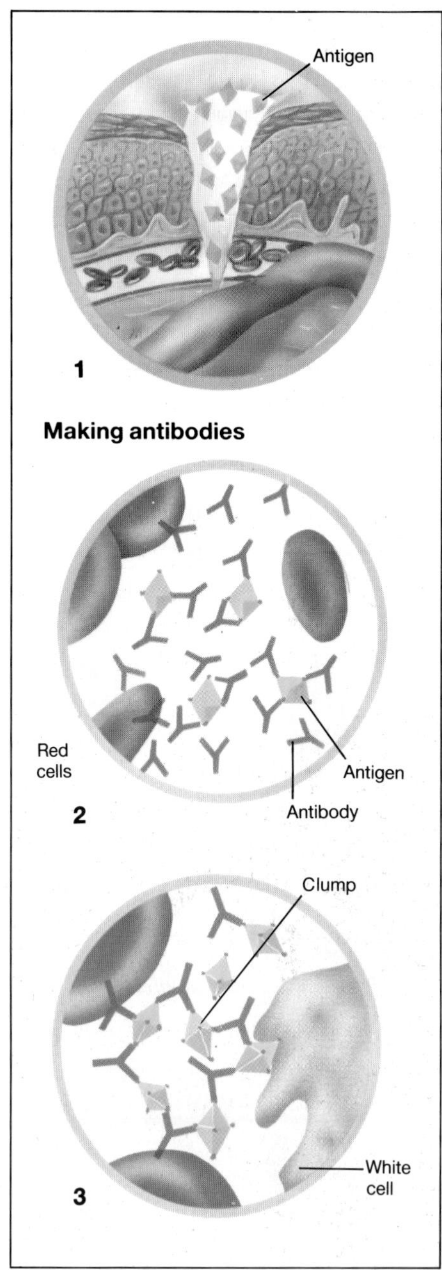

▲White blood cells attack invading germs in several ways. One method involves making substances called antibodies. Germs, shown by the green diamond shapes, enter the skin through a cut (1). White blood cells release Y-shaped antibodies (2), which are specific for that type of germ. The antibodies stick to the germs and make them burst or clump together. The germs are then eaten by other white cells (3) in the way that amoeba eats its food.

EXCRETION, WATER BALANCE

After a long trek across the desert, the camel looks thin and straggly. It is only two-thirds of its usual body weight. The other third was water which it has lost despite producing only small amounts of very concentrated urine. It has not had a drink for about 10 weeks. At the water hole, it makes up for this – by drinking 130 litres of water at one session!

The processes of life produce waste substances. Chemicals like urea and ammonia are wastes that come from the breakdown of proteins. Animals need some way of getting rid of these. This is the job of the excretory system.

Small and simple animals can lose wastes from the body by diffusion (page 16). But in larger animals it is not so easy. A variety of excretory systems has evolved. These control both the disposal of wastes and the ins and outs of water balance. In complex animals, the main excretory organs are usually called kidneys.

ADDING AND SUBTRACTING

Although the organs differ, the basic process of excretion is the same across the Animal Kingdom. Body fluids flow into the hollow part of the excretory organ, which is often tube-shaped. As the fluid moves along the tube, cells in the lining absorb water from it. Or, they may add water to the fluid, depending on the animal's water balance at the time. The cells get rid of wastes into the fluid. They can also take in or remove salts, again depending on current needs. Finally the fluid, containing wastes and excess water, leaves the animal as urine.

Sometimes these substances are moved in the opposite way to the way they would go by diffusion. This is because the excretory cells have "pumps", which use energy to force substances from one place to another against the flow of diffusion. So excretion is a process that needs energy, like muscle action.

SUCKING IN THE SEA

Sea water has substances dissolved in it. Most invertebrate animals such as jellyfish and starfish, and some fish such as sharks and rays have body fluids with the same concentration of dissolved substances as sea water, or slightly higher. This means they are in balance with their surroundings, or water tends to flow in very slowly. But the excess water is not too great, and

►On the hot, dry African grasslands, a daily trek to the water hole is essential for animals such as this Brindled gnu. It loses water continuously as breathed out moisture from its lungs, and through its skin. Making urine also uses up the body's water supply.

▲Sea snake

◄Angel fish

►Pigeon

▲►Animals in different environments face very different problems of water balance. Fish body fluids are less concentrated than sea water, so water tends to pass out through their body walls. To replace this, they drink water and make only small amounts of urine. A sea snake also gradually loses water into the sea, but can get water from the animals it catches, which are less salty than the sea. Seed-eating birds such as pigeons get little water in their food and drink wherever they can. Birds make a paste-like urine.

Water balance and excretion

►These types of blood flukes cause the disease bilharzia in people. They live in a watery environment inside a human. Water balance and excretion are not a great problem. But they may have to fight the host's immune defence system.

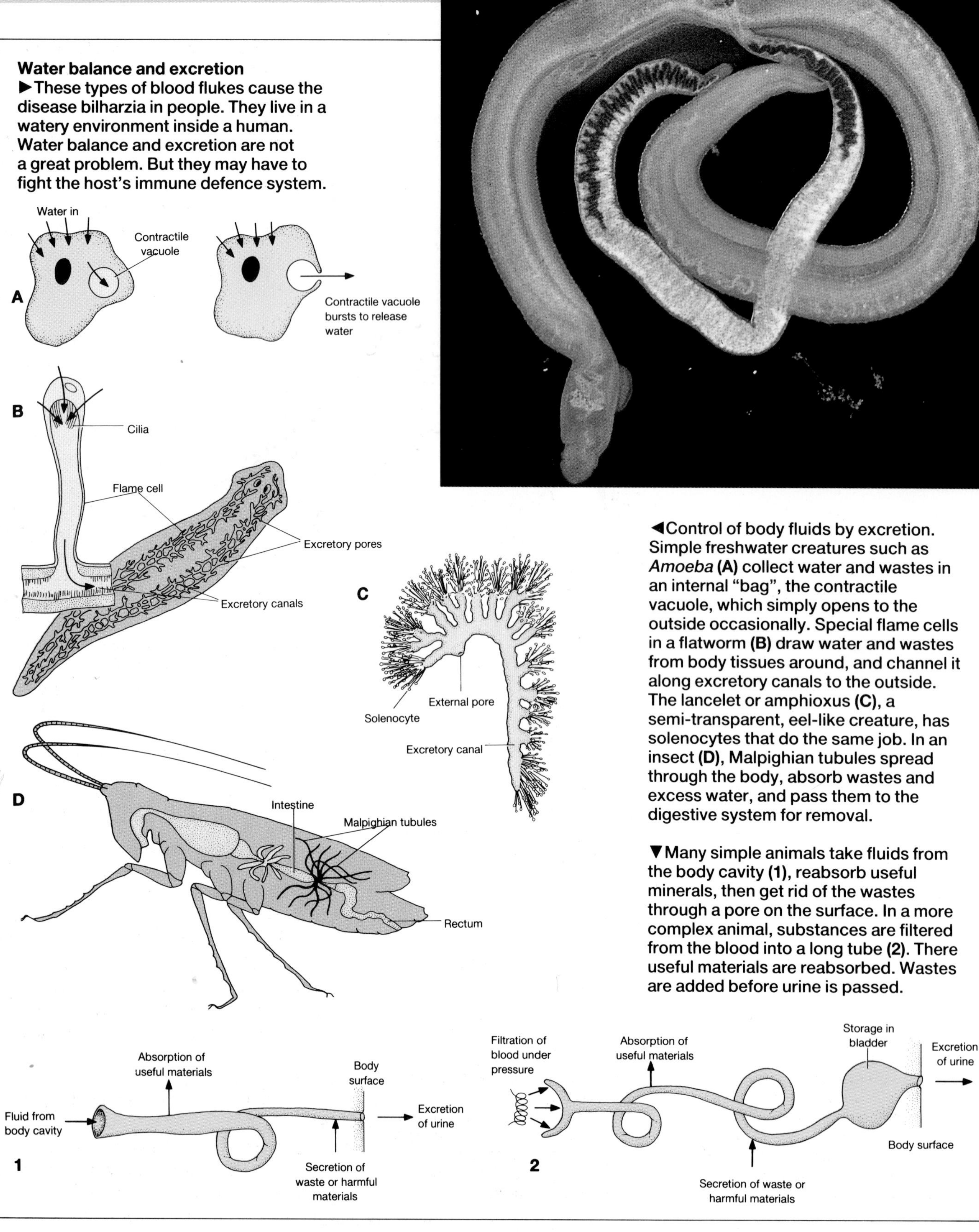

◄Control of body fluids by excretion. Simple freshwater creatures such as *Amoeba* **(A)** collect water and wastes in an internal "bag", the contractile vacuole, which simply opens to the outside occasionally. Special flame cells in a flatworm **(B)** draw water and wastes from body tissues around, and channel it along excretory canals to the outside. The lancelet or amphioxus **(C)**, a semi-transparent, eel-like creature, has solenocytes that do the same job. In an insect **(D)**, Malpighian tubules spread through the body, absorb wastes and excess water, and pass them to the digestive system for removal.

▼Many simple animals take fluids from the body cavity **(1)**, reabsorb useful minerals, then get rid of the wastes through a pore on the surface. In a more complex animal, substances are filtered from the blood into a long tube **(2)**. There useful materials are reabsorbed. Wastes are added before urine is passed.

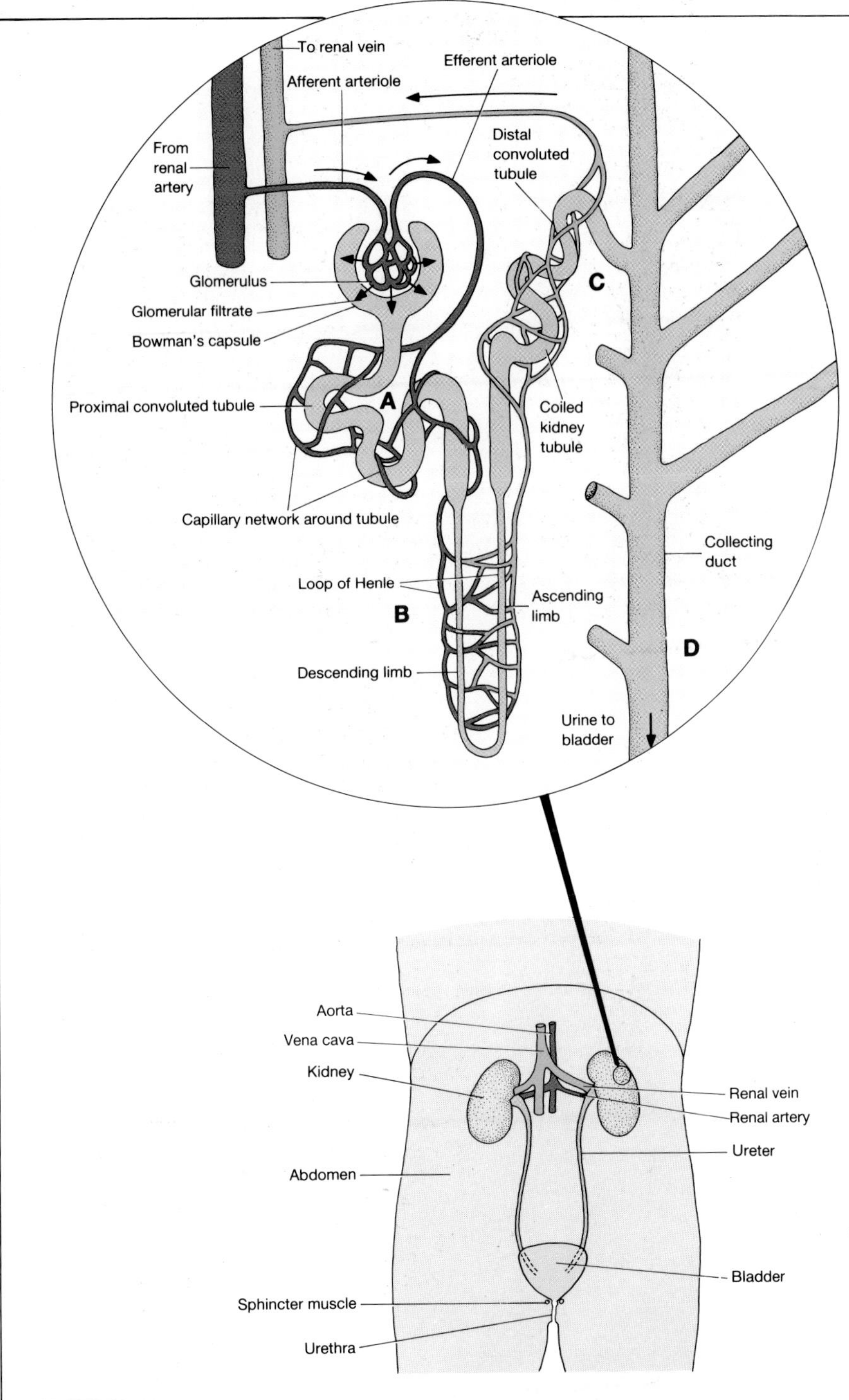

The human kidneys
In each human kidney are 1 million tiny filtering units (above). Blood from the renal artery flows through a knot of capillaries, the glomerulus. Many substances are filtered from this into the tubule (A). Farther along the tubule, useful water and mineral salts are taken back into the blood (B and C). The resulting fluid, urine, flows into a collecting duct (D). Many ducts in each kidney come together at its centre, and urine trickles down the ureter into the bladder.

the excretory organs such as kidneys can cope with the rate of inflow.

DRINKING THE SEA

A second main group of sea creatures includes crabs and other crustaceans, and most kinds of fish. Their body fluids are less concentrated than sea water. So water tends to be lost from their bodies.

These animals obtain extra water from three sources. One is water in food, which is especially important in plant-eaters such as surgeonfish and sea-cows. Another is water obtained from chemical breakdown of food. The third source is sea water that they drink. They quickly get rid of the extra salt they take in, pumping it out through the gills. They lose some salts in their faeces, and make very concentrated urine. Water is left, available for body tissues.

Freshwater animals such as worms, crayfish and fish have the opposite problem. Water floods into their bodies from the weaker solution that surrounds them. Their kidneys make large amounts of dilute urine. This gets rid of wastes and extra water.

HIDING FROM THE SUN

On land, animals dispose of body wastes in urine, along with some water. They also lose water in breathed-out air, and as sweat.

Many are able to control their waste and water loss by behaviour. For example, desert-dwellers such as gerbils stay in the cool shade during the day. They also make extremely small amounts of concentrated urine, and use little water in their faeces. Several kinds of desert insects can absorb water vapour in the air through their body coverings.

Some creatures get all their water supplies from food. Mosquitoes and leeches have plenty of water in the blood they suck. Mountain gorillas eat large quantities of succulent leafy plants, and rarely need to drink.

KEEPING CONSTANT

In the cool morning, just after sunrise, a group of Australian children walk to their outback school. As they pass a stony outcrop they disturb a lizard basking on a rock. It waddles slowly for cover. When the children return at midday, the lizard has gone. They wonder: is it hunting for food somewhere, or is it now too hot in the Sun for the lizard?

Single-celled animals live in a wide variety of surroundings, from freezing polar seas to hot-water springs. But they cannot survive in deserts or up in the air. Some multi-celled animals, from tiny insects to mighty eagles, can live in such places. In multi-celled animals, different parts of the body can have specialized functions. This means that each one of the many different types of body cells does not have to be adapted to withstand extremes of temperature, dryness and other difficult conditions. Instead, the cells can be adapted to do their jobs and work together, to make the whole body more efficient. Multi-celled animals may live in amazingly varied surroundings, but keep conditions inside their bodies much the same. This process of keeping internal conditions of the body constant is known as homeostasis.

BODY HOUSEKEEPING

The body cells of most animals are about 60 to 80 per cent water. Most have fairly similar concentrations of dissolved substances. The temperature at which the cells can live ranges from about 0°C to 45°C.

Yet animals exist in surroundings which differ greatly from these internal conditions. One example is living out of water. A land animal must have a fairly waterproof skin to keep in body fluids. It must also take in water regularly, to replace the water lost.

Also, an animal has to keep up the supply of nutrients to its cells and must get rid of wastes before these build up and become poisonous. All these processes are examples of ways in which the body's internal environment is regulated.

HEAT FROM OUTSIDE

Another example of homeostasis is the way that some animals control their body temperature, so that they neither overheat their body cells nor freeze them to death. Almost all animals depend on warmth coming from their surroundings to maintain their body temperature. They are often called "cold-blooded", but this is not a very accurate term. On a hot day a "cold-blooded" desert snake may be much warmer than the "warm-blooded" jerboa it catches. A more accurate term is *ectothermic*, which means "heat from without".

Creatures that cannot move about, such as barnacles and mussels, must withstand a wide range of temperatures, as the hot Sun shines down and then cold waves cover them a minute later. Their shells help to protect them from these extremes, as well as from the drying effects of Sun and wind.

SUNBATHING IN THE SHADE

Of the ectothermic creatures that can move about, many are able to control their body temperature by their behaviour. Scarab beetles and horned lizards are especially good at this. Their behaviour is adapted to finding places which are warm when their bodies are too cold, and then locating cool places if they become too hot. These types of animal often follow a

◀Some creatures that live through freezing conditions, like fish in polar seas, and this hibernating Peacock butterfly, have special "antifreeze" chemicals in their blood and body fluids.

▲As winter approaches, the Arctic hare grows a thick white coat of fur. This not only keeps it warm in the bitter cold, but also makes it hard to see against the white snowy background.

▼As the temperature drops to 20°C below freezing, Gentoo penguins endure an Antarctic snowstorm. They keep the body centre warm and the outer parts, like feet, just above freezing.

▶The penguin's flippers and feet have a heat-exchanging system. Warm blood from the body centre passes heat to the cold blood returning from the limb. Along the limb temperatures drop.

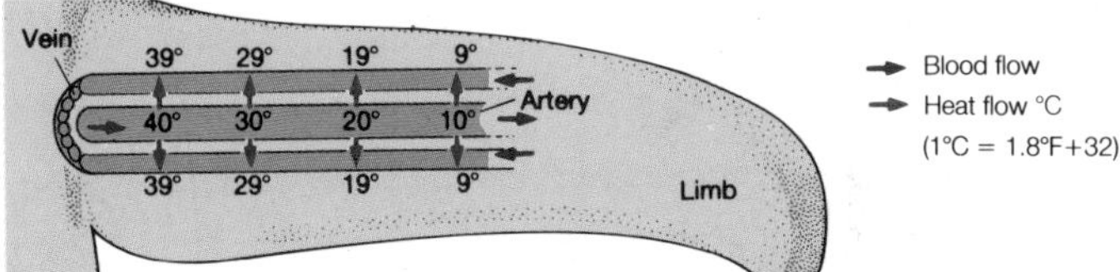

daily routine. At night they shelter in or near large trees, rocks and other places that have absorbed the Sun's warmth during the day. The warmth is given out slowly during the cool night.

At dawn, they come out to bask in the Sun's rays and warm up their bodies, ready for activities such as feeding or nest-building. During the midday heat, they shelter in the shade, often where there is a breeze. At dusk they sunbathe once again, to absorb as much warmth as possible before night begins again.

WARMTH FROM WITHIN

A few groups of animals can regulate their body temperature using heat generated within the body by its own chemical processes. These animals are called *endothermic*. The two main endothermic groups are mammals and birds. A few insects such as bees and moths are also able to warm themselves from within.

Most mammals maintain their body temperature at about 37°C. Most birds function at around 39°C. To keep this internal temperature constant while the temperature outside varies, they need to adjust the amount of heat made or lost from their bodies.

Since the ectotherm's body tends to be warmer than the surroundings, controlling heat loss is important. Mammals have fur and an insulating layer of fat under the skin, while birds have feathers to keep heat in. In the cold, they fluff up the fur or feathers so that they trap more air and improve insulation. Muscles may also "shiver", creating more heat.

◀Northern elephant seals bask on a beach off the coast of California. The Sun could cause overheating and sunburn. These seals have thrown a layer of sand over their backs. The light-coloured sand reflects the Sun's rays and keeps the animals cool and safe from sunburn. Sunbathing is often a useful way of conserving body warmth, and therefore saving energy.

KEEPING COOL

Animals cool themselves in several ways. Blood vessels near the surface widen to lose extra heat. Sweat evaporates from the skin. Fluids can evaporate from the mouth and breathing airways. This is what happens when a dog pants.

Endothermic creatures that live in cold seas, such as whales and seals, do not try to keep the whole of the body warm. They have a network of blood vessels at the base of each limb that acts as a heat-exchanger. This helps keep the heat in the body centre.

►Any small patch of shade is welcome in the heat of the African Sun. This cheetah family rests under the shadow of a small tree, their mouths open and panting to lose body warmth.

▼After a morning in the blazing Australian Sun, this Perentie monitor lizard has become too hot for comfort, and is cooling off in the shade of a fallen tree trunk.

SENSES

In autumn, two scuba-diving scientists swim in shallow water off the east coast of North America. Rounding a rock, they see the astonishing sight for which they have come. Hundreds of Spiny lobsters are walking purposefully in single file along the sandy bottom, heading for deeper water. How do they know where they are heading? This is what the scientists wish to study.

Animals obtain information about their surroundings using their senses. These detect danger, food, shelter, mates and the other essentials of life. The Spiny lobsters use their sensory information to know when and in which direction to migrate to remain in favourable conditions.

Our own senses are dominated by sight (see page 44). We also use our hearing (page 50) extensively, the sense of touch on our skin (page 54), and taste and smell (page 56). These senses are dealt with on the relevant pages. There are other kinds of senses in the animal world, some of which are described here.

A WORLD OF SENSES

Senses detect many aspects of the outside world. Sight detects light rays. Smell and taste register airborne or waterborne chemicals. Hearing interprets vibrations in air or water. Touch detects physical pressure.

But other senses can detect many other features of the world around an animal. These include the pull of gravity, the speed and direction of movements, the weak lines of magnetic force around the Earth, currents in air and water, humidity, temperature, and electrical signals generated by muscles and other living tissues.

We should be aware that other animals "see" the world in some very

▲This Common cuttlefish has just caught a Common prawn. It hunted it using its large and sensitive eyes. Once it holds the prey, it receives more sensory information from touch detectors on its tentacles.

▼This pit viper shows the heat-sensitive pit in front of each eye. Inside the pit is a membrane which detects temperature differences of just 0.02°C and is used to hunt warm-blooded prey. A mouse can be found in total darkness.

▲The chimaera or ratfish, which is a relative of the sharks, lives deep down in cold seas. The skin on the head, and especially on the rostrum (the "nose" part), is covered with chemical and electrical sensors. Perhaps the ratfish uses these to find prey or breeding partners, in the darkness of the vast ocean depths.

different ways to ourselves – perhaps as a complex pattern of water currents and magnetic forces, or as a kaleidoscope of smells.

In complex animals, sensing is the function of receptor cells. These are specialized to detect an aspect of the outside world, change it into tiny electrical nerve signals, and send these signals along nerves to the brain. Sensory cells may be single and scattered in the body, or grouped into specialized parts called sense organs.

TALKING DRUM

Our ears detect airborne vibrations, but vibrations occur in water and in solid objects too. Fish have lateral lines that tell them of vibrations and currents in the water (page 55).

In certain types of spiders that live on banana plants, the male uses vibrations to find his mate. When he detects the scent of a female, he shakes his body and legs. The vibrations pass through the plant to the female, who gives an answering shake. The male then follows the vibrations to find his partner.

ANIMAL COMPASSES

We have invented the magnetic compass to show the direction of the weak lines of magnetic force around the Earth. But experiments have shown that many animals have a magnetic sense – a sort of built-in compass. They include dolphins, birds, mice, snails, bees, butterflies and moths. Many animal migrators navigate at least partly by this magnetic sense.

Scientists do not yet know how the magnetic sense works. They have discovered small particles of magnetic material in the skull and neck muscles of birds such as pigeons, which are well-known for their homing abilities. Studies have also shown that some birds use the Sun as a compass pointer on long flights, and that the bird must first "set" the Sun compass using the magnetic compass, before it can use the Sun's direction for navigation.

Among butterflies, the Monarch has the most magnetic particles in its body. This long-distance flier migrates from North America to winter in Mexico. A body compass presumably helps it to find the way as it flies hundreds of kilometres southwards.

ELECTRIFYING SENSES

A sense which is very important to some fish was discovered in 1951.

Fish such as elephant-snout fish and knifefish produce a continual discharge of electrical pulses from specialized muscles near the tail. These travel through the water and are detected by electrical sensors near the head, which have evolved from part of the lateral line (page 55). Any objects in the water change the pattern of pulses, and the fish senses this. These fish live in murky water. They use their electrical sense for navigation. They can detect plants, riverbanks and other animals up to 1m away.

Other fish, particularly sharks and rays, have electricity sensors on their skin, but do not produce electrical pulses themselves. They can pick up the weak electrical signals of other animals. Rays detect flatfish buried in the sand, picking up signals from the muscles around the gills of their prey.

Yet other fish, the electric eels and rays, have massive electrical organs that produce shocks of 500 volts or more, to stun their victims (page 55).

CHECKING FOR CHANGES

One feature of sense organs is their ability to stop responding when the same stimulus keeps occurring. It is said: "We cannot afford to feel our socks on our feet all day long." This means that when a sense first detects something, we become aware of it and consider whether we need to take any action. But if the stimulus is of no real importance, the sense organ and brain gradually "ignore" it. Only if it changes, do we take notice again. Our senses, and those of other animals, respond mainly to change.

◀Migrating geese fly in family groups, so the young have the benefit of older geese to guide them along the route. Even so, they can still find their way by instinct alone. They may navigate by the Sun, Moon and stars, and by detecting the Earth's magnetic field.

▲The Emperor tamarin, like other monkeys, relies greatly on its sense of balance while leaping about the forest trees overhanging the River Amazon. It uses its long, furry tail as a counterweight while balancing, and as a steering rudder when jumping.

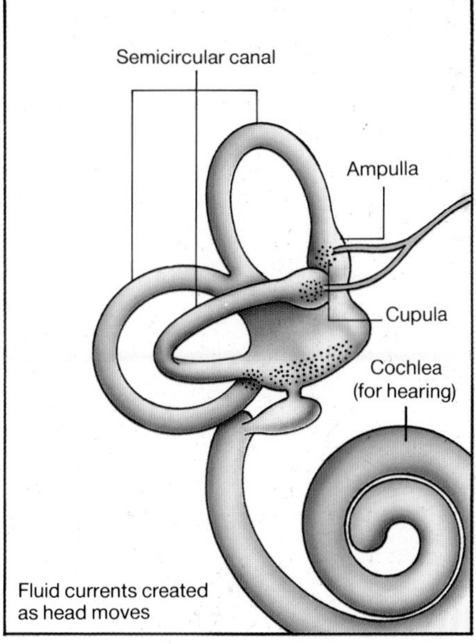

◀Mammals such as tamarins and humans have balance organs inside the ear. These are three curved tubes, semicircular canals. The canals contain a fluid that swishes round as the head moves. The fluid bends a jelly-like lump, the cupula, in the bulge (ampulla) at the end of the canal. Sensitive hairs embedded in the cupula create nerve signals when they are bent, which are sent to the brain. There is one canal in each dimension (up-down, front-back, left-right), so however the head moves, the fluid flows in at least one of them.

SEEING

In the far north of Scandinavia, a Snowy owl peers into the gathering gloom over the marsh. Unusually for an owl, it hunts mainly by day, although its great eyes can still pick out prey even in the failing light. Spotting a lemming on the far side of the clearing, it swoops down on silent wings. The lemming's poorer vision did not see the owl coming ...

Of all senses, vision is the most valuable for finding out about objects in the landscape. An animal with keen eyes can spot danger far away, so that it has time to escape. Senses such as taste and touch would work too late to avoid the danger.

Sight dominates our own lives so much that we think of the views we see with our eyes as the "real world". It is estimated that four-fifths of the information in the human brain came in via the eyes. A large part of our brain is devoted to analyzing and interpreting what the eyes see.

However, our eyes are only one of many types in the Animal Kingdom. Creatures with other types of eyes may have a very different view of the world. Also, we should remember that many other creatures rely less on vision and more on other senses such as smell or hearing.

EYE AND BRAIN

Animals make use of their eyesight in many ways. Even the simplest eye, which detects only light or dark, can help its owner to select more suitable surroundings. Scallops and fanworms, with several small simple eyes, use them to detect movements nearby. These can give warning of an approaching predator.

Other eyes form an image of the scene before them, in the form of a two-dimensional "picture". What the animal does with this information depends not on its eyes but on its brain. By itself, an eye is of little use.

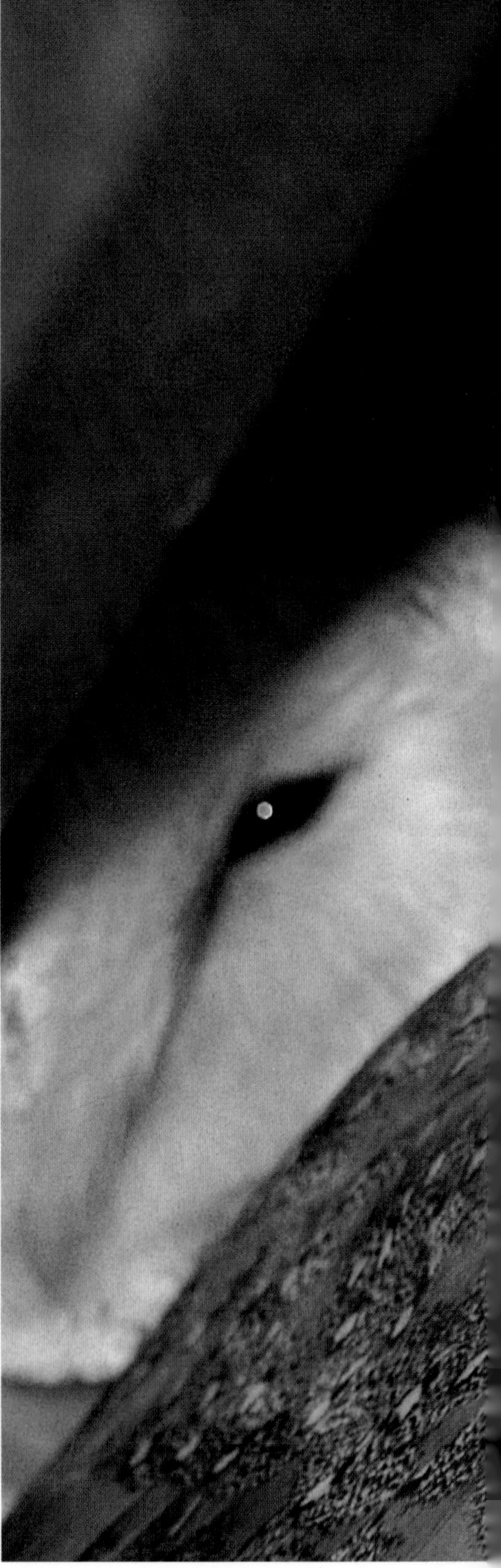

►A large part of an owl's head is taken up with its enormous eyes. Active mostly at night, an owl needs eyes which can gather as much light as possible, so it can see to hunt its prey.

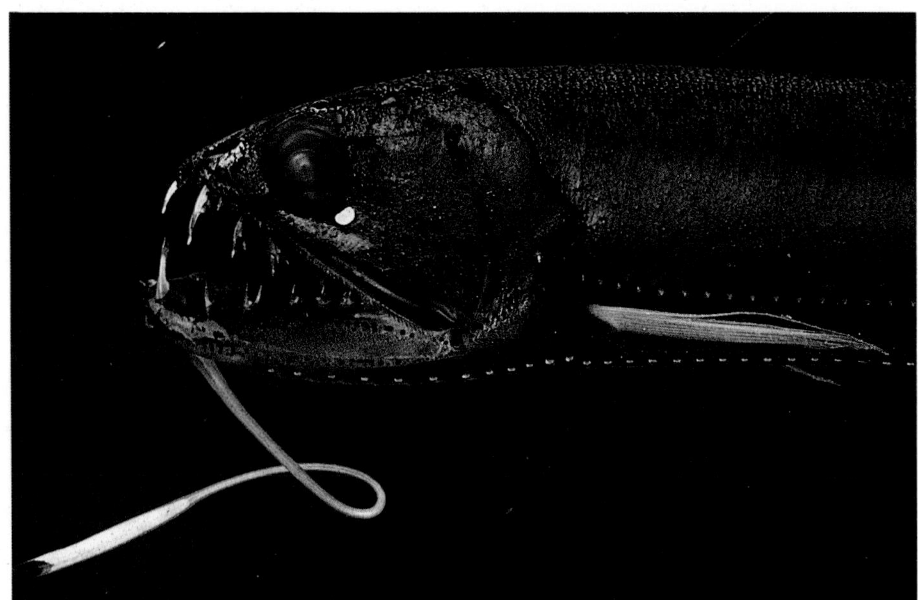

▼The deep-sea Viper fish lives where light seldom penetrates, and meals are few and far between. Its huge eyes collect what light there is, and its long fangs do the same for prey.

The brain must be able to process what the eyes see and then act on the information they provide.

FROM LIGHT TO ELECTRICITY

The essential part of any eye is the light-sensitive receptor cell. This cell generates nerve signals when light rays fall on it. An example is the rod cell, one type of light receptor cell in the mammal eye.

The rod cell contains a substance which is called visual pigment. This changes its structure when struck by light, which is a form of energy. The energy in the light ray changes the pigment into a more "excited" form. This sets off a series of chemical changes that affect the cell's membrane, closing some channels in the membrane which are usually open when there is no light.

As the channels close, they prevent other electrically-charged substances (mineral ions) from passing into or out of the cell. An imbalance soon builds up, in the form of an electrical charge. This is the beginning of the electrical nerve signal, which flashes along the nerve fibre towards the brain (page 66).

The eye has done its job: light has been turned into nerve signals. The whole process is completed in just a fraction of a second, and the visual pigment reverts to its original state and awaits more light rays. Without this quick recovery an eye would have very limited use.

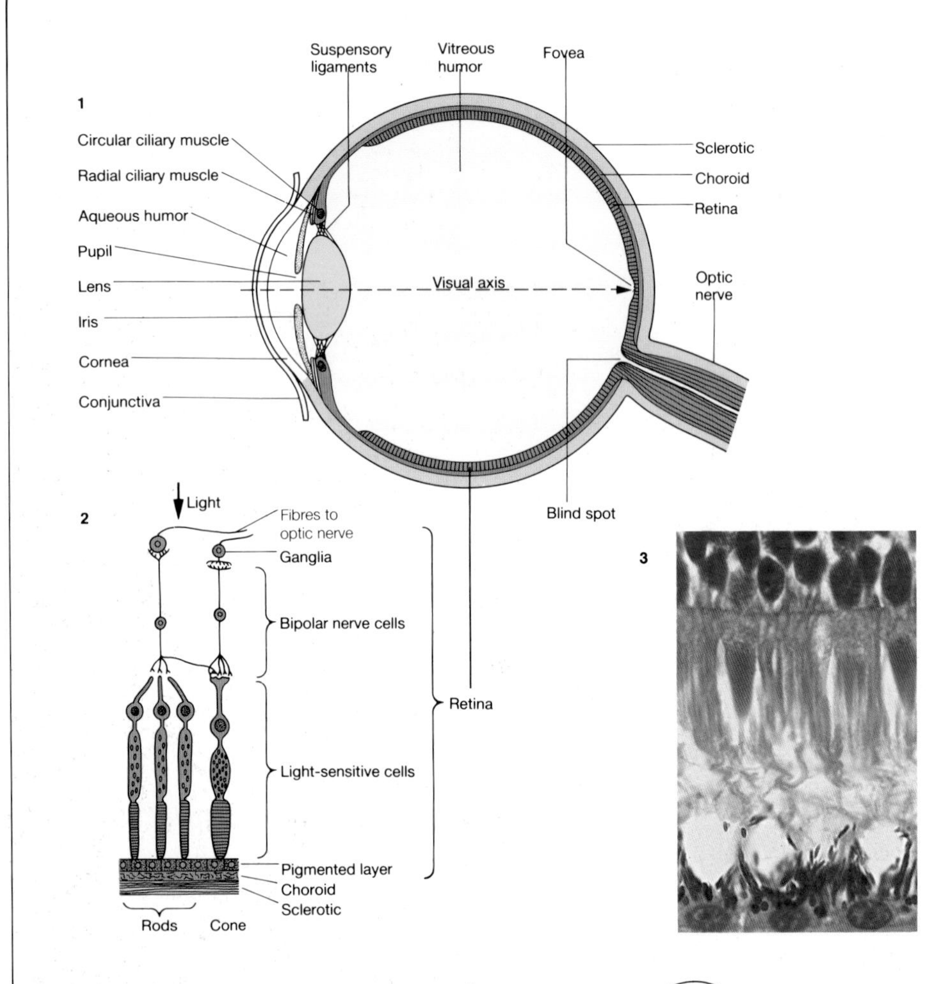

Different types of eyes
The human eye (1) has the typical mammalian design. Light comes in through the thin, transparent covering, the conjunctiva, which is kept moist by tear fluid smeared on to it by blinking. The light rays are partly focused by the cornea. The iris becomes larger to let more light through the pupil (the hole in its centre) in dim conditions, and smaller to stop bright light damaging the inside of the eye. Fine focusing is added by the lens, and the rays then pass through the jelly-like vitreous humour and shine on to the retina. This is a layer of light-sensitive rod and cone cells (2, and as seen under the microscope, 3). The rod cells work well in dim light but see only shades of grey. The three types of cones work well only in bright conditions. The choroid contains blood vessels that nourish the eye tissues.

▼Light rays from nearby objects (3a) are spreading apart when they reach the eye, so they need a stronger lens to focus them exactly on to the retina. The lens changes to its thick shape to do this. The rays from far away objects (3b) spread less, so the lens becomes thin and less powerful.

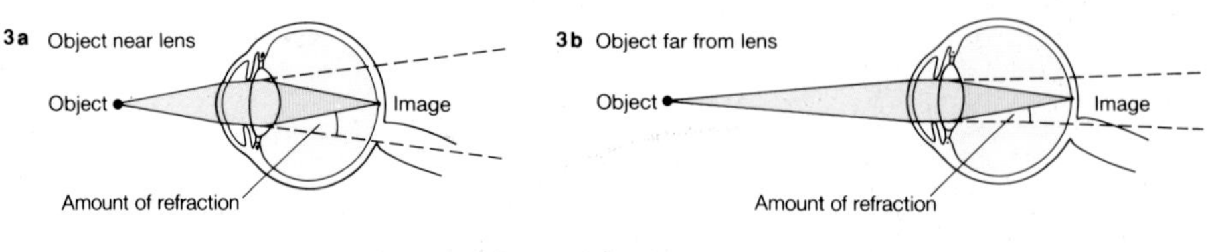

SIMPLE ANIMALS, SIMPLE EYES

A layer of light receptor cells packed closely together is known as a retina. In the course of evolution, about eight different ways have been tried of arranging the retina and other eye parts to produce an image.

The simpler animals, such as flatworms and earthworms, have simple types of eyes. These have a retina that lines a cup-shaped chamber of black pigment in the skin. When light comes from one direction, the pigment cup casts a shadow over the retina on that side. So a very simple image is formed by shadowing, as in a pinhole camera.

A variation on this design is to place each light receptor at the bottom of its own cup or tube. Eyes of this pattern are found in several species of fanworm and tube worm.

LOOKING THROUGH LENSES

Eyes with lenses have evolved many times. The eye lens works like a camera lens, to bend light rays and bring them into sharp focus on the retina. Without a lens the retina just sees a multi-coloured blur. Several animal groups have evolved separately eyes comprising a single chamber with a lens inside to focus light on the retina. These include fish, cephalopod molluscs such as the octopus and cuttlefish, gastropod molluscs like conchs, and some types of worms found in the sea.

EXTRA BENDING POWER

In water, light rays bend little as they pass from water to the watery fluid inside the eye. To focus an image on the back of the eye, a fish needs a powerful spherical lens.

Out of water, light rays bend a lot as they go from air to the watery fluid in the eye. Most of the bending in the eyes of land animals takes place at the cornea. This is the curved, transparent "window" at the front of the eye. The lens then adds fine-focusing adjustments, and may be much thinner than the lens in the eye of a water animal such as a fish.

This type of eye is found in the amphibians, reptiles, birds and mammals, and also in spiders. Some kinds

▼Animals whose eyes face forwards, like this Red fox, see a similar scene in each eye – although from slightly different angles. The brain compares the two views and works out the distances of objects. This is called binocular vision. Binocular vision is especially important for hunters as it helps them judge the distance when pouncing on prey.

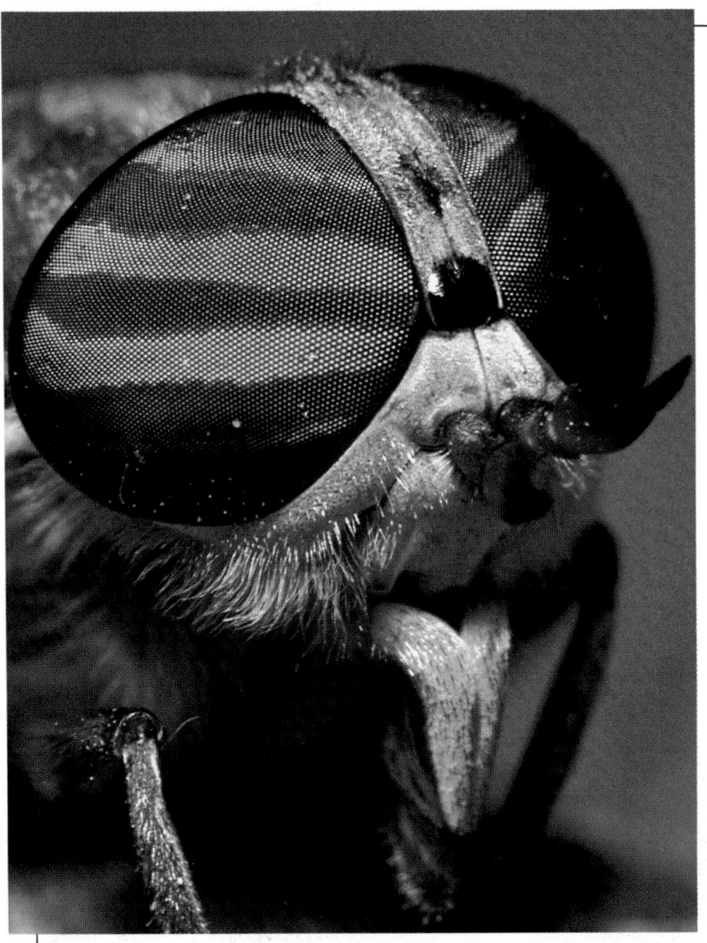

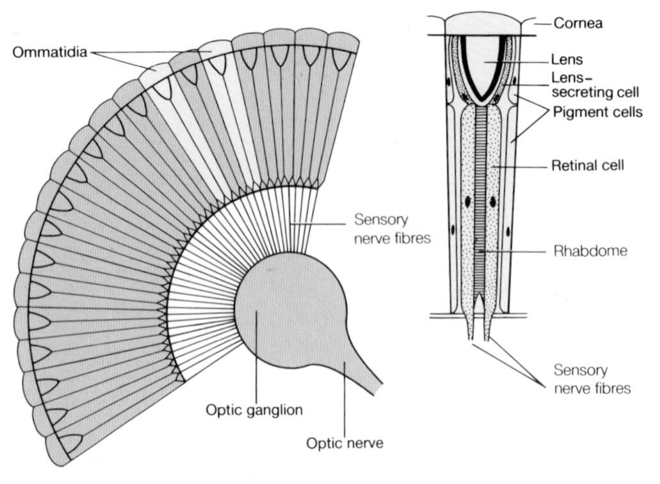

Insect eyes

◀Each of the horsefly's eyes is made of hundreds of separate units, called ommatidia. They see a mosaic-like view of the world. The eyes of the dragonflies can contain up to 30,000 units and give these hunters sharp vision to help find prey.

▲An insect eye with one ommatidium enlarged. The lens carries out some focusing, and the retinal cells in the cone-shaped tube detect the light rays. Nerve fibres run from these to the optic ganglion, and then down the optic nerve to the insect's brain.

of jumping spider, which hunt by sight, have vision almost as good as that of monkeys.

MANY EYES MAKE LIGHT WORK?

In contrast to the single-chambered eye of vertebrates some animals have compound eyes. In these there are many separate units. Each has a lens or other focusing system, and retinal cells that turn the light rays into nerve signals. Compound eyes occur mainly in insects and crustaceans.

A bee's eye has about 5,000 of these separate optical units, called ommatidia. They fit snugly together like the hexagonal cells of a honeycomb. The two compound eyes can see almost all around the bee. The compound eye probably forms a mosaic type of image, although we cannot be sure how the nerve signals are interpreted in the animal's brain. However, calculations show that a bee's vision is, at best, 60 times less detailed than our own.

A variation on the compound eye is the superposition eye. It is found in night-time insects and deep-sea crustaceans, which live with very low light levels. The individual lenses or mirrors do not each form a separate image, but send their light rays on to the retina lying below. The combined image is considerably brighter than individual ones would be.

WHO CAN SEE COLOURS?

Light rays of different colours have different wavelengths. Those with longer wavelengths are red, progressing through the other colours of the spectrum (the "rainbow") to the violet of the shorter wavelengths of light.

Our eyes have two main kinds of light receptor cells – rods and cones. In each eye there are about 120 million rods and 7 million cones. We have three types of cones. Each type is most sensitive to light of a certain wavelength, depending on the type of visual pigment it contains. Our three cone types pick up mainly blue, green or yellow light. The other colours we see are mixtures of these three.

Many other animals can see in colour. The eyes of gorillas and baboons have the same three visual pigments as us. Frogs have good colour vision and are especially sensitive to blue.

Squirrels and dogs have only two types of visual pigment, so the colours they see may not be as varied as those we can detect. Birds have five types of pigments, and also a filtering system based on droplets of oil in the cone cells, so they can probably distinguish many more colours than us. As scientists continue their research, they are discovering that more and more animals can see colours in one form or another.

SEEING INVISIBLE LIGHT

The shortest wavelength of light that we can see is violet. Yet some insects can see even shorter wavelengths – that is, light which is invisible to the human eye. This is called ultra-violet light. Many flowers have markings that we cannot see, but which bees can see and use to identify the flower and guide them to the source of nectar at a petal's base.

The longest wavelengths we can detect are red. Again some creatures, such as butterflies and snakes, can see light of even longer wavelengths, known as infra-red. Warm objects give off infra-red rays, which are sometimes called "heat waves". Snakes such as pit vipers and rattlesnakes have infra-red detectors in pits on either side of the head, in front of their real eyes. The detectors pick up infra-red rays coming from warm-blooded prey such as mice. These snakes can judge the direction and distance of their prey, and strike with deadly accuracy – even in what looks to us like complete darkness.

Light waves can vibrate in different directions, but to our eyes these differences (of "polarization") are not apparent. Some animals, including insects such as bees, have their light-receiving apparatus ordered in a such a way that they see light differently according to which way it is polarized. The pattern of polarization of light from the sky can indicate the Sun's direction even when it is behind cloud. So bees can often "see" the Sun when we cannot.

WHOSE EYES ARE BEST?

Because eyes are specialized for different roles it is hard to say which is best, but birds of prey may see things clearly six times as far away as us. Owls see when it seems pitch black to us.

The size of an eye gives a rough indication of how sharp its owner's vision is likely to be. Ostriches have the largest eyes among all the land animals. The largest eyes of all are the Giant squid's. These can be up to 40cm across, and allows the animal to catch prey such as fish and smaller squid deep in the sea.

▲A lioness and cub seen at night with the aid of an image intensifier. This magnifies each photon of light to levels that the human eye can see. There is obviously enough light at night to see clearly if eyes are sufficiently sensitive, like those of many nocturnal animals.

▼The angwantibo's eyes shine in the African night, reflecting the photographer's flash. This animal has a reflecting layer, or tapetum, behind the retina, which sends light back through the sensitive rod cells, giving a second chance of making use of it.

HEARING

Sitting in their country garden on a summer evening, the family talk quietly about plans for the next day. Suddenly the youngest child hears very high-pitched squeaks from nearby. The older child thinks she can hear something, but the parents cannot detect any such sounds. Then a bat flits over the hedge. They realize that the squeaks are being made by this tiny mammal.

Not all ears hear the same sounds. In humans, a young child is able to hear much higher-pitched sounds than older people. The ear's sensitivity to high notes falls with age.

Other animals hear sounds that are much higher, or lower, or quieter, than we can detect. Small mammals like shrews communicate by a range of very high-pitched whistles and pips. Birds such as pigeons may hear some extremely low-pitched noises such as stormy seas throwing waves on the shore.

Sounds too high-pitched for us to detect are known as ultrasound. Those that are too low-pitched we call infrasound. Air, water and solid substances like rocks all carry these sound vibrations. For some animals, sound is the main sense. They "hear" the world in the way we "see" it.

PICKING UP VIBRATIONS

Hearing organs such as ears are specialized to detect vibrations. In air, the vibrations are in the form of sound waves – air molecules moving to and fro at great speed. In water too sound travels through the vibrations of the water molecules. Sound travels even better in water than in air.

These vibrations are a form of energy. The hearing organ changes them into a different form of energy, electrical nerve impulses, which are interpreted in the brain.

USEFULLY DEAF

Surprisingly, some creatures that are otherwise well equipped with sensory organs, such as octopus and squid, lack true ears. However, this may be useful. Some of their main predators are toothed whales such as the Sperm whale, which are thought to stun their prey with incredibly loud bursts of sound. No squid could escape such a powerful noise at close range, but deafness may protect it while the predator is some way off, and let the squid escape.

►A Red-eyed tree frog blows up its vocal sac as it croaks to other frogs nearby. It then listens with its ears, the green discs just behind the eyes. A frog's hearing is mainly limited to the calls of other frogs of its own kind. It cannot hear many other sounds.

▼Red howler monkeys use sound as a form of communication in their South American tropical forest home. It is difficult to see other members of their group or rival groups among the trees. So the regular dawn chorus of howls lets each monkey know the whereabouts of other howlers more than 1km away.

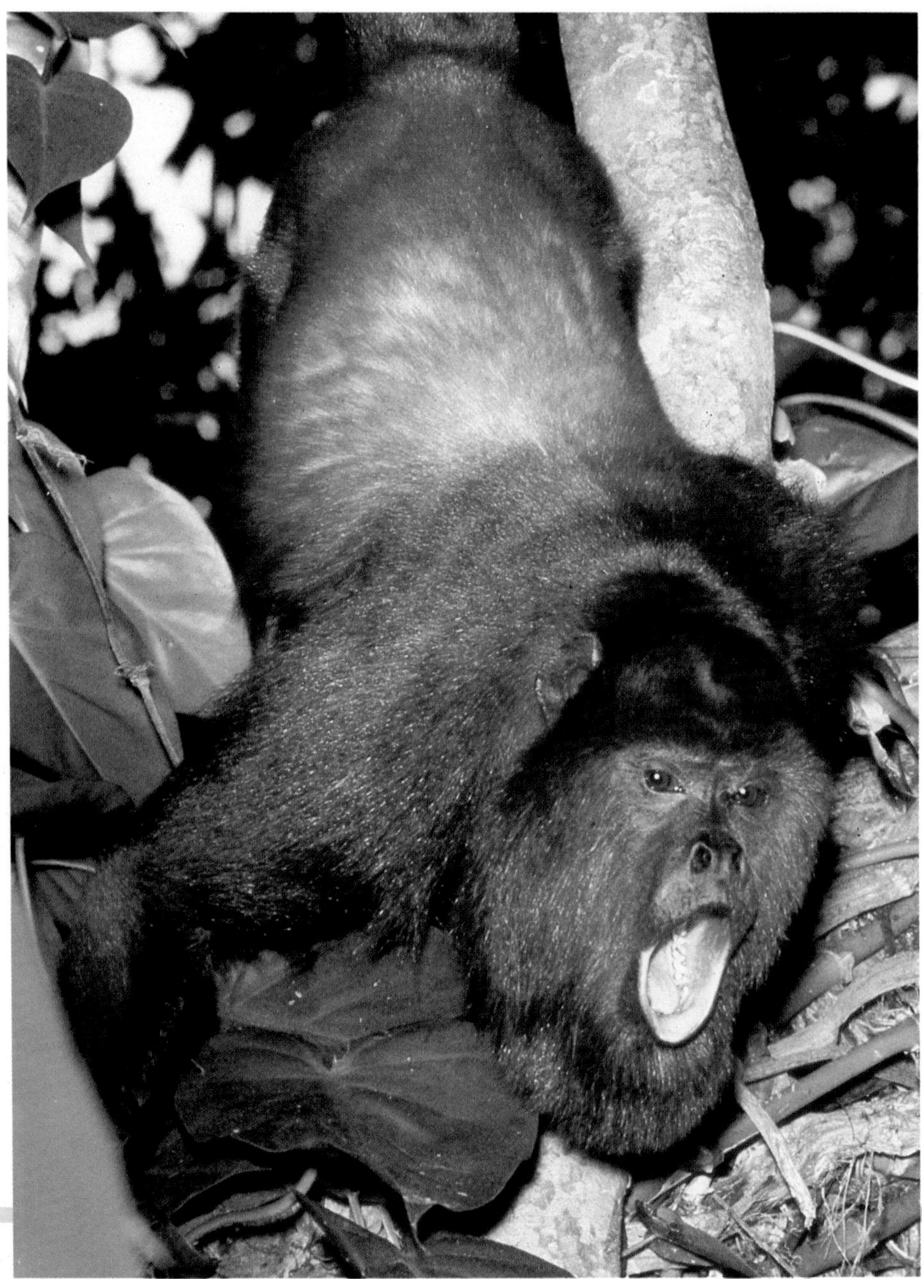

INSIDE AN EAR

Hair cells are the basis of many sensory organs, such as those of balance (page 43). The most intricate use of hair cells is in the mammalian inner ear, in the cochlea.

In mammals, sound waves are collected by the pinna, or ear flap – what we usually call "the ear". Our own pinna is not particularly good at funnelling sound waves into the ear, but that of a horse or rabbit is much better, and it can be swivelled to pinpoint the direction of a noise.

Sound waves travel along the ear canal and bounce off the ear drum, making it vibrate. These vibrations are transmitted through the middle ear cavity by three small bones (ossicles) to another membrane, the oval window, which is the entrance to the cochlea itself. The vibrations pass through the window into the fluid within the cochlea.

SNAIL-SHAPE CANAL

The cochlea has the coiled shape of a snail shell. But, to understand its workings, imagine it uncoiled becoming a long, cone-shaped tube. Inside it is a stretched sheet, the basilar membrane. This is the part that enables

The human ear
◀The human ear senses sounds. It also detects movements of the head and helps keep the balance. Inside the middle ear, sound waves are converted into vibrations of the ear drum, then vibrations of the tiny bones known as ear ossicles, and then vibrations in the fluid of the cochlea, where they are changed into nerve signals. The three numbered circles show the main sensory area. Gravity detection takes place in the utriculus, or utricle **(1)**, where tiny hairs (cilia) register movements of a tiny stone (otolith), sideways head movement is detected in the ampulla of the semicircular canals **(2**, and page 43), and sound is registered by the cochlea itself **(3)**, shown here in side-on view.

◀A Greater horseshoe bat swoops on a moth, having homed in on it by a "sonar" system of high-pitched sound pulses. The battle is not one-sided, since some moths have listening membranes that hear the pulses, giving time to escape.

▲Sound waves made by whales travel through the oceans for hundreds of kilometres. The whale makes its eerie "song" by moving air from one part of its body to another. This is a Humpback whale mother and calf.

mammals to detect the pitch, or frequency, of sounds so well.

Hair cells are in contact with the basilar membrane along its length. At the end nearest the oval window, the membrane is quite wide and vibrates best to low frequencies such as a bass drum. At the far end it is narrow and vibrates most strongly to high frequencies, as from a flute.

When sound of a certain pitch reaches the cochlea, it causes the strongest vibrations in just one region of the basilar membrane. This stimulates hair cells in that region and generates a particular pattern of nerve signals. From this the brain recognizes the pitch of a sound. Many noises contain sounds of several pitches.

SONAR HUNTER

Bats use their ears for navigating in the dark. They send out extremely high-pitched clicks, pips and squeaks which are reflected off nearby objects. Their ears detect the returning echoes, and from their pattern, the bat's brain can work out the size of objects and their distance away. They can detect objects as thin as a human hair. A bat uses this echo-location system, which is similar to the sonar "pings" of submarines, to track and catch insects in mid-flight – even in complete darkness.

A few birds, and many whales and dolphins, also listen for the echoes of their own voices, and use them to gather useful information.

CHIRPING AND SINGING

Reptiles, amphibians and fish have simpler ears than mammals. They detect a smaller range of sounds, but can still give useful information to their owners about their own kind. Frogs make many sounds at breeding time, and the sea can be full of fish noises ranging from grunts to a variety of percussion effects. Among the animals without backbones the only really noisy group of animals, with a sense of hearing to match, is the insects. Their only ears are vibrating drum-like membranes with a few receptor cells attached. They are sited on the middle or back part of the body, or on the legs in some grasshoppers.

Most of these simple ears do not have a wide range of pitch. They are tuned into the calls of rivals or mates. The main information in insect song is contained in the pattern of pulses – the way that the sounds start and stop in rapid bursts.

TOUCH

Sitting by the river, the boy sees a fish close to the bank. He creeps forward, trying to stay out of sight. He slowly puts his hand under the surface, to grasp the fish. But as he opens his fingers, he creates a slight ripple in the water – and the fish has gone.

With our fingertips, we can feel vibrations too small for the eye to see. Skin is, in a sense, our biggest sense organ. It detects not only touch but also pressure, heat, cold, and pains caused by extreme heat, crushing pressure, a wound or some other damage.

Receptors that indicate contact with the body surface, which is the basic form of "touch", are found in all animals. In insects they take the form of bendable hairs, each with one or more sense cells making contact with the base. As in other senses, one form of energy – the energy of movement of the hair – is turned into electrical nerve signals, which are sent along nerves to the brain.

SENSITIVE SKIN

In many other animals, including ourselves, modified nerve endings in the skin, tell us if we have touched something, and also give information on the texture, or feel, of its surface. Each nerve ending has an elastic capsule around it called a corpuscle.

▼Structure of skin A step-like cutaway diagram of human skin shows its main layers and the microscopic sensors they contain. These include cold and heat receptors, which are buried quite deeply, and deep pressure receptors which are at the very base of the skin, almost in the fat layer beneath. Light touch receptors, and free nerve endings to sense pain, are near the surface. There are also sensors in the hair root which can feel the hair shaft being pulled or tilted. Skin contains many other structures too, such as blood vessels and sweat glands.

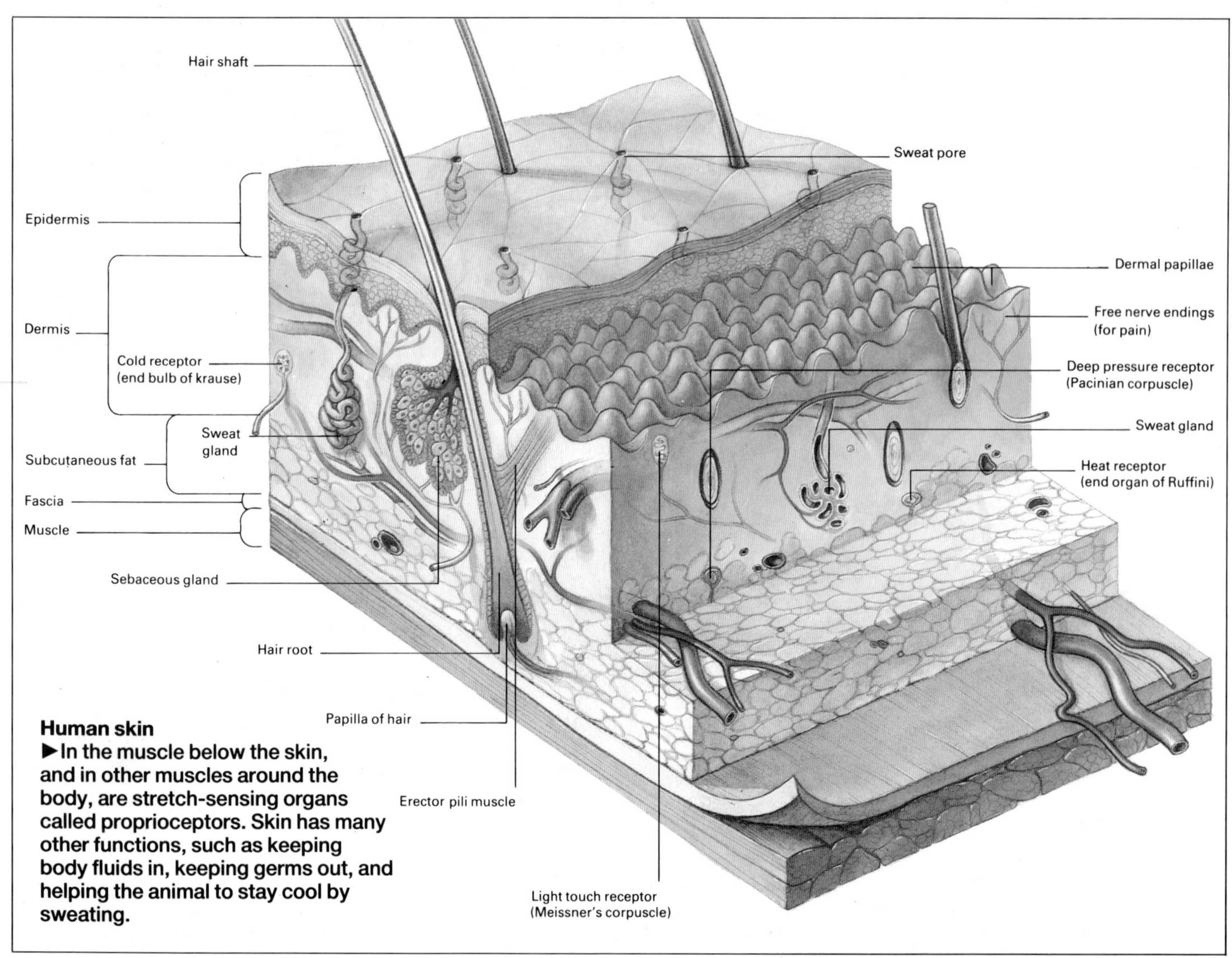

Human skin
►In the muscle below the skin, and in other muscles around the body, are stretch-sensing organs called proprioceptors. Skin has many other functions, such as keeping body fluids in, keeping germs out, and helping the animal to stay cool by sweating.

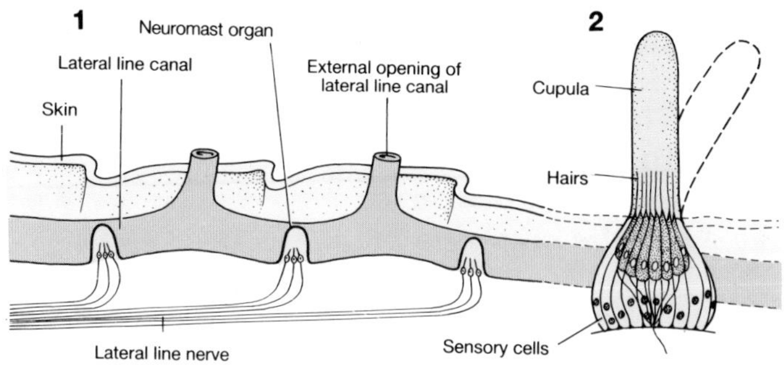

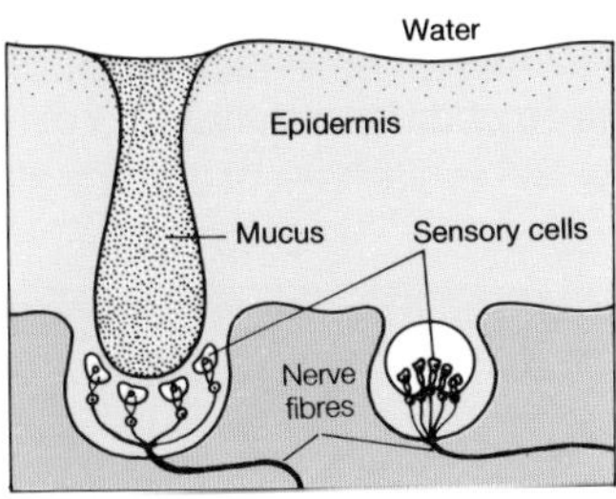

Two types of fish electro-sensors.
▲◀The Electric ray produces massive electrical shocks to stun prey. These are made by specially developed muscles along the body sides. Rays and other fish have electricity sensors in the skin, to detect weak electrical pulses given off by the muscles of other animals. They are good at finding flatfish buried in the sand, and feed on these.

▲(Top) The bleak shows the silvery lateral line on the side of its body. (Above) The lateral line is a groove or tube under the skin (1), with tubular openings to the surface. A single pressure receptor in the line (2). These receptors stick up from the base of the lateral line, as neuromast organs.

It has the effect of transmitting fast events, such as sudden taps which change its shape, to the nerve. But the corpuscle stays bulging out when constant pressure is put on it, and makes few signals. This is why we can no longer really "feel" something in contact with the skin after it has been there for some time, such as the pressure of socks and shoes on our feet (page 43).

INNER FEELINGS

Sensors which detect deformation, or change in shape, are also found in other parts of an animal's body. In the muscles, they measure the stresses (tensions) and the strains (length changes), as the muscles contract and relax when the animal moves. This is known as the proprioceptive sense. It helps the animal to tell the position of the various parts of its body. Muscle length is measured in many animals by elastic, spindle-shaped receptors in the muscle itself. As the muscle is lengthened the receptor is stretched and sends out nerve signals.

Changes in muscle tension are also measured. Insects, with hard, shell-like outer skeletons, usually monitor changes using receptors embedded in the skeleton itself. In mammals, which have an internal bony skeleton, tension is measured in the rope-like tendons that join the muscles to the bones of the body.

DISTANT TOUCH

Water, being much thicker than air, transmits vibrations and ripples well over short distances. Fish can detect these water currents by a type of "touch-at-a-distance" sense organ, the lateral line. In most fish, the lateral line shows as a thin strip along each side of the body, from behind the gill cover to the tail base. The line is a channel, groove or tube under the skin. It has slits or pores opening to the water above. At intervals along the line are clumps of sensory hair cells, with their tips embedded in a jelly-like mass, called the cupula.

Water currents ripple along the lateral line and bend the cupulae. This stimulates the hair cells to make nerve signals. This enables the fish to feel water currents around its body surface, made by the water flowing around rocks and other obstacles or by animals moving nearby.

A modified version of the lateral line sensors is found in the electricity detectors, or electro-sensors, of many fish. These are usually scattered about in the skin, particularly on the head, of fish such as sharks, rays and chimaeras. The electrical "ripples" are focused into a mucus-filled pit and affect the sensory cells there, which pass nerve signals to the brain.

SMELL, TASTE

A kiwi creeps through the dense forest of New Zealand, scratching with its powerful claws and dipping its long beak into the ground, in the search for food. Suddenly it catches the scent of a juicy worm and sticks its beak deep into the leaves, sniffing through its nostrils at the beak's tip. Within a second the prey is located and is on its way down the kiwi's gullet.

Smell and taste are often referred to as the "chemical senses", because they are concerned with detecting certain chemical substances in the animal's surroundings.

Our sense of taste detects the nature of chemicals in the mouth. These are dissolved in water, either in watery fluids already in the food, or released into the watery saliva that we add to food as we chew it. In us, the sense of smell deals mainly with airborne chemicals that float from a distance. They are breathed into the nose and captured by the smell organs there.

However, dividing taste and smell in this way is a very human-based way of looking at these types of sense organs. It applies to mammals and birds, but in many other groups of animals, there is little or no difference. For example, for a snail living in the water, "taste" and "smell" become almost the same.

UNLOCKING SMELLS

Biologists know little about the way that smells are converted from molecules floating in the air into nerve signals passing to the brain. The chief theory is that there is some form of "lock-and-key" mechanism. The sensory hairs that line the top of the nasal cavity, inside the nose, bear millions of nerve endings. In a human, there are about 15 million receptor cells in the nose, covering an area of about 4sq cm. This is much less than in many mammals. A cat's smell receptors cover some 15sq cm, and a dog has a sensitive lining of more than 100sq cm.

The receptors may have molecule-sized locks on their surface. Their keys are smell molecules. As a smell molecule reaches the nose it becomes trapped by the mucus overlying the sensory hairs, and passes through to slot into one of the locks. Fitting the key into the lock sparks off a nerve signal in some way. The key may be a chemical reaction between the smell molecule and the nerve ending; it could be the radiation which some

▼Most people recognize these seven distinct smells. We can probably call up memories in our mind's eye – or rather, our "mind's nose" – of what they smell like. The human nose can tell apart hundreds of different odours. Yet it is insensitive compared to many animals.

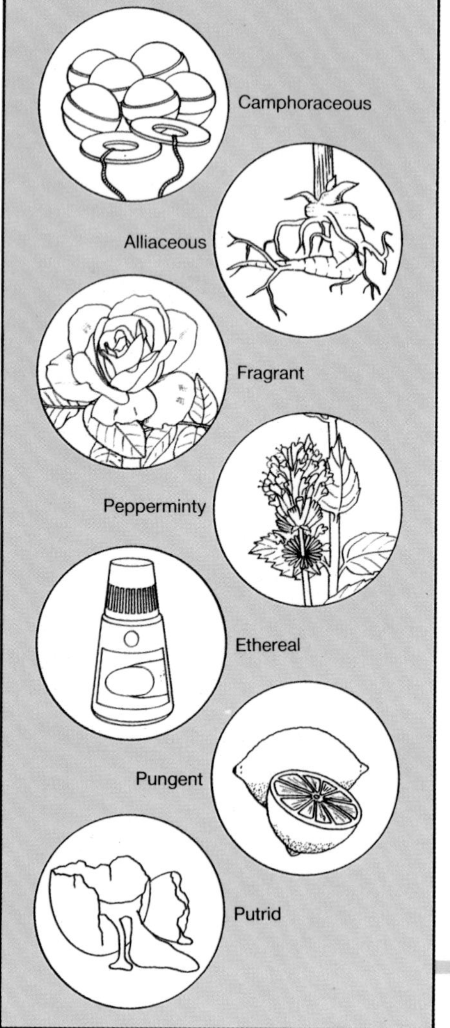

▼Taste buds in different parts of the tongue (1) respond most to one of the four main flavours that make up different tastes. A cutaway of the tongue (2) shows its surface, or epithelium, and the taste buds in deep grooves. Fluids collect in the grooves for tasting. There are also taste buds on the roof of the mouth, the throat and the tonsils. An enlargement of a single taste bud (3), with some 20 to 50 sensory and supporting cells grouped like segments of an orange.

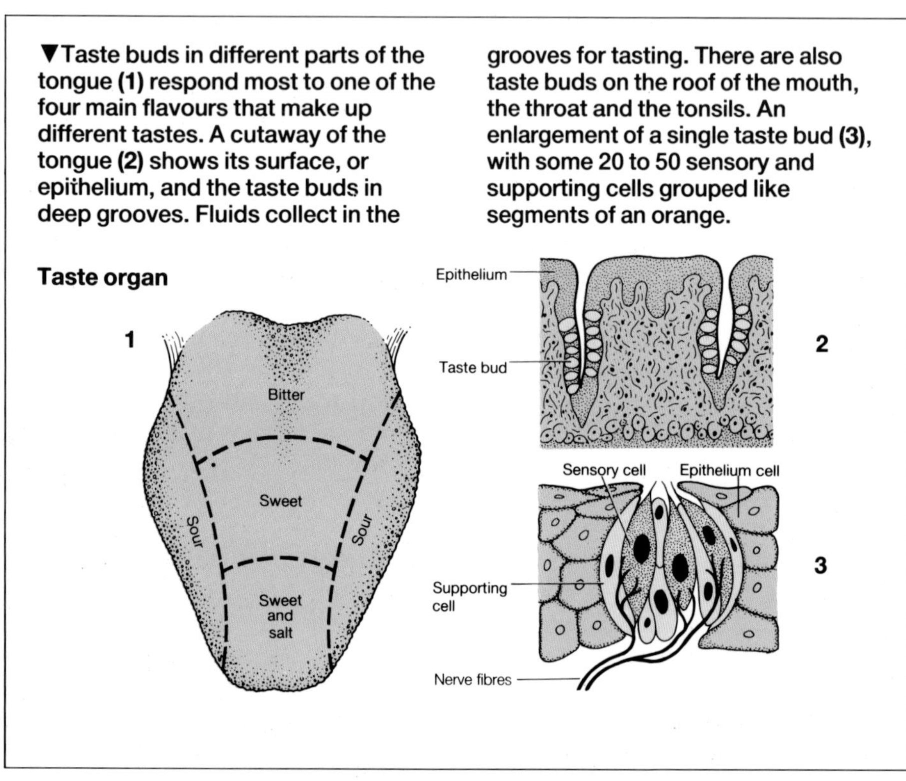

▼Many male moths have feathery antennae specialized for detecting a few odours which are important to the animal. This male Atlas moth has up to 10,000 receptors on his antennae, tuned to the female's sex-scent.

▲The snake's tongue "tastes" the air. As it flicks out, it picks up chemical signals. Back in the mouth, it is pushed into two pockets in the roof of the mouth, Jacobson's organs, where the chemicals are sensed.

▲A Brown hyena smothers grass with smelly substances from scent glands under its tail. The smell informs other hyenas that it has passed this way. Hyenas from other groups then know that the area is already occupied.

molecules give off; or it might be the particular properties of vibration that the molecule possesses.

THE "ODOUR IMAGE"

Whatever the process, a complex pattern of nerve messages is sent to the brain from the smell receptors. How the brain interprets these messages is also not clear. Tests on mammalian smell receptors show that they are not very specific, but that each is sensitive to a variety of odours, and sends a varied set of signals to the smell centres in the brain.

It may be that the brain constructs a sort of "odour image" from the overall pattern of signals it receives, and does not rely on specific kinds of smell receptors for a particular sensation.

SMELLS TO ACT ON

Smells have a number of uses. In many creatures, they are used to find food. A Polar bear can scent a seal carcass from 20km. Deer are alerted by the merest whiff of a wolf on the breeze.

Smell also warns if food has gone bad or if it contains possibly harmful substances. Dogs, whose smelling abilities are up to 1,000 times better than ours, sniff any unfamiliar food cautiously before they take a bite.

Many animals use special smells called pheromones for communication. In moths, the female moth releases a type of odour known as a sex pheromone into the air from her body. This can be detected by male moths hundreds of metres away, using their feathery antennae. The male moth then follows the odour trail to find and mate with the female.

THE ONE-SCENT SENSE

One of these pheromones is bombykol. It is made by unmated female Silk moths, in glands on the abdomen.

This chemical has been produced in the laboratory, and tried on the male moths. Tests show that the male's antennae bear 17,000 smell receptors, and at least 300 of these must be stimulated before the moth takes any notice of the chemical.

Chemicals very similar to bombykol have also been made in the laboratory, in which just one atom of the bombykol molecule has been altered. The male moth is up to 1,000 times less sensitive to the smell of this altered molecule. So, although the male Silk moth is incredibly sensitive to the odour of real bombykol, it seems that he can smell little else.

THE SMELL OF DANGER

Ants also use pheromones, of several different types. Scout ants lay a trail of odour when they find food, so that the other workers can follow this and bring the food back to the nest.

There are also alarm pheromones that warn the ant colony of danger, such as attack by an anteater. Upon smelling this warning signal in the air, the worker ants cluster round and try to defend the colony or repair the damage to the nest. Bees also use alarm pheromones to summon reinforcements. When a bee stings an intruder, she releases the pheromone and fellow workers come to help.

SMELL OR TASTE?

In insects, there are chemical receptors on the hairs of the body and limbs. It is often unclear whether, in human terms, these animals "taste" or "smell" a particular chemical. A fly has taste hairs on its feet and mouthparts. This is a sensible design, since these are the first and second parts to come into contact with food.

In water-dwelling animals, all chemicals are water-borne. The distinction between smell and taste is even less clear. Fish have nostrils, and also taste buds in parts of their mouths and elsewhere. Catfish have so many taste receptors all over their bodies that they have sometimes been called swimming tongues.

Like moths in the insect group, some fish are extremely sensitive to specific smells. Salmon can find their way back over hundreds of kilometres to their home stream to spawn, partly by following its smell.

A QUESTION OF TASTE

It is generally recognized that there are four different kinds of tastes: sweet, acid (sour), salty and bitter. Each part of the human tongue responds best to one of these main flavours. The many tastes that we sense in our various foods, whether ordinary or exotic, are built up from mixtures of the four basic flavours plus odours. So food does not taste the same when we have a cold.

Before we can taste anything, it must be dissolved in saliva. It then spreads to touch taste buds, microscopic groups of cells in grooves and pits on the tongue. The cells have projections or taste hairs, yet another example of the sensory hair cell common in other senses. As with smell, the way that the dissolved chemicals make the cells fire off nerve signals is not clearly understood.

An adult has about 9,000 taste buds on the tongue. Babies and children have more, which die as they grow older. Like eyesight and hearing, taste becomes less sensitive with age. This may be why our tastes in food change and why some parents do not always agree with their children about horrible-tasting food or the foul-flavoured medicines!

◀A goosefish stalks a crab. Many crabs feed on carrion and are able to home in on dead creatures by using their sense of smell. The antennules carry delicate hair-like sense organs which respond to chemicals in the water. But these organs do not seem to have alerted the crab to the approaching fish.

MUSCLES, SKELETONS

A large crab crawls hungrily over the sea bed. It notices a meaty-looking scallop, whose shell halves are slightly agape to reveal about 100 tiny blue eyes between them. As the crab nears, the scallop rapidly snaps its shell halves closed. Water shoots from between them, jerking the scallop backwards. It repeats the movement and rapidly "flaps" away from the startled crab.

The ability to move from place to place is known as locomotion. It has many different uses for an animal, including finding food and shelter, escaping from predators and locating a mate. Another type of movement happens inside the body. It moves body contents from one part to another, like food through the intestines or blood through the vessels.

Apart from the simplest creatures such as an amoeba, animal movement depends on muscles. Muscles are controlled by nerve signals, usually from the brain. However, muscles often act on the skeleton, which is the rigid structural framework of an animal. The muscle is attached to the skeleton via its long, tapering, rope-like end, called a tendon.

STRIPED OR SMOOTH?

There are two main types of muscle: smooth and striated. They are named from their appearance under the light microscope, striated muscle having regular light and dark stripes across its length. Striated muscles make those movements seen from outside, such as moving a limb or the whole body. An animal can make this kind of muscle move at will.

Smooth muscles lack stripes. They are concerned with the movements of internal organs. The control of these is largely automatic. For example, we do not control, or even usually notice, the movements of our intestines.

FIBRES AND FILAMENTS

A muscle is made of hundreds of small fibres lying side by side along its length. Inside each fibre are two kinds of even smaller filaments, thick and thin, arranged in regular bundles. These are, in fact, large molecules: the thick ones are a protein called myosin, and the thin ones are those of a protein called actin. The two sets of

►Some birds must run before they can fly, to pick up speed for take-off. These Greater flamingos patter rapidly across the water while flapping their great wings, before becoming airborne.

▼One wingbeat of a duck in flight. The downstroke (the five stages below), with feathers spread, produces the lift that keeps the duck up. It also gives thrust to propel the bird forwards. On the upstroke (the five stages on the opposite page), the feathers are opened to let air through and the wing is tilted in line with the direction of flight, so giving the least air resistance.

filaments are linked by chemical bonds called cross-bridges. In relaxed muscle, these sets of filaments only just interlock with each other, like the fingertips of each hand held just touching. When the muscle is sent a signal by a nerve to become shorter, the two sets of filaments slide past each other, like the fingers of both hands moving together to interlock. The cross-bridges break and then reform with the next link along. As the filaments slide, the muscle shortens.

The strongest muscle, for its size, is that which keeps the two halves of a mussel shell closed. Among the fastest-acting muscles are the finger muscles of mice, which contract 15 times more quickly than the muscles in the leg of a tortoise.

SKELETONS INSIDE

There are numerous types of skeleton among animals. In the vertebrates the skeleton is made of bones and it is inside the body. Some bones are fixed firmly to each other, as with the parts of the skull. Others are linked by movable joints. The joints are lined with smooth, shiny cartilage, to help easy movement. Bone tissue is about two-thirds calcium phosphate crystals embedded in the type of fibrous protein known as collagen.

OUTER FRAME

Other animals have their body frameworks outside. Crabs and other crustaceans are encased in a hard outer shell, which becomes thinner at the joints to allow movement. The shell is up to 90 per cent calcium carbonate (the same chemical as chalk), with protein and another fibrous substance, chitin.

Many molluscs, including snails and scallops, have hard outer shells for skeletons. These are almost entirely

▲Airborne animals **The Sugar glider (*Petaurus breviceps*) (1) glides on furred membranes. The Poplar admiral (*Limenitis populi*) (2) usually flaps but may glide on migration. The prehistoric pterosaur (*Pteranodon*) (3) was probably good at soaring. The Large mouse-eared bat (*Myotis myotis*) (4) is a true flier, unlike the gliding "Flying dragon" (*Draco spilopterus*) (5).**

calcium carbonate, with less than 5 per cent protein in the structure.

Insects also have a body with a hard outer casing, the cuticle. It is made up of chitin and various proteins.

Worms and similar creatures do not have hard, stiff parts in their bodies. Their "skeleton" comes from fluid under pressure, like water forced into a balloon. This is called a hydrostatic skeleton, and it is strong enough to enable an earthworm to tunnel through hard soil.

PULLING AGAINST PARTNERS

Muscles can only contract. They cannot actively lengthen. So how can animals carry out such complicated movements? The answer is that the muscles usually come in pairs. Each

◀Sharks lack swimbladders and so are not buoyant like other fish. They tend to sink unless they keep swimming. As they move forwards they obtain lift from the nose, wing-like fins and tail. This is a White-tipped reef shark.

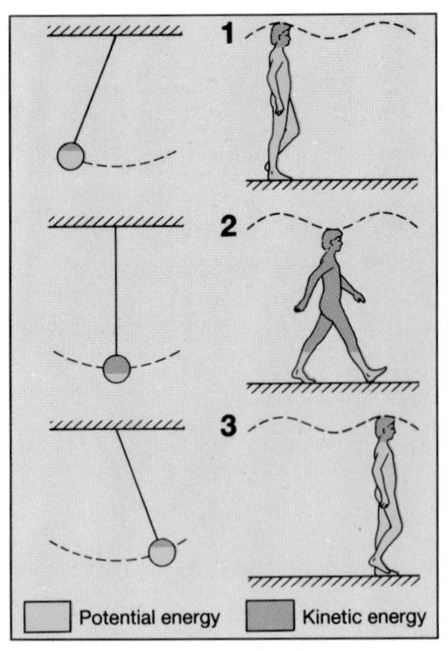

Walking
▲A walking human is rather like a swinging pendulum. The pendulum and body are both at their highest points (1). They use the pull of gravity to swing downwards and along (2), and then, with only a little added effort, back up again (3).

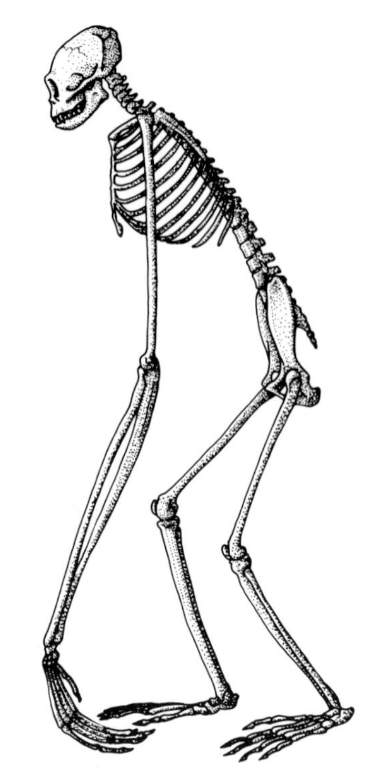

▼The skeleton of a guenon, a type of monkey. Its limbs are all of roughly equal length, since this creature walks on all fours as it runs along branches and leaps through the trees of the African forests. Its long tail aids balancing and is used as a rudder when jumping through the air.

▲In contrast to the guenon, the skeleton of this ape, an orang-utan, has quite different proportions. Its arms are extremely long because orangs move mainly by arm-swinging through the branches. Because they move this way apes do not need tails for balance.

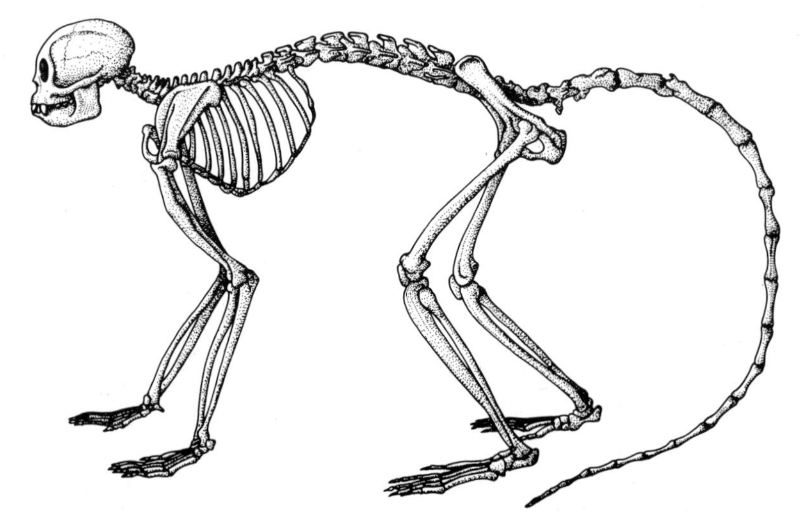

muscle in the pair reverses the effect of the other. As one contracts, it lengthens the other. We can see this in our own arm. Contract the muscle on the upper side of the upper arm, the biceps, and the elbow bends. Contract the muscle on the lower side, the triceps, and it straightens.

The same principle is used by worms. One set of muscles runs hoop-like around the worm's body, and another set runs lengthways along it. If the circular muscles contract, they make the whole body long and thin. Contraction of the muscles running lengthways makes it shorter and fatter.

PROPELLERS AND OARS

Water is a much thicker, denser substance than air. To move rapidly through it, an animal must be the right shape. This is the reason why most fast-swimming creatures, such as squid, dolphins, seals and speedy fish are long, slim and cigar-shaped.

There are four main kinds of swimming motion. One is rowing with oars. A water beetle has legs fringed with bristles. It pushes the legs back with the bristles spread out, and then brings them forwards with the bristles folded to reduce water resistance. In this manner it paddles along. Many slower-moving fish row with fins.

The penguin, and other birds that swim using their wings, move their wings up and down rather than forwards and backwards. The angle of the wing is adjusted to give it lift and push it forwards. A penguin really "flies" through the water.

Other water-dwellers swim by bending the body. S-shaped waves pass along the body as the muscles contract one after the other. Water snakes, leeches and fish such as eels use this method. In fish with powerful tails, like marlin and tuna, the tail is thrashed to and fro by the S-shaped curves, to give massive amounts of forward thrust. The fourth technique is the water-jet propulsion of squid

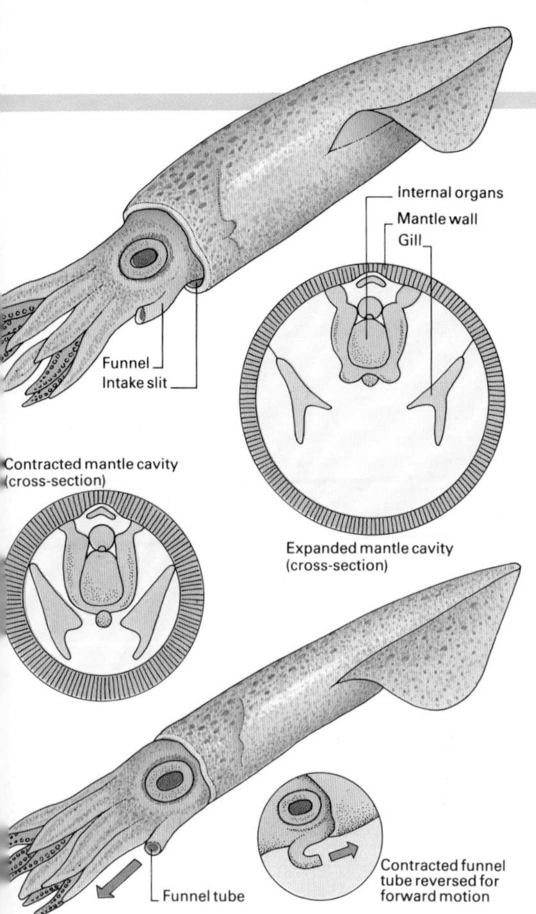

▲Jet propulsion in the squid. Water is sucked into the main mantle cavity through a wide slit behind the eye (upper diagrams). Muscles in the mantle wall then contract to squeeze the water out of the thin funnel (lower diagrams). It spurts forwards in a powerful jet, pushing the squid backwards. The whole process is repeated rhythmically for smooth swimming.

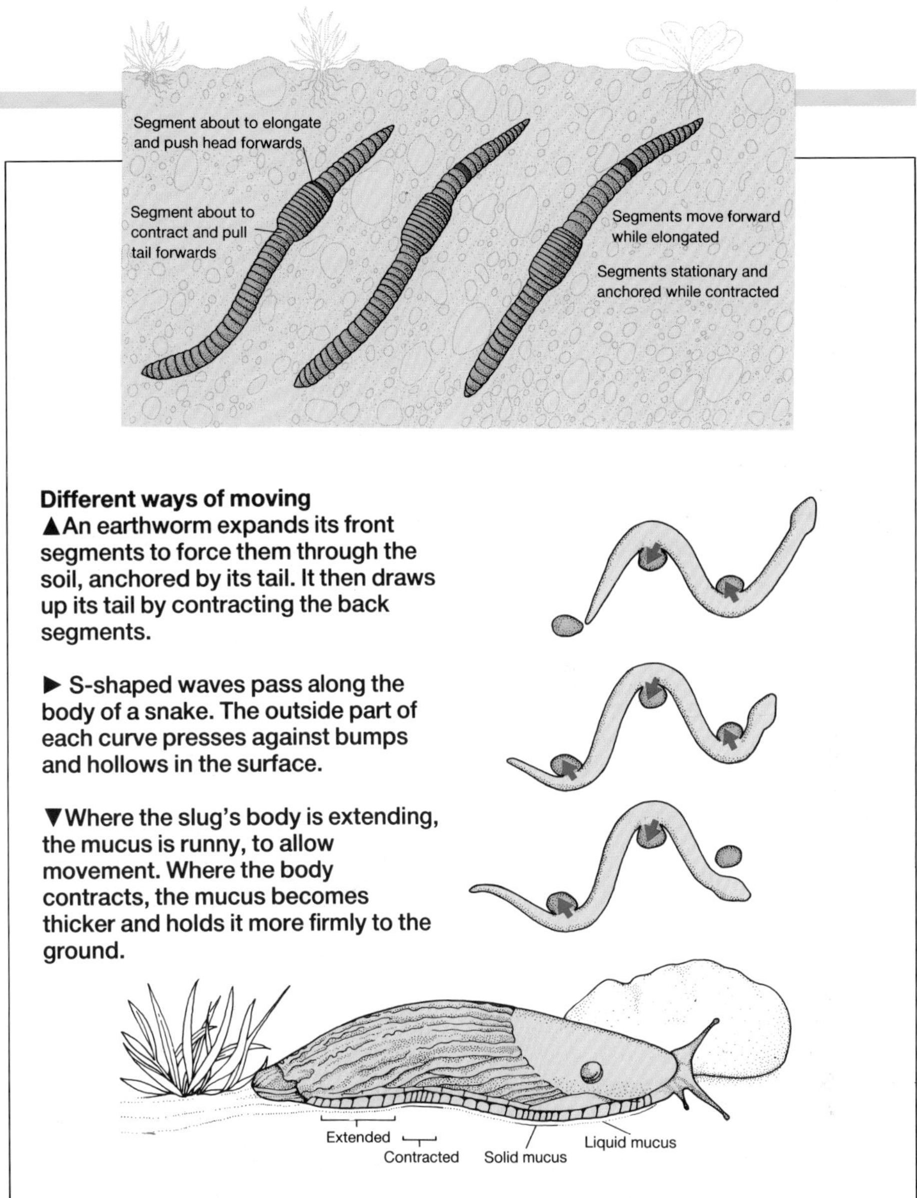

Different ways of moving
▲An earthworm expands its front segments to force them through the soil, anchored by its tail. It then draws up its tail by contracting the back segments.

► S-shaped waves pass along the body of a snake. The outside part of each curve presses against bumps and hollows in the surface.

▼Where the slug's body is extending, the mucus is runny, to allow movement. Where the body contracts, the mucus becomes thicker and holds it more firmly to the ground.

and scallops. It gives great acceleration for escaping enemies.

TAKING TO THE AIR

Insects, birds and bats are the only true flying animals, able to make long and controlled flights using flapping wings. In the hovering flight of hummingbirds, and insects such as moths and hoverflies, the animal's body is more or less stationary and the wings move very quickly. In the forward flight of larger insects, bats and most birds, the body travels along and in many cases the wing acts like the aerofoil of an airplane wing, to give added lift.

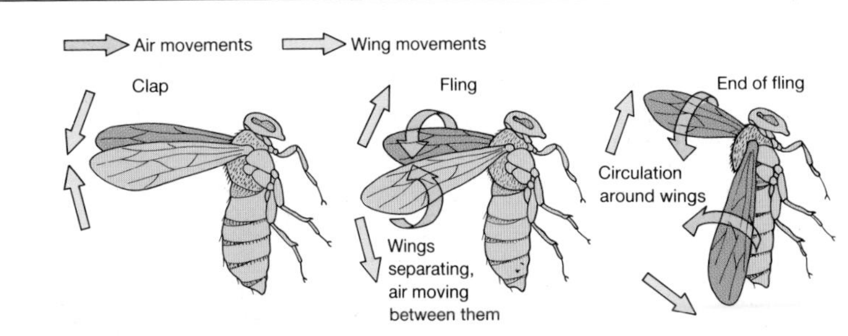

Clapping wings
▲Three stages in the "clap-and-fling" wingbeat method used by some hovering insects. The basic movements of the wing push air downwards to keep the insect airborne. In addition, the wings clap together over the back, and then fling outwards. The sudden rush of air into the space between the separating wings provides extra lift. In a mosquito, each wingbeat lasts only two-thousandths of a second.

BRAINS, NERVES

A soccer player receives a high pass on his chest and traps the ball with his foot. He dribbles past one opponent, and dodges around another. He approaches the goal and after a final sideways swerve, he kicks the ball hard towards the net – and scores! His brain has made dozens of muscles cooperate so that he can carry out the complicated actions of controlling the ball.

Animals use their muscles to make enormously powerful movements. Yet they can also make incredibly fine or gentle movements. But what makes the muscles do what they do? Why do they work together, rather than against one another?

THE NEED FOR NERVES

Control of the muscles is carried out by a system of nerves. The nerves in an animal's body work in a similar way to a telephone system. The "wires" of the system are the nerves themselves. They carry nerve messages, in the form of tiny electrical signals, quickly from one part of the body to another. This means body parts can keep in contact, so that one is affected by what happens in another.

In many animals there are "telephone exchanges" where messages are received, sorted and passed on to other body parts. These exchanges are made of many nerves gathered together. Such a bunch of nerves is called a ganglion. If there is a really large gathering of nerves, usually at the front of the animal, we call it a brain.

Some nerves send messages to muscles. Others carry messages into the body from sense organs such as eyes or touch receptors.

MESSAGE CARRIERS

The main part of a nerve is the nerve cell, or neuron. In most animals, nerve cells have the same basic build. There is a cell body that contains the nucleus, and a long, thin extension like a wire, known as the axon. The axon acts like a wire, too, carrying signals along its length. At its tip, the axon splits into branches. Each branch ends in a button-shaped pad that almost touches the next cell, which may be another nerve cell or a muscle cell. At the other end of the nerve cell, projecting from the cell body, there are also many branches, called dendrites, that receive messages from other nerves (see page 70). The axons of some nerve cells are more than one metre long, a great length for something so thin that it can only be seen under a microscope.

The thicker the axon of the nerve cell, the faster messages travel along it. In many animals, special thick axons carry messages that may mean life or death, making the animal take evasive action. For example, in the squid, giant axons run from the brain to the muscles that shoot water from its body, when the animal needs jet propulsion to escape from enemies. These axons are 0.5mm thick, which is huge – for a cell! Because they are so large, they have been used by many scientists studying how nerves work.

Some kinds of nerve cell have a coating or sheath along much of the axon. This is made of myelin, a fatty substance. The myelin makes nerves work faster and more efficiently.

ONE-WAY TRAFFIC

When a message passes along a nerve cell, it is in the form of a small pulse of electricity. The fatty myelin sheath is an insulator, which is why it helps

▶British golfer Tony Jacklin prepares to strike the ball. The white line is the path taken by his right hand on a practice swing, and the red line traces the path of the golf club head. Actions such as this are the result of marvellous coordination of the senses and muscles, by the brain and nerves.

transmission. In theory, a pulse could travel either way along an axon. In fact, nerve signals only travel in one direction. This is because of the way that messages are passed to the next cell in the network.

There is a tiny gap (the synapse) between the "button" at the end of the axon, and the dendrite of the next nerve cell. When a signal reaches the button it produces a chemical that travels across the gap. This makes a change in the cell membrane of the next cell, which starts a new electrical pulse travelling through that cell. Only buttons at the end of the axon produce the chemical, and not the dendrites of the next cell. So the nerve signal can only travel one way.

ALL OR NOTHING

A single nerve cell cannot transmit different strengths of signal. Either it is inactive, with no pulses at all, or a standard strength pulse travels along it. The only way it can change its signal is by sending pulses at a faster or slower rate.

Other ways in which different messages can be sent between parts of the body include using more or fewer nerve cells, or by using different combinations of nerve cells.

WIRE NETTING

Some of the simpler multi-celled animals, such as jellyfish and sea anemones, have their nerve cells connected in a network around the body, which looks like wire netting or a fishing net. For simple swimming, a nerve signal can spread around the net and start the muscles contracting in the correct order.

For a circular animal, the system seems fine. When a sea anemone is touched, a signal goes through the nerve net to contract the stalk muscles as an escape reaction. It is less easy to see how such a nervous system can control a sea anemone's movements as it "shuffles" from a rock on to a shell

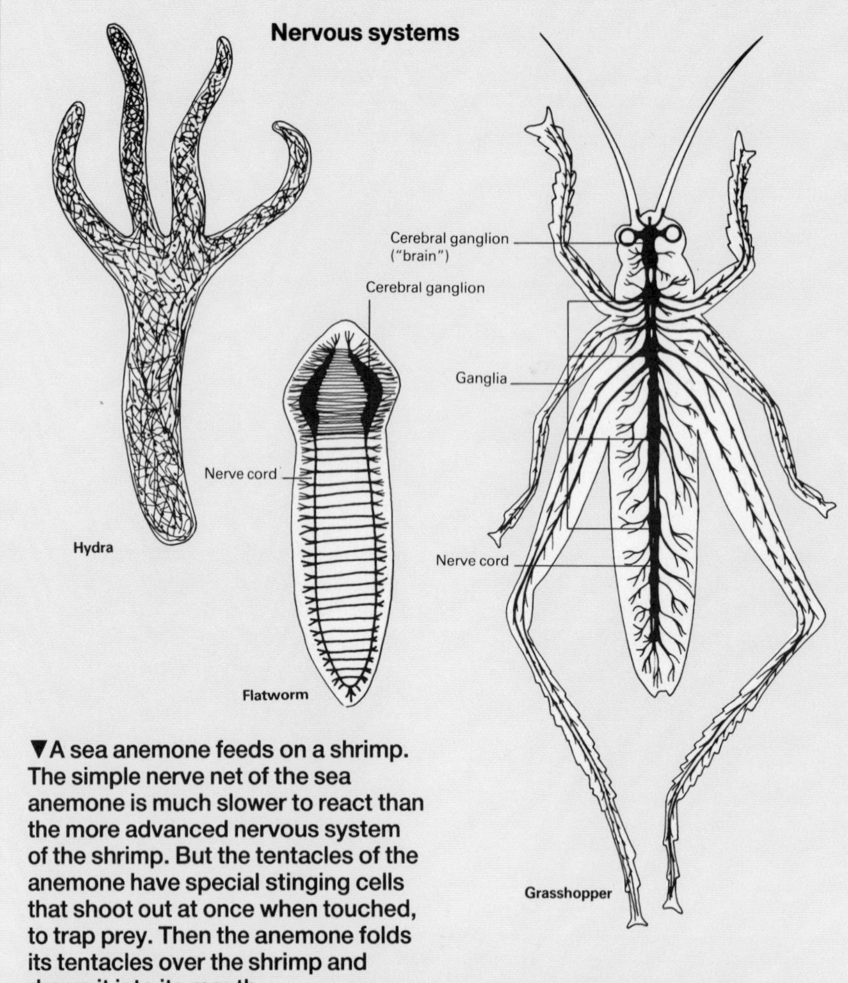

▼A sea anemone feeds on a shrimp. The simple nerve net of the sea anemone is much slower to react than the more advanced nervous system of the shrimp. But the tentacles of the anemone have special stinging cells that shoot out at once when touched, to trap prey. Then the anemone folds its tentacles over the shrimp and draws it into its mouth.

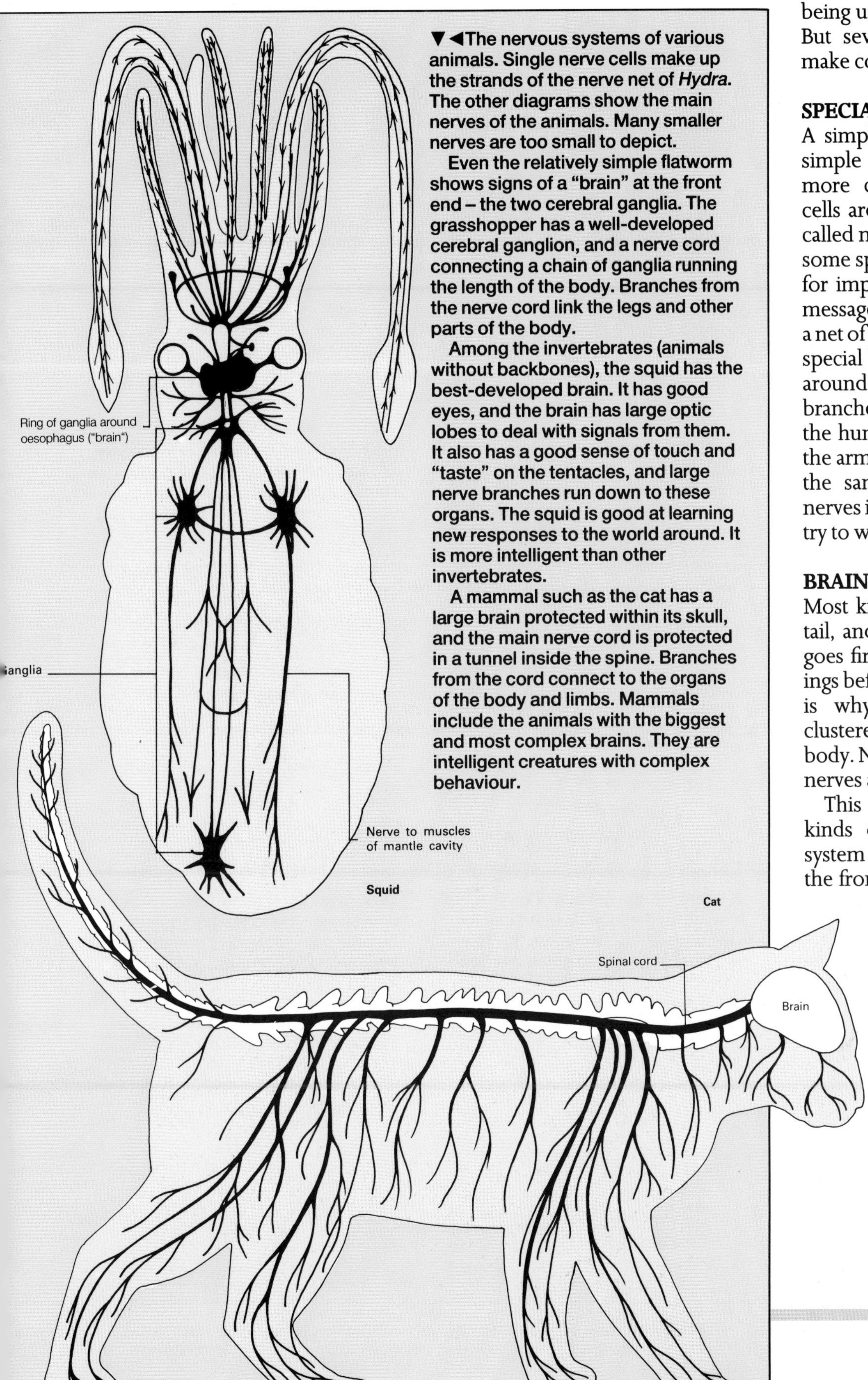

▼◄The nervous systems of various animals. Single nerve cells make up the strands of the nerve net of *Hydra*. The other diagrams show the main nerves of the animals. Many smaller nerves are too small to depict.

Even the relatively simple flatworm shows signs of a "brain" at the front end – the two cerebral ganglia. The grasshopper has a well-developed cerebral ganglion, and a nerve cord connecting a chain of ganglia running the length of the body. Branches from the nerve cord link the legs and other parts of the body.

Among the invertebrates (animals without backbones), the squid has the best-developed brain. It has good eyes, and the brain has large optic lobes to deal with signals from them. It also has a good sense of touch and "taste" on the tentacles, and large nerve branches run down to these organs. The squid is good at learning new responses to the world around. It is more intelligent than other invertebrates.

A mammal such as the cat has a large brain protected within its skull, and the main nerve cord is protected in a tunnel inside the spine. Branches from the cord connect to the organs of the body and limbs. Mammals include the animals with the biggest and most complex brains. They are intelligent creatures with complex behaviour.

being used as home by a hermit crab. But several kinds of anemone can make complex movements like this.

SPECIAL PATHS

A simple nerve net is enough for a simple animal. But to coordinate more complex animals, the nerve cells are bundled together as groups called nerves. These are laid out along some special pathways that are routes for important or commonly needed messages. A starfish, for example, has a net of nerves around the outside, but special bundles of nerves make a ring around the middle of the body, with branches into the arms. These control the hundreds of tiny tube feet under the arms, making sure they all walk in the same direction. If the ring of nerves is damaged, different arms may try to walk in different directions.

BRAINS AND CORDS

Most kinds of animal have a head, a tail, and two similar sides. The head goes first, so it meets new surroundings before the rest of the animal. This is why sense organs are usually clustered in the head at the front of the body. Nerves run from these, so many nerves are clustered at the head too.

This arrangement has led to many kinds of animal having a nervous system with a "brain" of some kind at the front. A large bundle of nerves (a nerve cord) projects from the back of the brain, into the body. In an animal such as the human, the brain and main nerve cord (spinal cord) is called the central nervous system. Branches from this link to all parts of the body.

A simple animal like a flatworm shows the beginnings of such a system. Worms and insects have more developed brains and nerve cords, although the details of the parts differ. In insects, for example, the main nerve cord runs along the underside, and not along the upper side. In other complex animals the shapes and sizes of nervous systems vary, but the basic organization is similar.

BRAIN SIZE

As a rough-and-ready rule, we might expect that the bigger the brain, the more intelligent the animal. This is not entirely true. An elephant has a bigger

Types of nerve cell

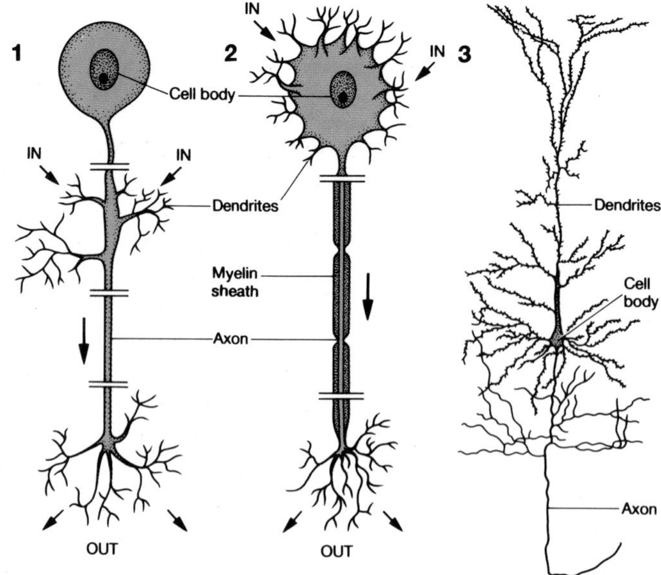

▲A Crayfish motor nerve cell (1), or neuron. (Motor nerves carry signals from the brain to muscles.) Other nerves connect with dendrites a little way down the axon. In a human motor neuron (2), the incoming connections are to dendrites on the cell body. Nerve signals pass on from the far end of the axon. In a brain neuron (3), the dendrites are finely branched.

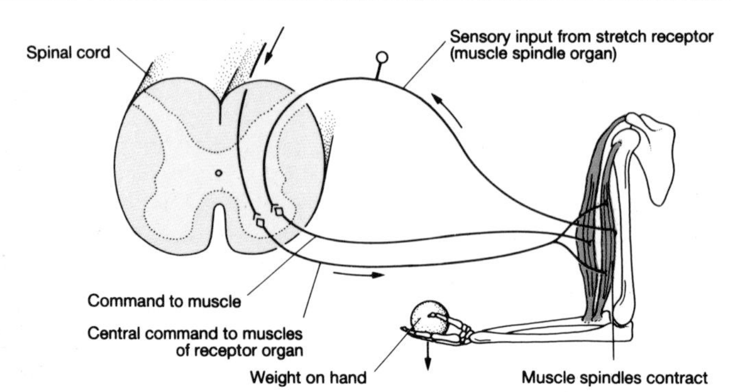

▲How a simple reflex works. Placing a weight in someone's hand causes the hand to move downwards. This stretches the muscle spindle organ and starts nerve signals. The signals travel to the spinal column, where the nerve's ending connects to a motor neuron running to the arm muscle. Signals pass along this and command the muscle to contract, moving the hand up to support the extra weight. The whole sequence is automatic.

Brains

▼►The brains of vertebrates differ in overall size, and also in the relative sizes of their parts. In the lower vertebrates such as fish (1) and amphibians (2) the medulla, the part of the brain responsible for automatic control of simple body functions, is the largest part. In the more complex reptiles (3), birds (4) and mammals (5), including humans (6), other parts of the brain become more important. The cerebellum (blue) coordinates the balance and control of movements. The cerebrum (brown), originally a small area at the front of the brain, has expanded in the human to cover the rest of the brain. Its huge numbers of nerve cells allow our intelligent and varied behaviour.

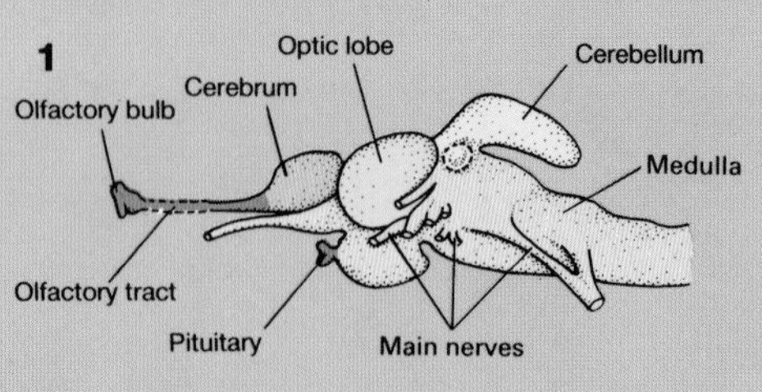

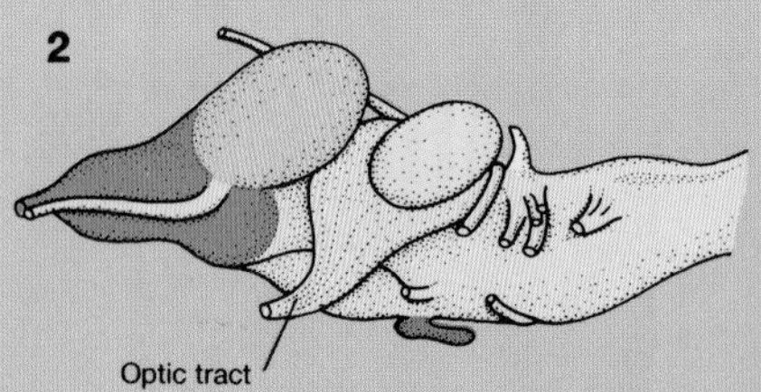

brain than a human. It is intelligent compared to many animals, but not compared to us. Big animals usually have large brains simply because so many nerves supply their big bodies.

A better guide to intelligence, though still not completely true, is brain size compared to body weight. Here, humans come out on top. There are also ways of packing in more nerve cells to increase "brain power". For example, the surface of the human brain is folded and crossed by many little valleys which increase its surface area, and which are lacking in less "brainy" animals.

A simple animal with a simple life-style may need few nerve cells. Some roundworms manage with less than 100 in their body. In contrast an active, alert, intelligent animal may have millions. An octopus has up to 200 million nerve cells in its brain alone. A human brain contains 10 billion (10,000,000,000) nerve cells.

BRAINS IN ACTION

How does a brain work? We know part of the story, but not all of the details. It is known for some animals that nerve cells with a particular function always occur in the same place. For example, in a crab, two nerve cells are responsible for making the eye "blink" into its socket. They are the same shape and in the same place in every member of the species. The locations of cells involved in other simple actions are also known. But when it comes to looking at a whole brain, the sheer scale and complexity of its construction makes it hard to study.

A single nerve cell in a human brain may have more than 250,000 connections from other nerve cells joining to it. In every cubic centimetre of the outer layer of the brain, there may be 1,000km of tiny fibres connecting the cells. We can recognize some of the main pathways in the brain, but we rarely know exactly which cell is connected to which.

In spite of this, scientists have shown that some parts of the brain have particular jobs. In an octopus brain, one area seems to be responsible for learning. If this part is destroyed, the octopus can no longer learn, although in other respects it works well enough. In humans, different areas of the brain receive input from different parts of the body. Similarly, there are specific areas responsible for moving the muscles of particular limbs. Such aspects of the mind as memory, emotions, learning, dreams and language ability also seem linked to a particular part of the brain.

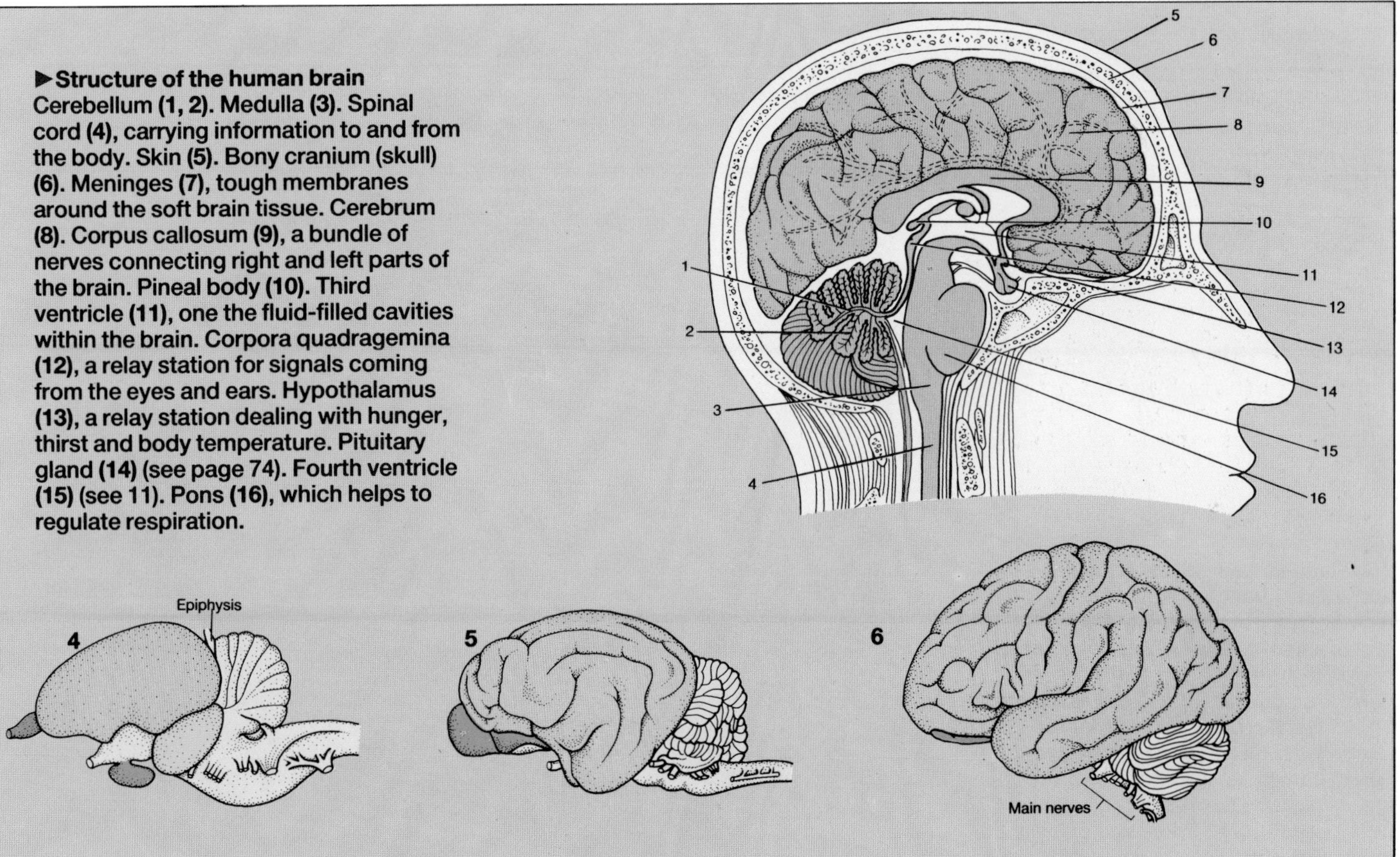

▶Structure of the human brain Cerebellum (1, 2). Medulla (3). Spinal cord (4), carrying information to and from the body. Skin (5). Bony cranium (skull) (6). Meninges (7), tough membranes around the soft brain tissue. Cerebrum (8). Corpus callosum (9), a bundle of nerves connecting right and left parts of the brain. Pineal body (10). Third ventricle (11), one the fluid-filled cavities within the brain. Corpora quadragemina (12), a relay station for signals coming from the eyes and ears. Hypothalamus (13), a relay station dealing with hunger, thirst and body temperature. Pituitary gland (14) (see page 74). Fourth ventricle (15) (see 11). Pons (16), which helps to regulate respiration.

HORMONES

Walking down a jungle path, a villager suddenly finds his path blocked by a leopard. Almost immediately, his heart starts pumping harder and faster. His hair stands on end and the pupils of his eyes widen. Both he and the cat are frightened, yet alert and ready to run. The leopard moves off at last. Safe again, the man's body gradually relaxes.

The "emergency reactions" that take place in a frightened person prepare the body for fleeing or fighting the danger. The airways widen and breathing increases, the surface blood vessels contract and make the skin pale, and more blood is sent to the muscles. More sugar is released into the blood to provide easily used energy. The heart steps up its work. In ourselves, we notice other reactions, like the hair on the back of our necks standing up.

Similar reactions take place in other animals. A frightened cat's heart beats faster and its fur stands on end.

These "fight or flight" reactions are caused by a chemical, adrenaline, flooding through the body. It is made in special glands, the adrenals, and is released into the bloodstream in times of stress. The chemical travels rapidly around the body in the blood and affects just a few "target organs", such as the heart and lungs, in the ways described.

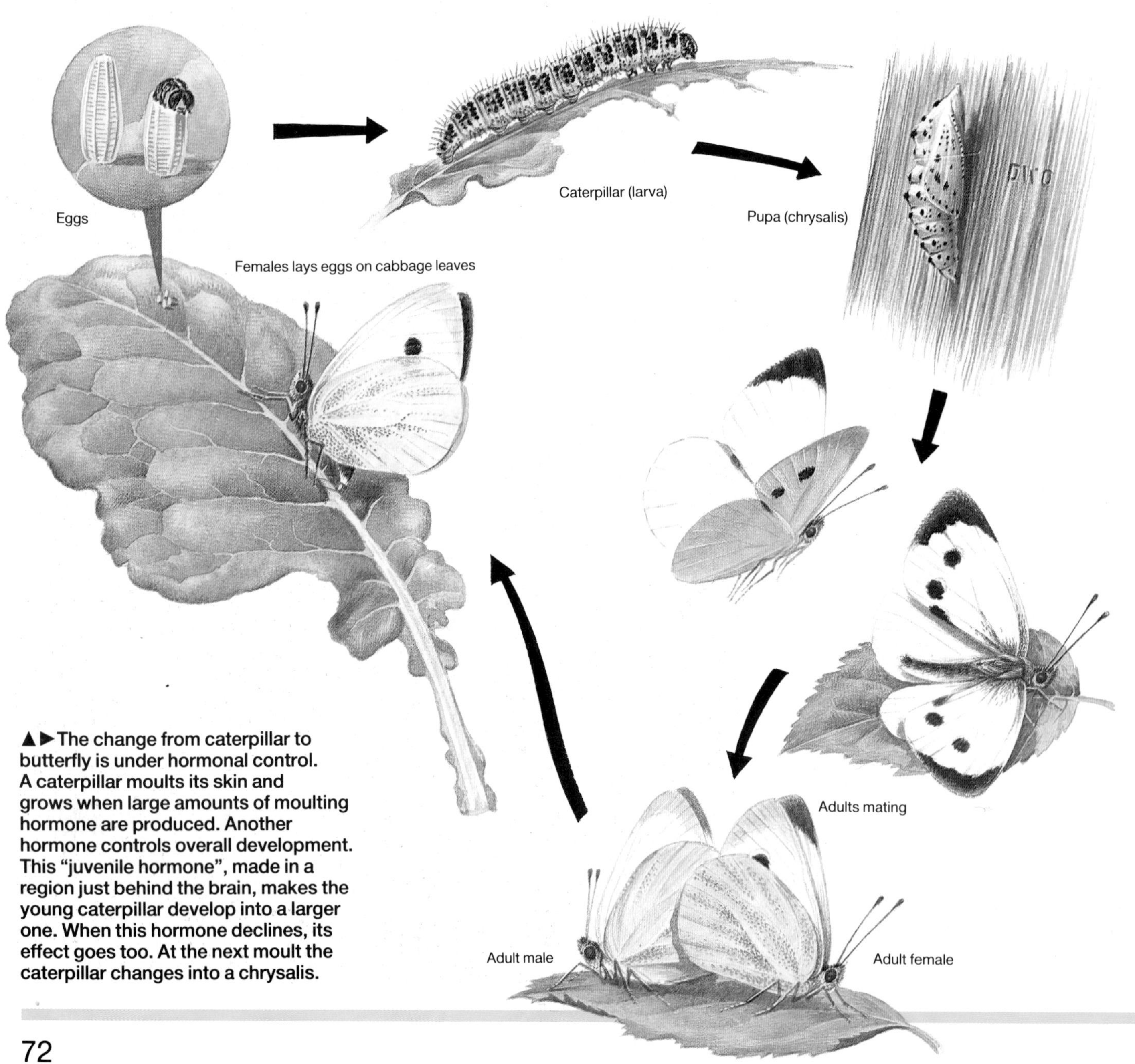

▲►The change from caterpillar to butterfly is under hormonal control. A caterpillar moults its skin and grows when large amounts of moulting hormone are produced. Another hormone controls overall development. This "juvenile hormone", made in a region just behind the brain, makes the young caterpillar develop into a larger one. When this hormone declines, its effect goes too. At the next moult the caterpillar changes into a chrysalis.

LONG-LASTING MESSAGE

The chemical adrenaline acts as a messenger. Such a chemical, creating an effect in another part of the body from where it was produced, is called a hormone. Many hormones act in our bodies, and in those of other animals. Like nerves, hormones allow body parts to communicate with each other. But although a few produce effects very fast, like adrenaline, many hormones have a longer-term action. Their effects happen over days or months, rather than in a flash, like a nerve's action.

Hormones are powerful chemicals. They circulate in the body in very low amounts but have large effects. They are made in certain organs called endocrine glands. These glands have no special ducts or other outlets. They release their hormones into the surrounding fluids, to be carried away in the blood.

BEARDS AND ANTLERS

One of the first hormones to be discovered was the male sex hormone, called testosterone. This is made in the testes, the sex glands of male vertebrates. It causes growth and development of the male sex organs. It also triggers "secondary sexual characteristics", which include a deep voice, and facial hair in men. In deer, the male sex hormone causes larger body size than the female, and the development of antlers. In chickens, testosterone produces the rooster's fine tail feathers, large comb, and his ability to crow.

Hormones can affect behaviour as well as bodies. Male hormones make animals such as stallions or bulls more

►A newly-emerged adult of the Mexican grasshopper *Taeniopoda auricornis*. The moulted skin of its previous stage is still attached to the plant. Moulting hormone is made by a gland in the thorax, the central part of the body. This gland is itself controlled by a hormone made in the brain.

aggressive than the females. For thousands of years, farmers have known that castration (removal of the testes) quietens down such animals. A castrated ox, known as a bullock, is a placid animal. Only in the last hundred years have scientists discovered why this should be.

HORMONES AND CHANGE

Many hormones help to maintain the balance of chemicals in the body. But some bring change. The change from tadpole to frog is brought about when the tadpole's pituitary gland at the base of the brain is stimulated, perhaps by an increase in temperature. The pituitary releases a hormone which activates another gland, the thyroid, in the neck. This makes the hormone thyroxine.

Thyroxine affects some parts of the tadpole's body by making them grow fast, or change shape, and it causes the tail and gills to shrink. The result is a change from tadpole to frog. If, for some reason, no thyroxine is produced, then the tadpole stays as a tadpole. On the other hand, miniature frogs can be produced from young tadpoles by feeding them extra amounts of thyroxine. The axolotl, a Mexican salamander, normally keeps its gills and stays in water all its life. If it is fed extra thyroxine, it becomes a land salamander.

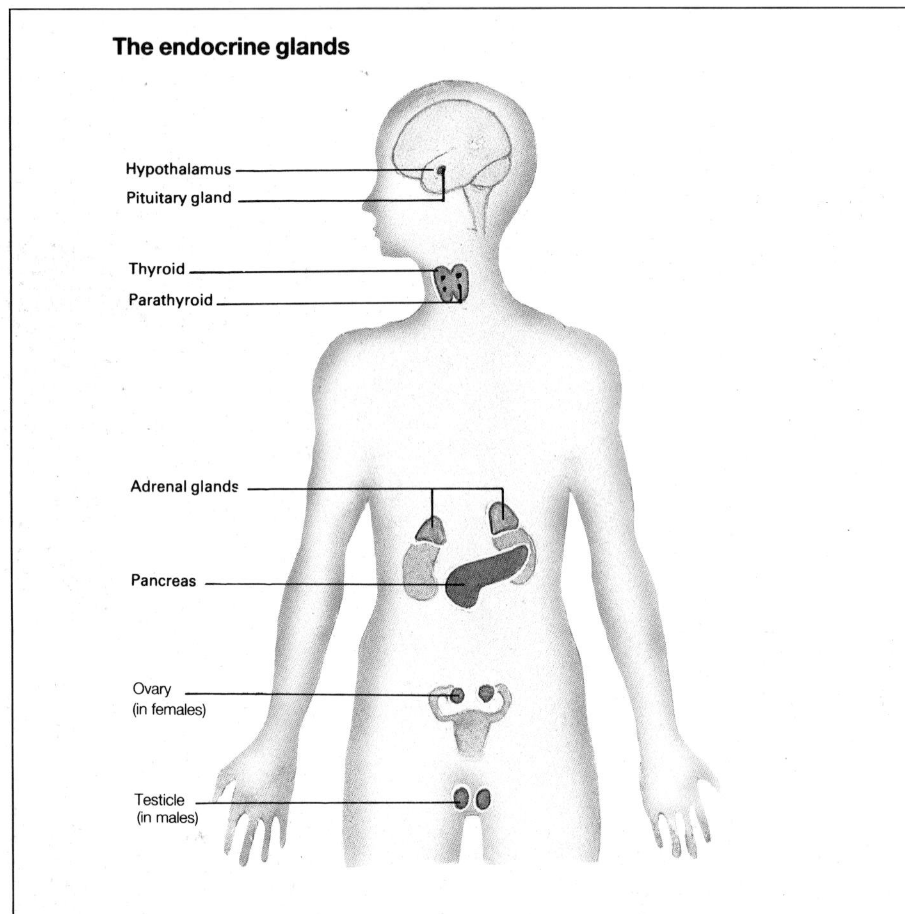

The thyroid controls energy use in the body. With the parathyroids, it also affects calcium levels. The pancreas hormones control sugar balance. The adrenals above the kidneys make hormones that regulate salt balance in the body, plus some sex hormones. Also they produce adrenaline and other hormones which help the body react to emergencies. Testes (in males) or ovaries (in females) make hormones affecting reproduction and sexual development. Some of the pituitary's hormones control other endocrine glands. The hypothalamus links the brain to the pituitary.

LIFE PUT ON HOLD

When days are short, in spring, the female silk moth *Bombyx mori* lays colourless eggs that soon hatch and develop. When the days are long, in summer, she lays coloured eggs that have a long resting period. They do not hatch until early next spring. The difference is because of a hormone produced by the moth's brain, which is only made when there are long periods of daylight. The hormone affects the ovary, so that the special resting eggs develop.

FEEDBACK

The quantities of many hormones are controlled by "feedback". If enough hormone is circulating in the body, this slows down production by the gland. This is called negative feedback. It is typical for many of the glands that control the balance of chemicals in the body.

In a few cases, hormones produce positive feedback – they encourage the gland to produce even more of themselves. This happens when the amphibian thyroid gland secretes thyroxine. It may explain why, after weeks as a tadpole, the change to an adult comes with a rush.

►Mating lions. Their behaviour and appearance are influenced by hormones. The male hormones produced by the testes of the male lion make his body large and his mane grow. They also affect his voice, so that he has a deep-throated roar. Female hormones from the lioness's ovaries help bring her body into breeding condition, and influence her readiness to mate.

CELL DIVISION, GENETICS

A family lines up for a photograph. The oldest boy looks very like his father. His sister looks like her father too, with dark hair and dark eyes. But her younger sister and the baby brother take after their mother, with fair hair and small noses. The photographer notices and wonders why some children look like one parent, while others take after the other parent.

For thousands of years, people have realized that children tend to look like their parents. Young animals, too, usually take after their parents rather than other members of their species. What makes us look like our parents? Indeed, what makes dogs look like dogs, and not like giraffes or squirrels? Now we know that the answer lies in almost every cell of an animal's body.

MENDEL'S PEAS

The first experiments about family likeness, which eventually led to the answer, were made by a monk called Gregor Mendel in the mid-1800s. He worked with plants rather than animals. He grew certain types and colours of peas, then carefully bred the offspring together in various combinations. He made meticulous notes and counted the number of offspring with particular features, such as colour, plant size, and wrinkliness.

When Mendel bred tall pea plants with short ones, all the offspring were tall. But if he bred some of these offspring together, one quarter of their offspring were short plants. His experiments seemed to show that one feature was passed on more strongly than another. It took over, or dominated, the weaker feature. But the characteristic that did not show in the offspring had not disappeared entirely. It re-emerged, in turn, in some of their offspring.

This experiment, as well as others Mendel made, could be explained if every plant had two sets of the characters. One was inherited from its father, and one from its mother. When it bred, each of the pair of characters was passed on separately, or independently. Nowadays, we call the characters that Gregor Mendel discovered "genes".

TALL AND SHORT

In the tall and short peas, for example, the pure-bred tall peas each had two genes for being tall. The pure-bred short peas each had two genes for being short. Together, they produced offspring which each had one gene for being tall, and one for being short. But the gene for being short was overshadowed by the tallness gene. In other words, the tallness gene was "dominant", and the gene for being short was "recessive". But when this generation bred together, some of the offspring (one in four) had both genes producing shortness, so these peas were short.

Since Mendel's time we have found that all living things work in much the same way as peas, passing on genes to their offspring. In some cases the genes behave in a more complicated way, but the basic principles are the same. Mendel, the discoverer of these principles, was unfortunate in that, during his lifetime, his experiments did not lead to a greater understanding of the science of genes. Today, we know this science as genetics and it is fast growing in importance and in its ability to produce practical results.

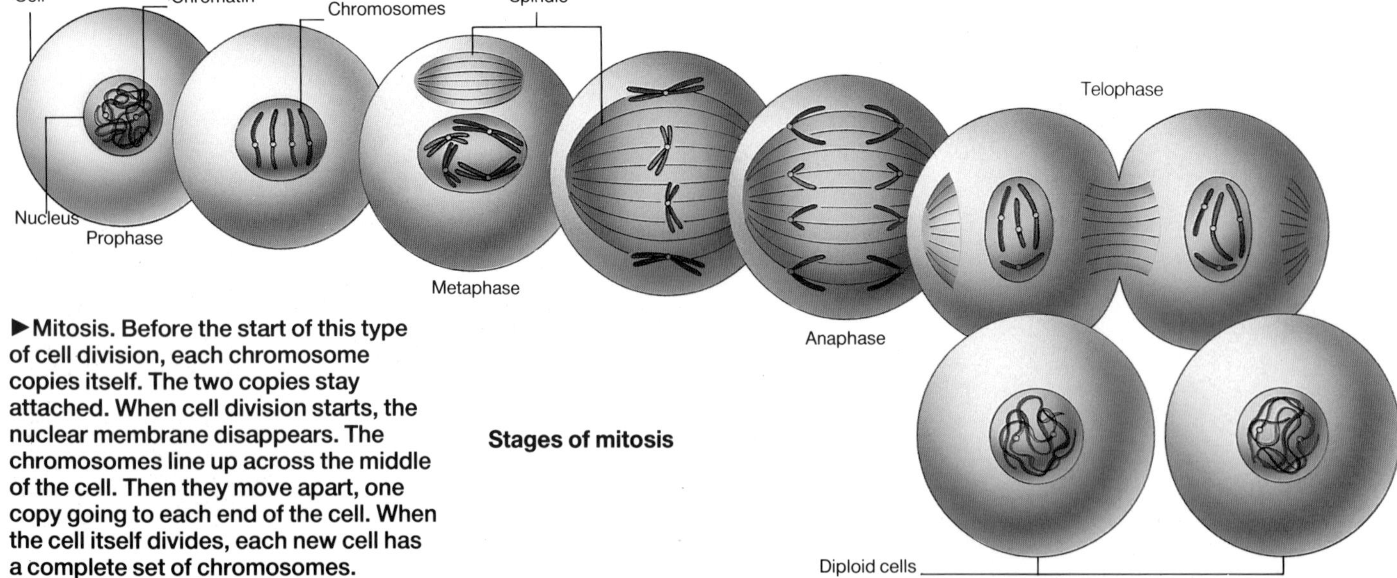

►Mitosis. Before the start of this type of cell division, each chromosome copies itself. The two copies stay attached. When cell division starts, the nuclear membrane disappears. The chromosomes line up across the middle of the cell. Then they move apart, one copy going to each end of the cell. When the cell itself divides, each new cell has a complete set of chromosomes.

20TH-CENTURY SCIENCE

From the early years of the 20th century, the science of genetics began to progress. Many new experiments were carried out, and Mendel's pioneering work was recognized. The basis for the way characters were inherited was discovered in cells. From the 1950s onwards, the search was on to discover the molecular basis of genetics. The second half of the 20th century has seen huge leaps in our understanding of genes and molecular biology.

VITAL CHROMOSOMES

Scientists realized that in each cell there are parts which are passed on in much the same way as genes. These parts are called chromosomes, and they are in the cell's nucleus. Much of the time they are difficult to see, but

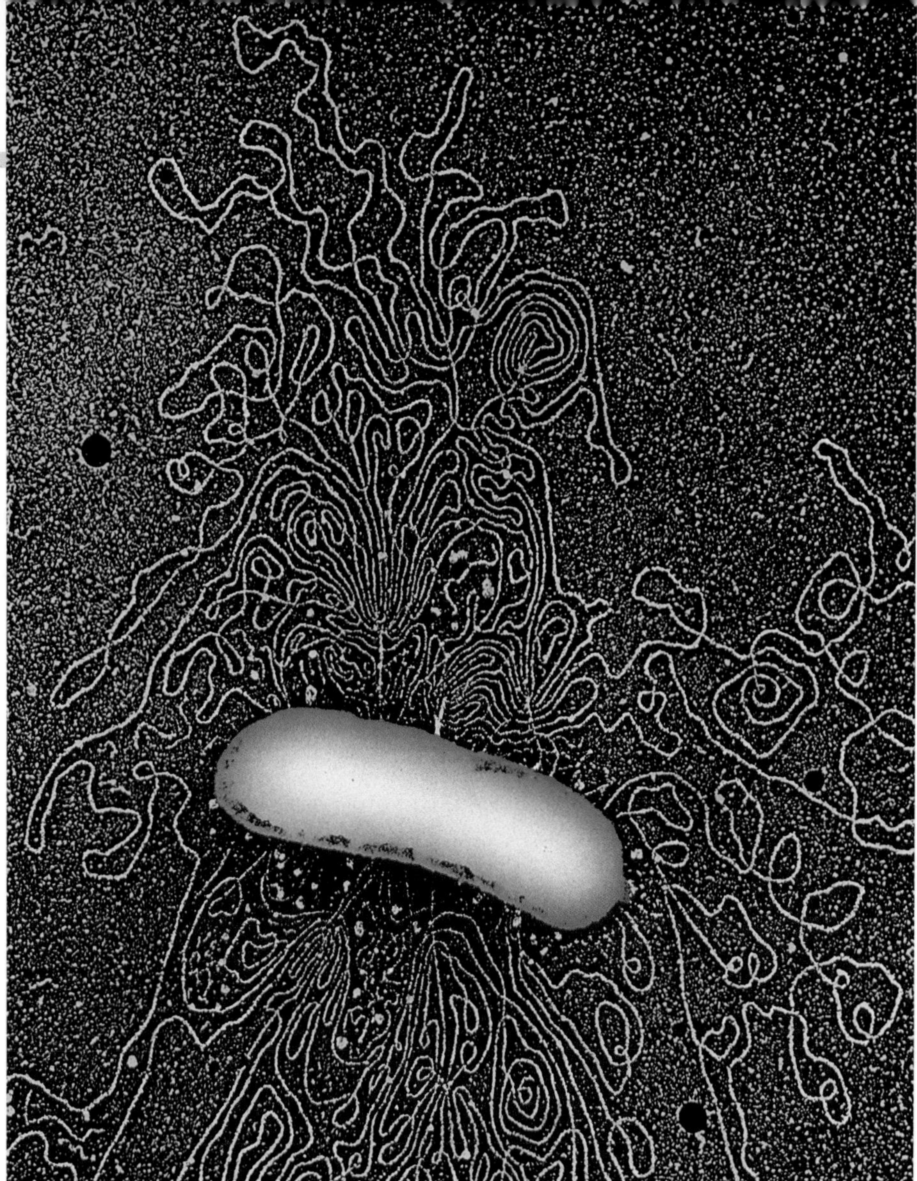

►The chromosome of a bacterium. This *Escherischia coli* bacterium has been treated so that its cell wall has broken down and released the chromosome contents. The long strands seen all around it are normally folded inside the cell. They contain all the information required to make the substances that it needs during its life, and to pass on its "blueprint" to the next generation.

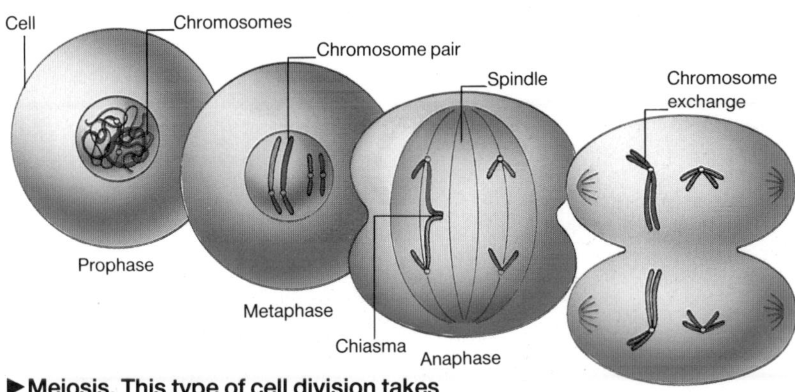

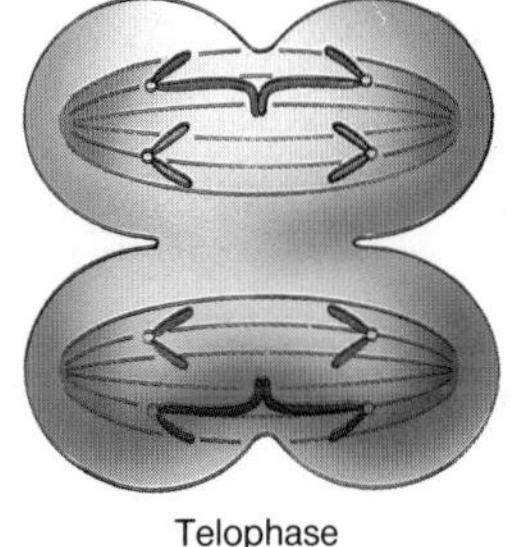

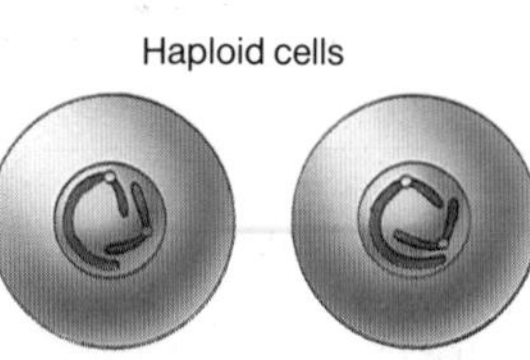

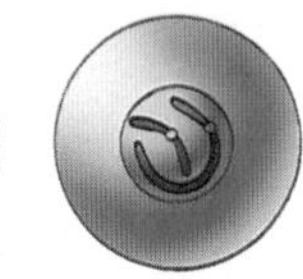

Stages of meiosis

►Meiosis. This type of cell division takes place when sperms or eggs form. The chomosomes come together in matching pairs along the middle of the cell. One of each pair goes to each end as the cell divides. Then each chromosome splits in two, the two halves move apart, and the cell divides again. Each of the four new cells contains only half the original number.

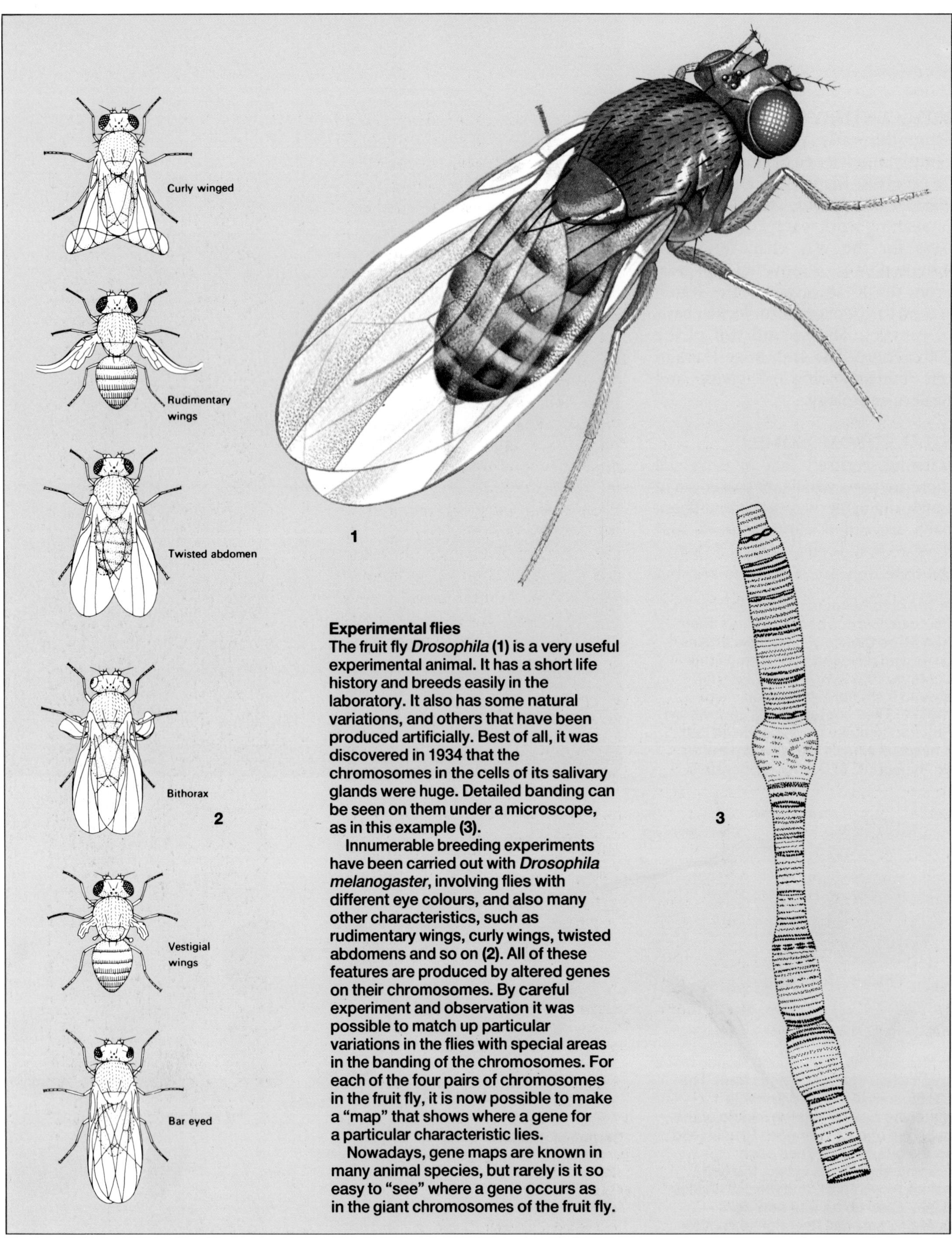

Experimental flies

The fruit fly *Drosophila* **(1)** is a very useful experimental animal. It has a short life history and breeds easily in the laboratory. It also has some natural variations, and others that have been produced artificially. Best of all, it was discovered in 1934 that the chromosomes in the cells of its salivary glands were huge. Detailed banding can be seen on them under a microscope, as in this example **(3)**.

Innumerable breeding experiments have been carried out with *Drosophila melanogaster*, involving flies with different eye colours, and also many other characteristics, such as rudimentary wings, curly wings, twisted abdomens and so on **(2)**. All of these features are produced by altered genes on their chromosomes. By careful experiment and observation it was possible to match up particular variations in the flies with special areas in the banding of the chromosomes. For each of the four pairs of chromosomes in the fruit fly, it is now possible to make a "map" that shows where a gene for a particular characteristic lies.

Nowadays, gene maps are known in many animal species, but rarely is it so easy to "see" where a gene occurs as in the giant chromosomes of the fruit fly.

when a cell prepares to divide, they become more visible, and they can be stained with a special dye to make them easier to see when viewed under a microscope. (Chromosome means "coloured body".)

Before a cell begins dividing, the chromosomes become rod-shaped. As it divides, the chromosomes are divided equally between the two new cells. But the way in which this happens differs according to whether it is a normal cell dividing to make two more normal body cells (the process called mitosis), or a cell dividing to make sperm or eggs (the process known as meiosis).

An ordinary body cell contains an even number of chromosomes which can be matched in pairs. Each member of a pair is the same size and shape, and controls the same characteristics, as its partner. This means it carries the same genes. So in a pea, the genes that decide whether the plant will be tall or short occur on paired chromosomes.

Before a body cell divides, it doubles up its chromosomes. When it divides, a complete set of all the pairs is passed to each of the new cells. But when sex cells form, the doubling does not happen. Division takes place so that only one chromosome from each pair goes into the resulting egg or sperm. So an egg cell or sperm cell has only half the number of chromosomes of a normal body cell. This "half set" of chromosomes is called the haploid number.

When a sperm fertilizes an egg, two half sets come together to make a full set. This full set is called the diploid number of chromosomes.

X AND Y

All the chromosomes in a diploid cell come in pairs. The two chromosomes in each pair look much the same – with one exception. In many animals, scientists have found that the partners in one pair of chromosomes do not look the same. One chromosome is larger than the other. This pair of chromosomes seems responsible for the difference between the sexes.

The larger of the chromosomes in an uneven pair is usually called an X chromosome and the smaller one a Y. In people and other mammals, an individual with two X chromosomes in the pair is female. An individual with one X and one Y is male. This is not always the case in other animals. Among birds, females have an XY pair and males have XX.

As well as having genes which control sex, the X and Y chromosomes have other genes that affect other body features. So sometimes we find features that are "sex-linked". These occur only, or much more commonly, in one sex rather than the other. In people, for example, colour blindness is much more common in men than in women. In cats, ginger colouring nearly always means a male cat, while tortoiseshell colouring indicates a female.

WHAT'S IN A CHROMOSOME?

As we have seen with the X and Y chromosomes, each chromosome can carry more than one gene. In fact, scientists have been able to find dozens of genes on a single chromosome, and map their positions along it. But what are genes, and what is a chromosome made of? Chromosomes contain large amounts of a substance called deoxyribonucleic acid, or DNA for short. This is a very

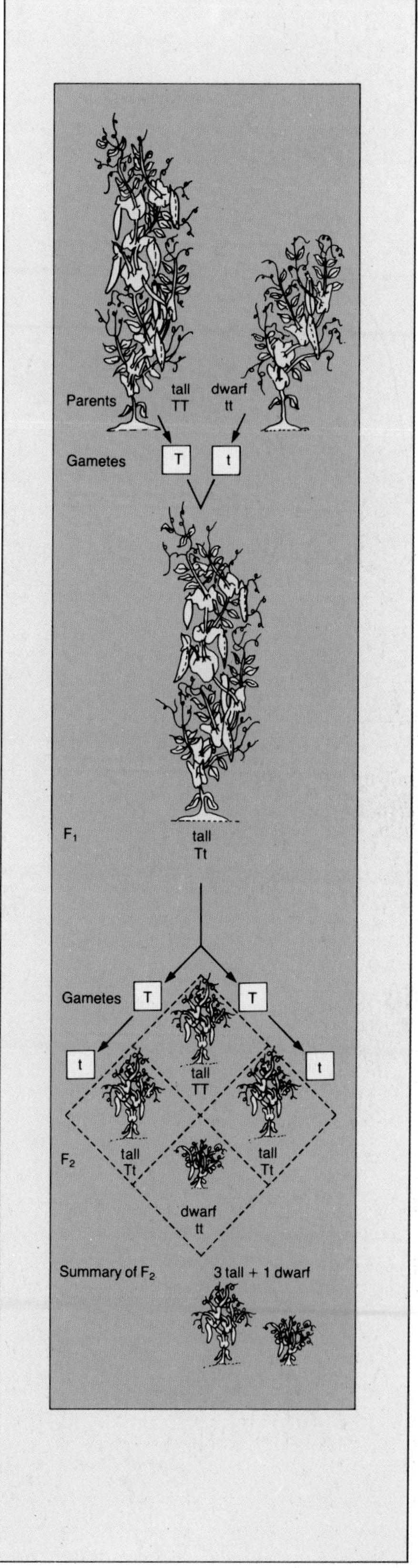

►**The first experiments in the science of genetics were begun in 1856 by Gregor Mendel, an Austrian monk. He carried out careful work breeding peas, and found that characteristics were always passed on in a certain way. His work was not really appreciated in his lifetime, but experiments like his became the basis of the modern science of genetics. He took great care in the way he designed and carried out his experiments. By counting and keeping records he was able to show the way in which living things passed on their characteristics.**

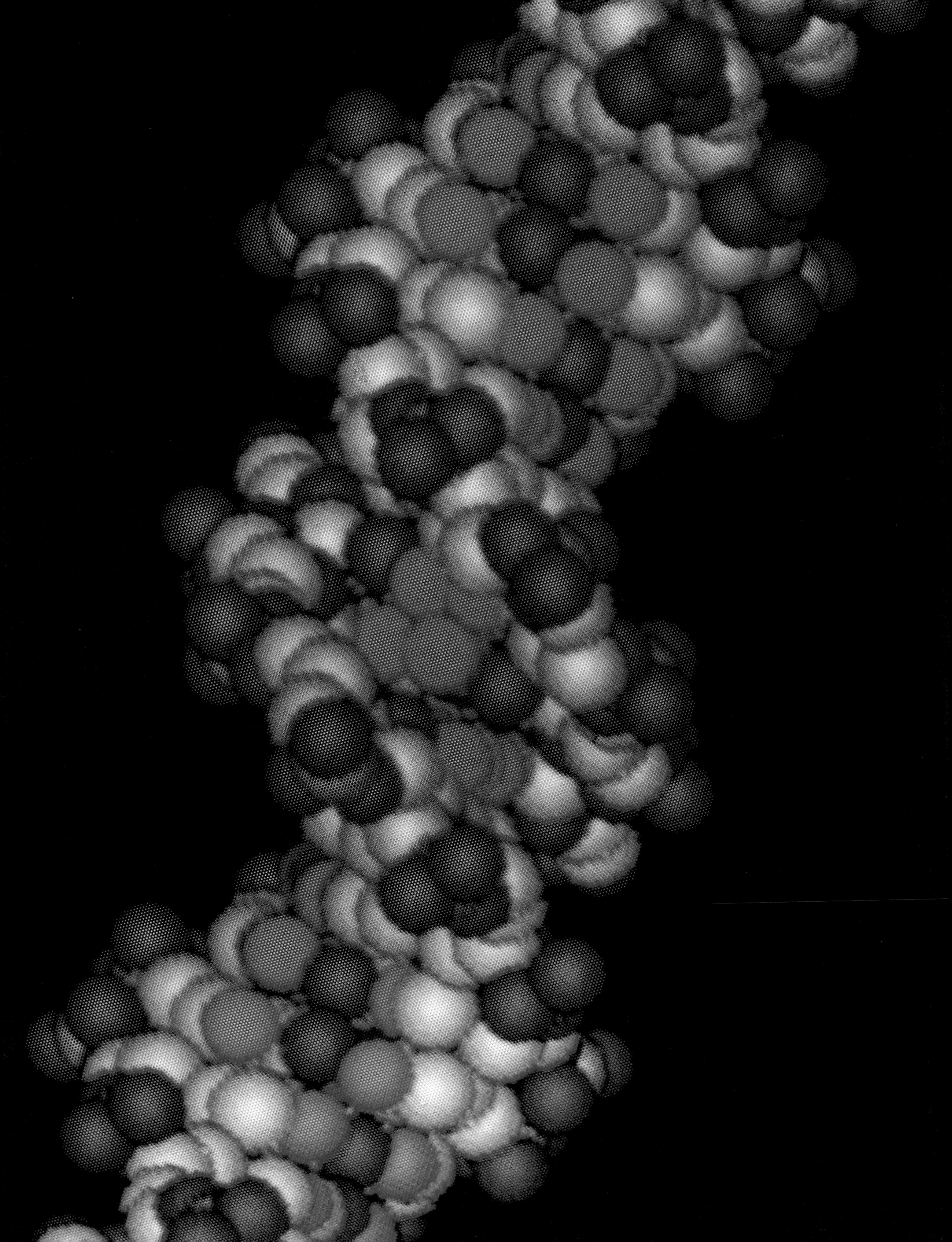

long molecule which is really a chain of repeating units. There may be tens of thousands of these units in a single DNA molecule. It is like a very long, thin thread, but in a dividing cell it coils up into the chromosomes we recognize. This long molecule carries a chemical code that holds all the basic instructions needed to make a working animal cell and, in the end, the whole animal.

THE STRUCTURE OF DNA

Although it is such a big molecule, DNA is built up in a fairly simple way.

◀A model shows that characteristic double helix structure of part of a DNA molecule. In every animal cell, DNA molecules carry the coded information needed for all its life processes.

It consists of two strands joined together. Each strand has a "backbone" of molecules of a sugar, deoxyribose, connected to one another. The strand has a helical shape, rather like a coiled spring. The two strands are like two intertwined springs, held together by chemical attachments.

Each of the sugar molecules along the strand has attached to it a molecule of a substance known as a base. There are many kinds of base, but DNA has only four. They are called guanine, cytosine, adenine and thymine. One strand of the DNA is connected to the other by links between these bases, in the same way that rungs of a ladder connect the upright parts. The bases only fit together in two ways. Guanine links with cytosine. Adenine links with thymine. So, if it is known which bases are attached to sugars along one strand of DNA, it is evident which bases will be attached with absolute certainty to the opposite strand.

This arrangement also gives the DNA molecule a perfect means of copying itself. If the two strands of DNA come apart, then new material can be assembled to make two new strands, which form double strands with those already there. The new double strands each have the same sequence of bases as the old. This is the secret of life – how DNA copies itself to make the next generation.

In the chromosomes of the cell's nucleus, then, are DNA molecules that can copy themselves. The DNA

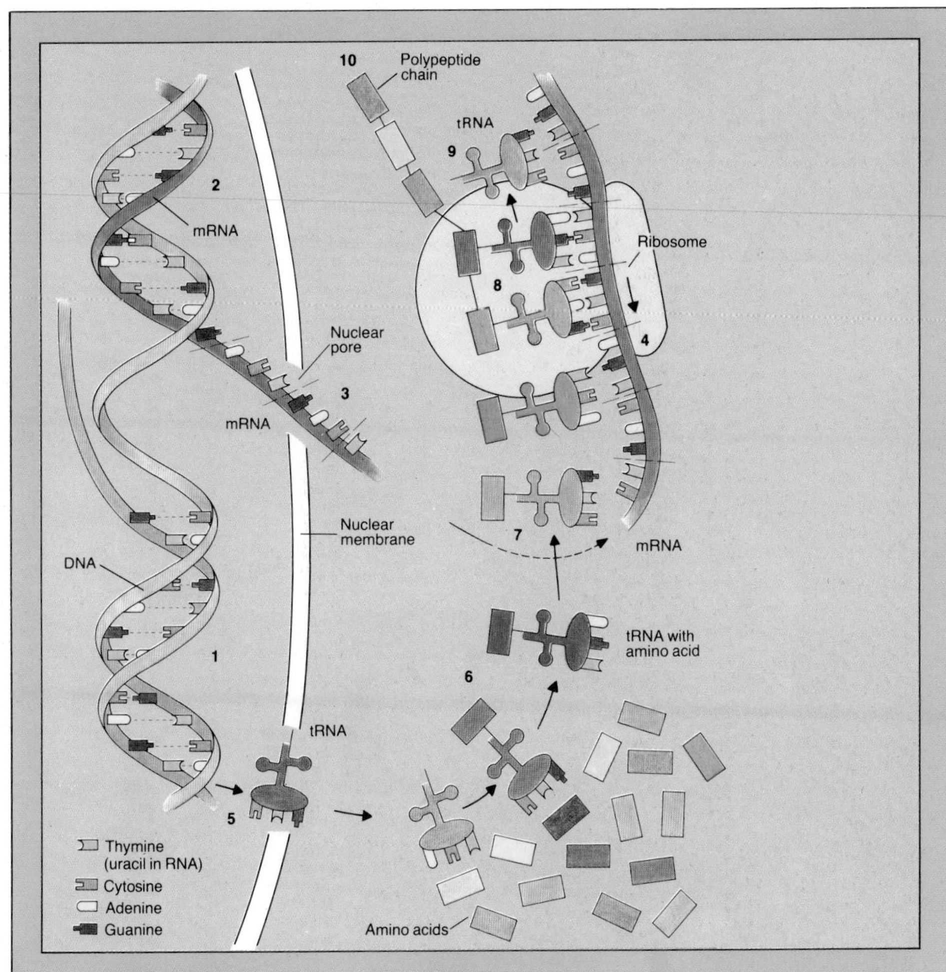

Making a protein

◀The "factories" of the body cells are the small structures called ribosomes (4), which are in the cytoplasm of the cell. The instructions for what is to be made come from the nucleus. Part of the DNA in there unwinds (2) and a chain of messenger RNA (mRNA) forms. The sequence of bases on this (shown as green, blue, yellow or brown attachments) is determined by the bases opposite them on the DNA strand. The messenger RNA moves into the cytoplasm through gaps in the nuclear membrane (3).

Another type of RNA, transfer RNA (shown as tRNA in the diagram), picks up particular amino acids (6) in the cytoplasm. (Amino acids are shown as coloured rectangles.) In the ribosome the transfer RNA links temporarily to a particular site on the messenger RNA, into which its bases fit (7). This gives a chance for the amino acid it is carrying to join the next amino acid along, to form a chain (8). The transfer RNA comes unstuck from both the amino acid it was carrying and the messenger RNA, and floats off into the cytoplasm (9). A chain of amino acids (a polypeptide chain) is created (10), and this forms the basis of a protein.

It takes only one second to form a chain of 4,000 amino acids.

"formula" of an animal (or a plant) is passed to every cell of the body as the cells form by cell division. The formula is also passed on to each of the eggs and sperm.

BUILDING BODIES

But how does the DNA molecule tell a cell what to be, and what to make? The sequence of bases along a DNA strand works like a kind of code.

The structure of a cell and its workings are brought about largely by protein molecules. A code which specifies which proteins are made is therefore a code which specifies a particular kind of cell or animal. The code which is built into the structure of DNA can do this.

A section of three bases in DNA makes the "code name" for one of about twenty kinds of amino acid. These acids are the building blocks which make proteins. A line of thousands of bases along a DNA molecule can code for whole strings of different amino acids. These amino acids, brought together in the correct order, form a protein molecule.

This "manufacture" does not take place in the nucleus itself. The DNA is like a "blueprint", which sends its instructions to the "factory" in the cytoplasm of the cell (see page 81).

WHEN COPYING GOES WRONG

DNA is a very long molecule. It carries an enormous amount of information in its codes. It has a mechanism for exactly copying itself. But, like any procedure where huge numbers of steps are involved, occasional mistakes occur.

In DNA , a base may get lost or added in copying. A tiny part of the molecule may become broken off. The result may be a copy that is not exact. Some of these copies will not work. If they are present in eggs and sperm they may be infertile, or the resulting embryo cannot develop properly or survive.

But some of these "different" copies may still result in a slightly different animal that works perfectly well. It is different, but not in dangerous ways.

Occasionally a new variation on DNA may actually be better than the original. This is probably how new animals have taken over from ancestors in the course of evolution.

VARIATION ON A THEME

The study of DNA has shown that this enormously long molecule has the capacity to code for huge numbers of substances. In a chromosome, some of the DNA is probably redundant, in that it repeats another section. Or it produces no effect at all.

Scientists have also realized that much of DNA, far from dealing with "life and death" necessities, can vary quite a bit, producing small and fairly random variations on a theme. Many groups of animals in nature seem to have quite a lot of natural variation in their genes. In some cases this is linked to their survival. For example, some snail species come in several colour varieties, and each variety survives best in different conditions. But

▼Genetic variation in the European adder. Brown or silver colours are found, with the typical zigzag marks along the back. Very dark individuals are also seen. Many are females. Many silvery snakes are males.

in many cases the variations seem to be neither good nor bad. Consider humans, who may be tall or short, fat or thin, and have a variety of hair, eye and skin colours. Their genes are slightly different, but it makes little difference to their survival.

MULES: THE END OF THE LINE

In most cases the difference between species of animals, in their structure and behaviour, is so great that they do not try to breed with one another. Even if they did, they would normally find that their combined chromosomes and DNA would not provide a working blueprint for an animal.

But there are a few exceptions. Some species are so closely related, with similar chromosomes and DNA, that they can produce offspring. Some kinds of pheasant, for example, can breed together to produce hybrids.

▼All of these colours can be seen in shells of one group of the Banded snail *Cepaea nemoralis*. In open areas pale shells are often common. In woods a high proportion have dark shells. Poorly camouflaged snails are probably soon caught by predators and never breed.

▲A zebroid. A cross between horse and zebra, two species similar enough to interbreed and produce offspring. But the chromosomes from the mother and father are not alike enough to make satisfactory eggs or sperm, so the zebroid cannot breed.

Lions and tigers living in captivity sometimes produce young. A male donkey may breed with a female horse, who gives birth to a mule.

In some cases the young produced by these mixtures are actually bigger or stronger than their parents. Mules are known for their toughness. But they are the end of the line. In nearly every case, these mixed-species hybrids cannot themselves breed and produce offspring. Almost certainly this is because of the mechanics of cell division. Their chromosomes are not true pairs, and so they cannot divide properly to form eggs or sperm.

REPRODUCTION, GROWTH

A young Blue tit's head peeps out from a hole in a tree. Then its owner appears, and launches into the air. It is followed by another, and still more, 13 in all. A pair of Blue tits have reared their young, who are now leaving the nest.

▼Cell divisions in the testes (shown blue) and in the ovary (shown pink). In many animals these sex organs are only active for part of the year, when conditions are best for breeding. Some animals, including humans, produce eggs and sperm at any time of the year.

For a species to continue, some of the individuals of that species must breed and replace themselves. This is the process of reproduction.

MULTIPLY AND SUBTRACT

When they reproduce, animals make a number of new individuals, usually more than two. But in many natural situations, where numbers of animals remain steady, two parents in one generation are replaced by two young in the next. This means most of the offspring produced have died. A female mouse can give birth to 50 or more babies in her lifetime. Yet only two, on average, will become adult and themselves reproduce. In some animals the wastage rate is much higher. Some fish lay millions of eggs at a time. A plaice may lay 20 million during its life. An oyster makes 40 million eggs. Nearly all die before they reach maturity.

Others take the opposite tack, and invest heavily in the care and protection of a few young. An elephant may produce only four or five calves in her lifetime, a rhinoceros perhaps only six. An albatross may only rear four chicks. But the period of care of these young is relatively long, and they set

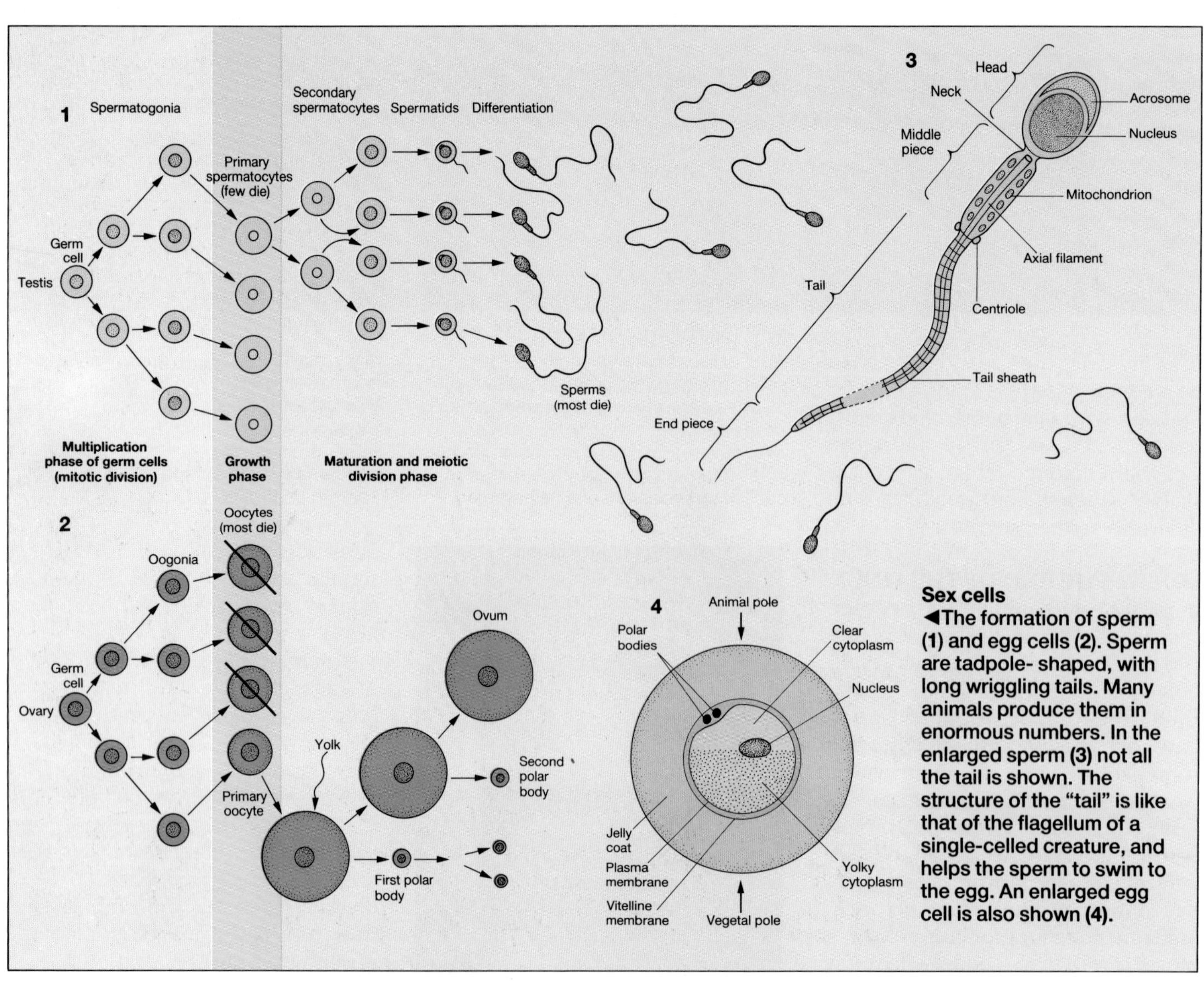

Sex cells
◀The formation of sperm (1) and egg cells (2). Sperm are tadpole- shaped, with long wriggling tails. Many animals produce them in enormous numbers. In the enlarged sperm (3) not all the tail is shown. The structure of the "tail" is like that of the flagellum of a single-celled creature, and helps the sperm to swim to the egg. An enlarged egg cell is also shown (4).

out into the world with a much higher chance of survival than the millions of scattered eggs of a fish.

BUDDING AND SPLITTING

Some animals produce new individuals that are genetically identical to themselves, simply by splitting. Many simple single-celled animals do this. Other simple animals, such as the freshwater *Hydra*, reproduce by budding. Part of the body develops an outgrowth that is eventually nipped off as a new individual. Some corals do much the same, as do sea-squirts. The cell divisions that make these new individuals are mitotic divisions (see page 76). The new individuals have exactly the same genes as the "parent".

If the parent is well adapted to the place it is living, then young produced in this way presumably will be too. Indeed this type of reproduction seems to be commonest in animals that travel hardly any distance in their lives. Those animals that disperse or travel around more commonly use sexual reproduction.

SEX AND VARIETY

In sexual reproduction, meiotic cell divisions (see page 77) produce eggs

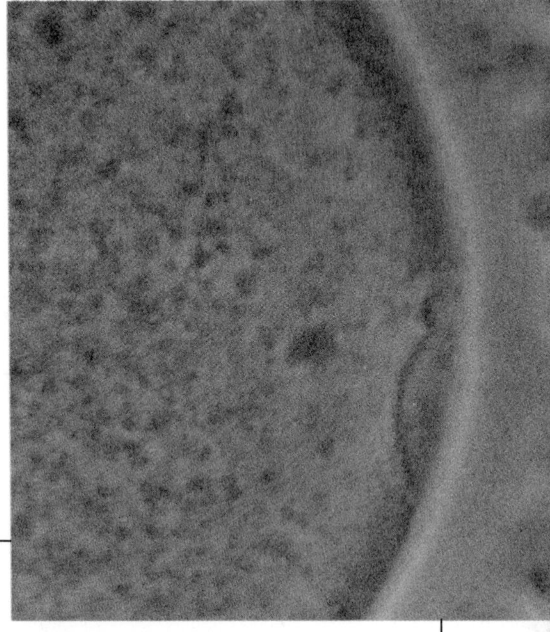

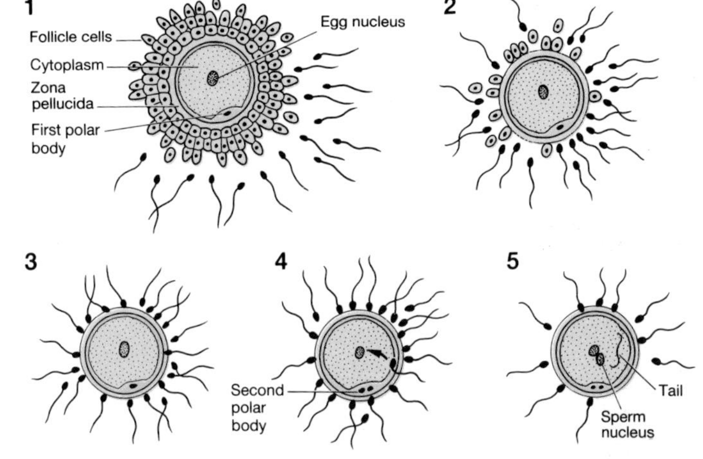

Fertilization
◀The coming together of egg and sperm. Sperm reaches the follicle cells surrounding the egg (1). The follicle cells disperse (2), and a sperm penetrates the outer layer or zona pellucida (3). A single sperm enters the egg cytoplasm (4), and the sperm nucleus and egg nucleus fuse (5).

▲An egg with a sperm inside (right).

▼Rabbit sperm seen through a microscope.

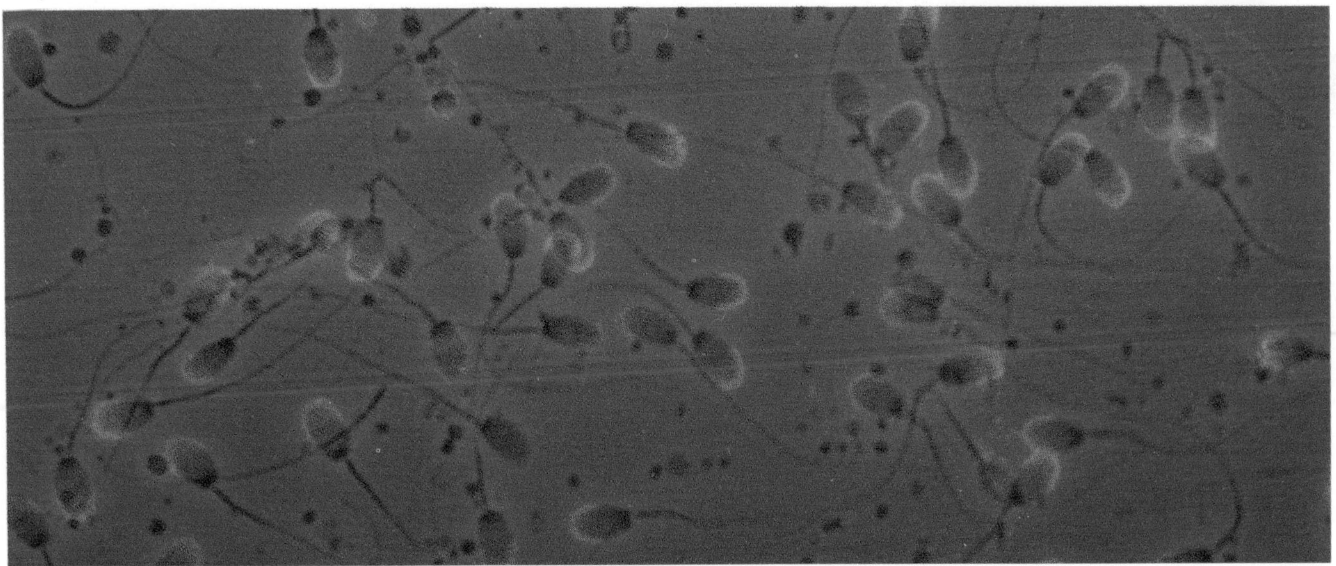

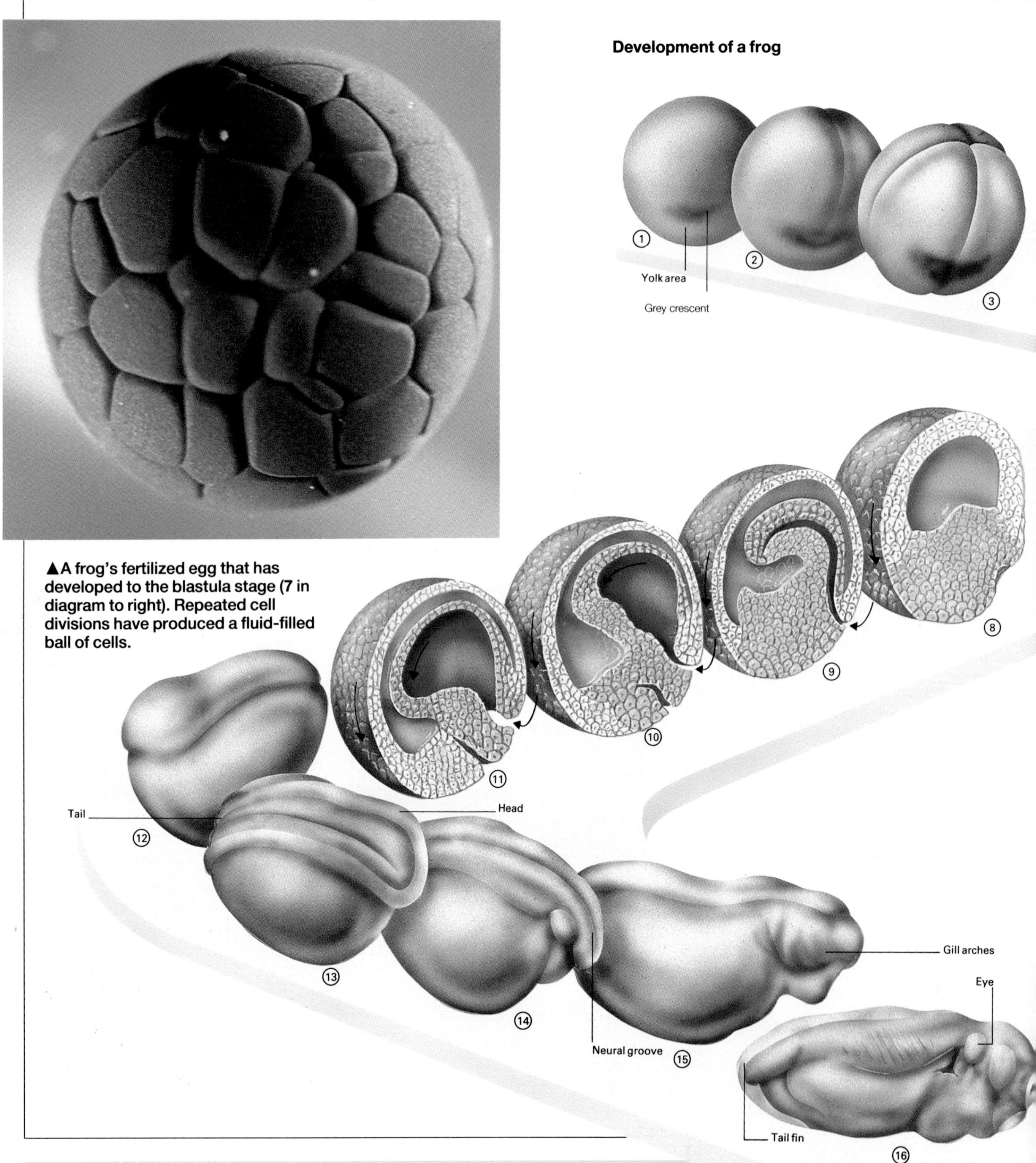

▲A frog's fertilized egg that has developed to the blastula stage (**7** in diagram to right). Repeated cell divisions have produced a fluid-filled ball of cells.

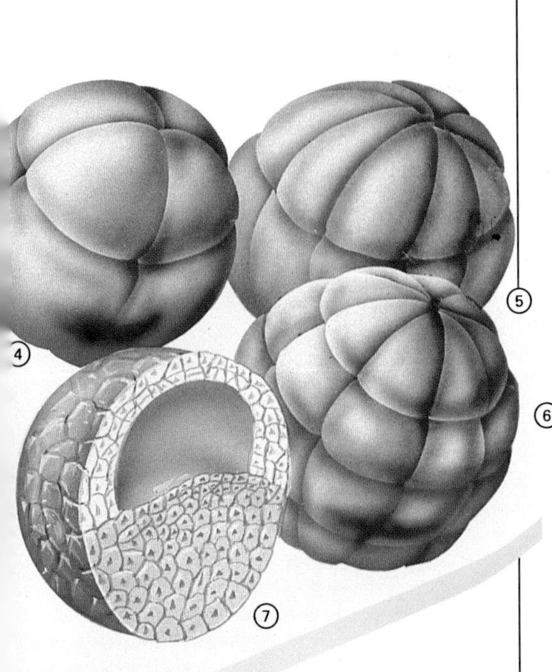

◀The egg **(1)** is pigmented above, the lower half yolky. At first, cell divisions are quite regular, producing 2, 4, 8, 16 and 32 cells **(2–6)**. Then they become more irregular. Cells divide faster in the lower half, and a cavity appears in the upper half **(7)**. A hole develops in the yolky area **(8)**. Coloured cells divide and move in through the hole to make a new inner layer **(9–10)**. The yolk is used up until there is just a plug left **(11)**. A groove forms on the upper surface and a head end becomes visible **(12–13)**. The groove closes up to make a tube, and gill arches form **(14–15)**. Then eyes and tail fin become visible **(16)**. By hatching **(17)**, the tadpole's gills, eyes and mouth are formed.

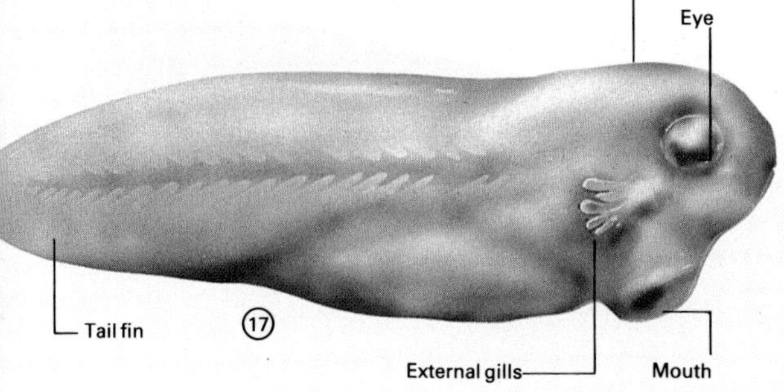

and sperm. Its advantage is that offspring are not genetically identical to their parents. From the variety produced, some will be less successful and disappear. But others may be very well adapted to the new place where they find themselves. These will thrive and themselves produce young.

A few animals can reproduce using either the sexual method or the simple copying of the parent, called asexual reproduction. The Water "flea" *Daphnia* is a small freshwater crustacean. In the summer, a pond will be full of female Water fleas. They may all be descended from a single female hatched in the spring. She feeds on the algae in the pond and, without needing to mate with a male, produces eggs that develop and hatch as small copies of herself.

This can carry on through several generations when life is easy in the pond, building up a huge number of individuals. But in a midsummer drought or the autumn cold, some of the females begin to produce male offspring. Mating between males and females takes place, resulting in special tough eggs that can survive the winter. From the variety of eggs produced, one will probably produce a female suited to the conditions of next year's pond.

MAKING EGGS

Eggs are the sex cells of female animals. They are usually made in special organs called ovaries. In insects and some kinds of worm, the ovaries are long tubes. Egg-producing cells are at one end, and as the egg travels along the tube, it matures. In mammals the ovaries are solid bodies that release eggs. These travel along tubes called oviducts, and are then ready for fertilization.

Most animal eggs spend a long time in the first stage of meiotic cell division. During this, much information from the DNA is transferred to messenger RNA. This mRNA is "packaged up" and is not used until development into a new animal has begun. During the process of egg formation, yolk, special membranes and perhaps a shell may be added.

Mature eggs may be thousands of times bigger than the original egg cell, as in birds and sharks. Mammal eggs have no yolk and are comparatively small, about the size of this full stop.

The process of egg formation can take only a few months, as in some worms and sea urchins. It may take two years, as in a frog. Or it may take much longer. In humans, a female begins the process while just a three-month old foetus in the womb. It is finished when she is a grown woman.

MAKING SPERM

Sperm (plural also sperms or spermatozoa) are the sex cells of male animals. They are produced in organs called testes. Some snails, worms and other species are hermaphrodite, with both sets of sex organs in the same individual. Even these generally mate with another individual so the young are not identical to the parent.

In many animals, sperm are produced in even greater numbers than eggs, and huge numbers never get to fertilize an egg. A human male may produce one million million sperm in his lifetime, but probably less than ten will be able to fertilize eggs and result in children. Unlike eggs, sperm are mobile, swimming with their tails. But they carry no food supply for the young. They just contribute their genes to a new individual, when fertilization takes place.

◀King penguin and fluffy chick. Only one chick is raised by the parents during each breeding season. At the end of the season, the chick is very fat and weighs more than the parent. Once on its own, it soon uses up the fat store.

▲Young Deer mice in their grassy nest. When they were born, after a pregnancy of just three weeks, they were blind and naked. Three weeks later in their protected nest, they are furry and active, alert and aware.

STARTING OUT IN LIFE

After fertilization, when sperm and egg join together, the egg begins to make mitotic cell divisions. It divides repeatedly to form a ball of cells. The sperm's genes seem to have little effect at this stage. The egg appears to be carried through these first stages of development using messenger RNA laid down in the egg during its early development, as explained above.

Once the embryo has developed to a ball of cells there is often a series of cell movements, as layers or sheets of cells fold and twist themselves. The position of the cells in the embryo now seems to cause their development in different ways. All the cells in the developing body have the same DNA in their nuclei, but now the position in the body helps to switch on particular sets of genes.

Gradually this switching-on of genes leads to groups of cells with specialized shapes or functions. The formation of tissues and organs has begun. The animal slowly takes shape.

GROWING

Some animals hatch or are born as small replicas of their parents. Newly hatched lizards and snakes may look little different from their parents. They are smaller, of course, and not yet ready to breed, but otherwise they are easily recognized for what they are.

Many crustaceans, and some insects such as grasshoppers and cockroaches, climb a "ladder" of juvenile forms. They go through a series of shape changes, with ever-increasing size, until they become full adults.

Other animals, including starfish, crabs and many insects such as flies and butterflies, hatch looking very different from their parents. They go through one or more larval stages before turning into the adult form.

Some animals, such as most mammals and birds, and also insects, reach a more-or-less fixed adult size, after which further growth does not occur. Other animals, like reptiles and some worms, carry on growing throughout their lives.

The "investment" in reproduction is probably greatest in birds and mammals. In both of these groups, adults spend a considerable part of their lives caring for the next generation.

FINDING FOOD

A blowfly lands on a table where there are the remains of a meal. The fly walks across the table and reaches a spot where some sugary fruit juice has been spilt. As its feet contact the sweet liquid it stops and puts down its mouthparts. These consist of a sponge-like tip and a tube up which liquids are sucked. The blowfly has fine hairs on its feet that can "taste" substances. When they find food, then the mouthparts get to work.

Feeding provides many examples of the way in which the shape of animals, their senses and behaviour have to fit together to achieve the best result.

THE NEED TO FEED

Every animal has to feed in order to live and grow. None can make its own food. All must get their nourishment either from plants directly, or else at "secondhand" by eating animals that themselves have eaten plants. But food can take a huge number of forms. There are thousands of plants, from almost invisible algae to trees. Possible animal prey can also vary

widely in size. Dead plants or animals, or the products of their decay, can also be used as food. Almost every substance that contains organic matter is eaten by some animal somewhere. The range of adaptations for feeding, both in body form and behaviour, is enormous. Animals that sustain themselves by killing and eating other animals are dealt with on pages 98 to 103. Those animals that feed on plants or less solid food are dealt with on this and the following pages.

◀▼A variety of feeding techniques
The moose (*Alces alces*) **(1)** browses on vegetation. A goshawk (*Accipiter gentilis*) **(2)** swoops on to its prey. The Common genet (*Genetta genetta*) **(3)** often climbs through trees after its food. The St. Andrew's cross spider (*Argiope aetherea*) **(4)** spins a web to catch prey such as this fly. Greater flamingos (*Phoenicopterus ruber roseus*) **(5)** strain out microscopic organisms from water with their beaks. Butterflies like the Gulf fritillary (*Dione vanillae*) **(6)** suck the nectar from flowers. The squid (*Loligo* species) **(7)** captures fish with the tentacles that encircle its mouth.

THE EASY OPTION

One of the simplest kinds of feeding behaviour is shown by those animals called filter feeders. They have some means of sieving tiny plants or animals from the water in which they live. Many groups of animals from sponges to coral, mussels and fanworms use this method. Some fishes, birds and whales are also filter feeders. The behaviour of filter feeders can be very simple. They may do little more than stretch out sticky tentacles, as do fanworms, to catch edible objects in the water that flows past. But filter feeding can be more active and complex than this. Mussels, for example, create their own currents of water through their gills to bring more food within reach. From among all of the material suspended in the water they take only some as food and pass it from the gill surface to the mouth. The rest is rejected and passed out of the

body in the water current. Particles of the wrong size or taste are discarded.

Many filter feeders, such as fanworms, do not move about when adult, relying largely on food to come to them. Some bony fish and basking sharks, though, swim through the water with their mouths open. This forces a stream of water through the gills which function as a sieve trap for microscopic food. Blue whales gulp into their mouths a mass of water containing a huge number of small shrimp-like krill, and then use their tongue to push out the water and trap the krill against the frilly plates of horn (baleen) in the roof of the mouth.

MUD PIE

Simply swallowing your surroundings is even less demanding than filter feeding in terms of senses and special behaviour, but this indeed is what some earthworms and lugworms do. They swallow mud, and their digestive system acts on any food particles as they go down the gut. The rest is just passed out as waste – worm casts.

GRAZING NOT LAZING

Eating grass would also seem to be a simple option. For an antelope or a buffalo, food is spread out like a carpet under their very noses. At many times of the year it may be plentiful and it would seem that the animal could just walk along like a giant mower eating everything before it. But cattle and other grazers make many choices while feeding. To help them they have their senses of smell and taste, and sensitive lips and whiskers. Some plants are preferred to others. A few, such as buttercups, contain bitter or poisonous chemicals and are avoided. If you look at a pasture where horses have grazed you will see that some plants are well cropped while others are not touched at all.

Even good grass, however, needs to be taken in quite large quantities to provide adequate nourishment. But still it is hard to digest and many grass-eaters rely on bacteria in the gut to ferment it and break it down. Most animals such as cattle "chew the cud" or ruminate, bringing up partly digested food to the mouth for more chewing before sending it back to complete its journey through the gut. Even when ruminants are at rest they are almost constantly chewing, and you can see balls of food travelling up the throat to the mouth at regular intervals. So, even if grazing seems an easy option it involves behaviour that may well take up most of the day.

KEEPING MOVING

Many grazing animals keep on the move in the wild so that they do not return to an area too soon before their food has a chance to grow again. In some species, such as wildebeest, long-distance migrations are undertaken to ensure that the herds do not exhaust their feeding grounds. On the other hand, some plants grow back very quickly. Brent geese crop down the marsh vegetation they feed on and then move on. But within 4 days the vegetation has grown back to grazing length again. A Brent goose flock will avoid an area where it has previously fed, but then fly back in about 4 days later to crop it again.

PICK AND MIX

Some plant eaters browse rather than graze. Goats, for example, pick individual leaves, buds or twigs from bushes or tall herbs. Browsers, like grazers, may spend much time in feeding and finding food, though the individual items they eat may be quite nourishing.

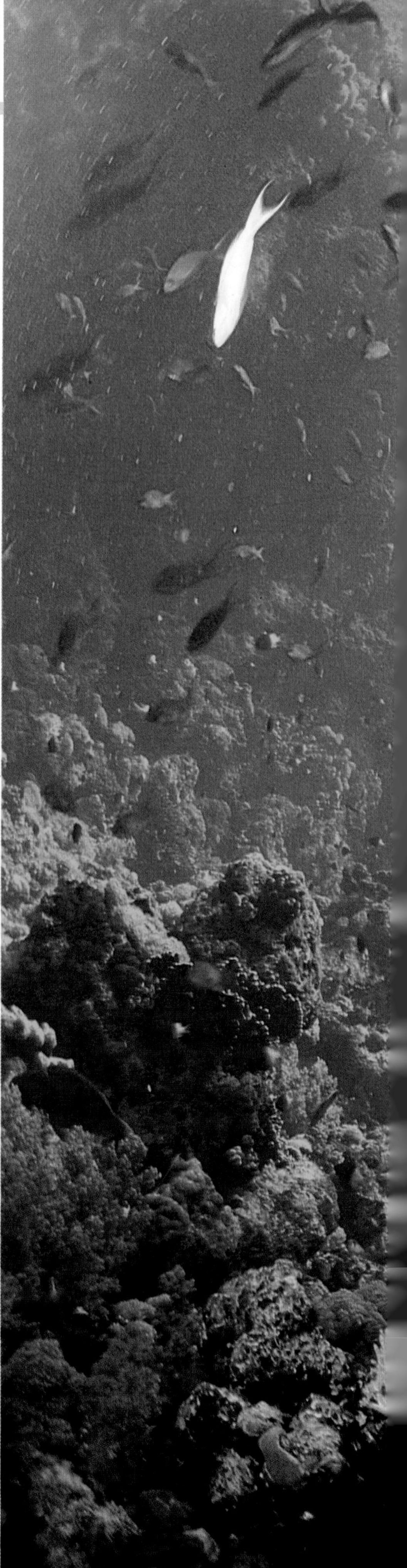

▶In the Red Sea, these corals use the stinging cells on their tentacles to capture small animals to eat. Large fish, such as this grouper, swim over the coral reefs, preying on smaller fish. Microscopic animals, the zooplankton, graze on the tiny plants that drift near the surface of the water.

LIQUID REFRESHMENT

Some of the most specialized plant-eaters are those that feed on nectar from flowers. They include insects such as butterflies, birds, such as hummingbirds, some bats and the Australian Honey possum. Many have long mouthparts or tongues to reach into flowers. They may also use specialized feeding techniques. Hummingbirds hover well, which enables them to feed from otherwise inaccessible flowers. Some animals feed on what may seem to us less appetizing fluids. A few of the most beautiful butterflies, for example, sip pools of liquefying dung on the jungle floor.

FOOD FINDING STRATEGIES

When food is scarce, or occurs only in particular places or at particular times, then behaviour that ensures finding it becomes very important. In winter a small bird such as a tit may spend 90 per cent of its time searching for food. Many animals, if they encounter one piece of food, will search around thoroughly in the immediate area. For a seed-eating mammal like a wood-mouse this strategy makes sense. Where there is one seed there may well be others.

But knowing when to stop looking is important too. As an animal eats its way through a bush full of berries, for example, the number of food items gradually diminishes and as a result each one will become more and more difficult to find. There must come a point where the animal would be better off looking for another large supply. This point will differ according to whether such supplies are plentiful or not. The behaviour of animals seems designed to cope with this. In an area where new supplies are sparse, animals will spend longer using the resource more thoroughly.

Nectar feeders have their feeding strategies too. The amakihi, a bird of the Hawaiian honeycreeper family, remembers where it has fed recently and avoids returning to an area from which it has exhausted the nectar. Bumblebees, when faced with a shortage of flowers, may take the maximum nectar from each. When flowers are plentiful, however, the bees may leave some nectar in every one they visit.

▲Instead of using its beak to crack seeds, like most other parrots, the Rainbow lorikeet uses the brush-like tip of its tongue to mop up the nectar and pollen from flowers.

1

◄▲**Some animals that store food when it is abundant** Various species create hoards and return to them when food becomes scarce. Rodents such as the woodmouse (*Apodemus sylvaticus*) **(1)**, store seeds and nuts in part of the burrow when they are plentiful in autumn. Acorn woodpeckers (*Melanerpes formicivorus*) **(2)** drill large numbers of holes in dead trees, then fill them with acorns. The nutcracker (*Nucifraga caryocatactes*) **(3)** stores small collections of food objects in thousands of places within its living area.

Large sized food items, or ones that are most abundant, are not necessarily the best. Small seeds may be easier to open than large ones, or scarce berries may be more nourishing than plentiful ones. Thus, within a given time an animal may get much greater nourishment from small, scarce food items than from larger, more plentiful ones. When we study animal behaviour we often find that our subjects are working in the "best" way, not the one that seems to us to be the simplest.

ANIMAL FARM

Humans make reasonably sure of continuing food supplies by growing their own on farms and storing it. Very few animals have developed behaviour that could be described as farming, but leafcutter ants do grow their own food, a fungus, in their underground nests. They bring back pieces of leaf into the "gardens" inside the nest and chew them to a pulp on which the fungus grows. Only one fungus type is permitted to grow. If any others appear, the ants weed them out. Some termites are also fungus farmers.

SELECTING A DIET

How do animals select what to eat? For some the body structure and the behaviour are so specialized that they are adapted to eating only one kind of food. But many animals have in theory a wide range of possible foods from which to make a choice.

Taste preferences may be important. For people the taste often helps decide whether something is good to eat. This holds for many other animals too. A blowfly prefers some kinds of sugar to others. Some animals are known to acquire a taste for a particular food from their mother. Young rats can recognize something as being good to eat because they have already received traces of its flavour in the mother's milk. Once they start feeding on solids they will show a clear preference for foods the mother had been feeding on.

Other factors can affect preferences too. If a rat falls ill due to the lack of some vital factor in the diet, but is then cured by eating a food that corrects the lack, it may afterwards prefer a diet that contains that food. The same may be true of many other types of animal.

LIVING TOGETHER

A huge fish approaches a coral reef. A small brightly coloured fish swims out. The big fish opens its mouth wide. It could easily gulp down the smaller fish but doesn't even try. The smaller fish begins searching the larger one's lips and gills. It even enters the big fish's mouth, stays there a few minutes, and emerges again.

The behaviour of fishes at a coral reef "cleaning station" is unusual. Hunting fish come to be cleaned of parasites and do not harm the cleaners. They even spread mouth and gills wide to allow the cleaners to work. Cleaner fish are brightly coloured and have a special way of swimming. The behaviour of the cleaner and its customer is a good example of symbiosis – a relationship between two species that brings benefits to both. The large fish have their parasites removed, the cleaner fish get a meal.

CROCODILE TOOTHPICK

A similar symbiotic relationship exists between the Nile crocodile and the Egyptian plover. The bird is allowed to scramble over a basking crocodile and even pick scraps of food from its teeth without coming to harm.

A different kind of symbiosis exists between some ants and aphids. The ants "milk" the aphids of their body waste, a sweet liquid called honeydew. They stroke the aphids with their antennae to make them release it. In return for this food the ants may move the aphids to new feeding sites, and will drive off predators. In some species the relationship is so close that an ant queen carries an aphid on her mating flight to ensure continuation of the honeydew supply.

TABLE SCRAPS

There are other types of association between animals. In some cases one benefits from another without doing it either good or harm in return. A gull feeding on a rubbish dump, or a raccoon eating from a garbage can, both show behaviour that enables them to benefit from associating with people, but without doing harm. This type of relationship is known as commensalism. In some situations, different forms of living together can occur on one animal. For example, as an African buffalo grazes, Cattle egrets hunt for insects it disturbs (commensalism) and oxpeckers search it for tasty parasites (symbiosis).

UNWELCOME GUESTS

Parasitism is, in fact, a third type of relationship. A parasite is an animal that lives in or on another – called the host – at its expense. The parasite survives usually by taking the host's food or by eating or otherwise damaging its tissues, so doing harm. Some

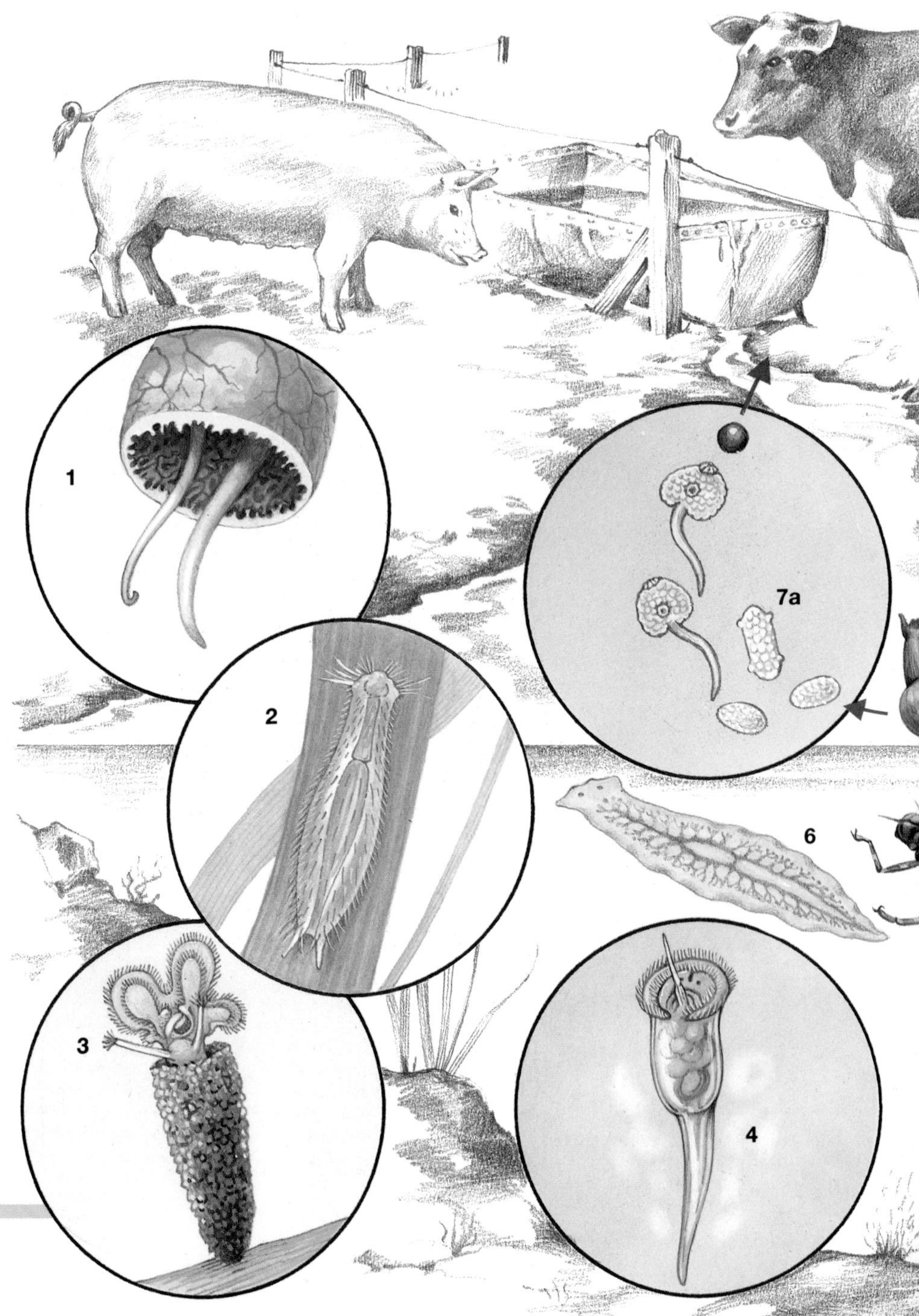

parasites eventually kill their host, but only when they can move on to a free-living stage in their life cycle. Many do not kill the host, however, for they need the host as a permanent home for themselves and perhaps their offspring as well.

A parasite such as a tapeworm living in the gut of a dog or a human needs no special behaviour. It fixes itself to its host, and remains in one spot, absorbing nutrients and dissolved oxygen from the food in which it is bathed. It lacks digestive and blood circulatory systems and sharp senses.

►A group of ants tends the aphid "cows" that supply them with honeydew. In return the ants provide protection.

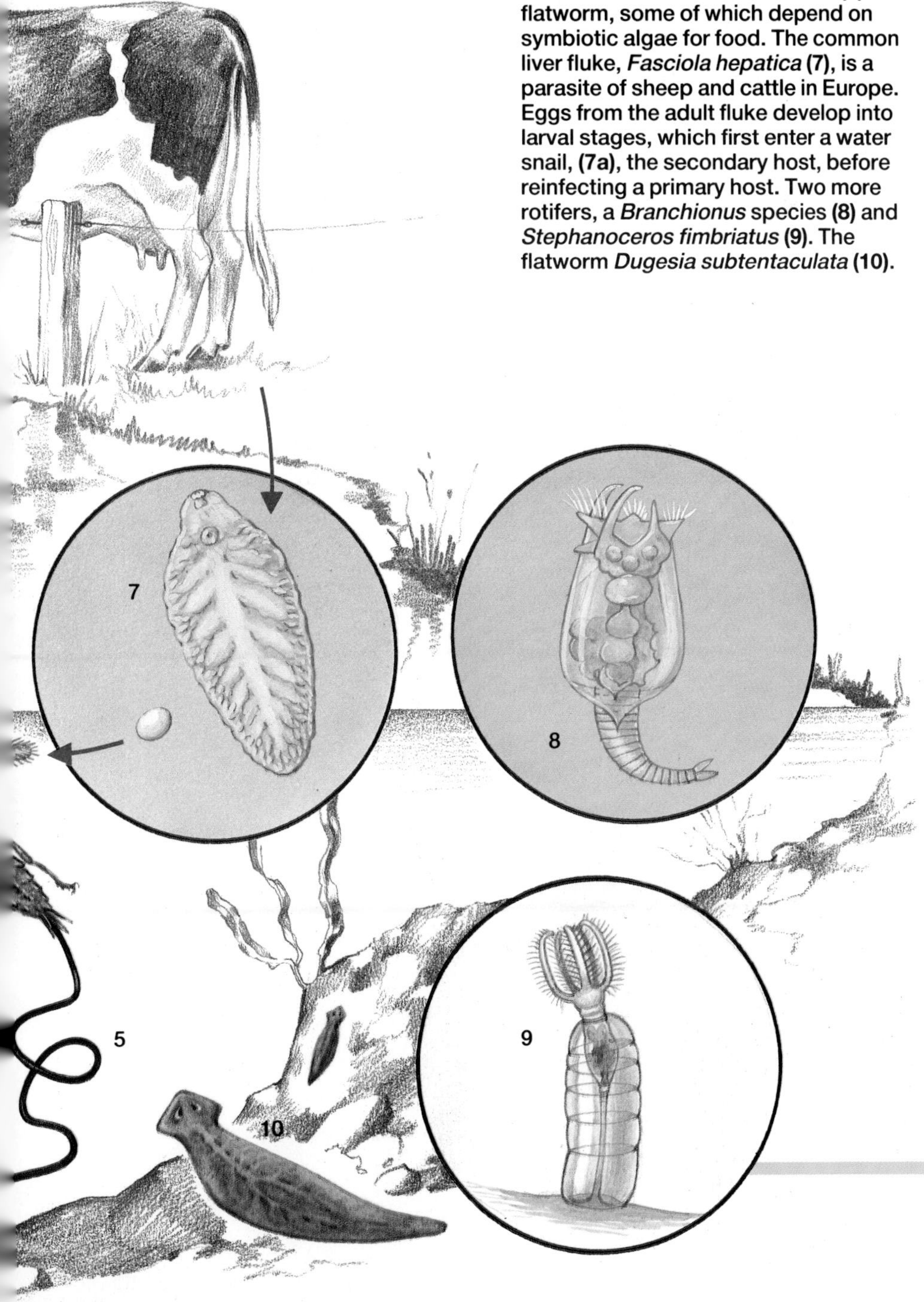

▼Worm-like parasites of farmland and some of their relatives Living in the gut of the domestic pig is the round worm *Ascaris lumbricoides suilla* **(1)**. The gastrotrich *Chaetonotus* **(2)**, and the rotifers *Floscularia ringens* **(3)** and *Conochilus hippocrepis* **(4)**, prey on bacteria and protozoans, some of which are parasites of mammals. A few rotifers are themselves parasites, as is the worm *Gordius* **(5)**, which lives inside aquatic insects. *Dendrocoelum lacteum* **(6)** is a flatworm, some of which depend on symbiotic algae for food. The common liver fluke, *Fasciola hepatica* **(7)**, is a parasite of sheep and cattle in Europe. Eggs from the adult fluke develop into larval stages, which first enter a water snail, **(7a)**, the secondary host, before reinfecting a primary host. Two more rotifers, a *Branchionus* species **(8)** and *Stephanoceros fimbriatus* **(9)**. The flatworm *Dugesia subtentaculata* **(10)**.

7

8

5

9

10

The most important behaviour for some parasites is that which gets them or, more importantly, their offspring, to a new host. One flatworm that lives in fishes has to transfer to a bird for one stage in its life cycle. At that time it burrows its way into the fish's eye. This makes the partly blinded fish swim near the surface, thus increasing the chance of being caught by a bird.

TIMING IT RIGHT

The behaviour of a parasite is often geared to coincide with that of the host in order to ensure survival. The Rabbit flea, which feeds on its host's blood, breeds in response to the chemicals produced in the blood by a pregnant rabbit. Young fleas therefore emerge just before the young rabbits are born. The increase in body temperature of the mother rabbit at this time makes the fleas more active, and therefore more likely to jump onto the newborn rabbits.

THE HUNTERS

A stalk of dry grass twitches. Over the grass the eyes and ears of a lion gradually appear. It concentrates on the herd of zebra in the clearing ahead. Its tail twitches. Then it suddenly leaps forward and rushes at a zebra. In the whirling dust and confusion the zebra dodges and runs. The lion has missed a possible meal.

Hunting animals, the predators, do not always catch the prey they are after. Lions may succeed in less than a third of their attempts. Leopards may catch their target only once in every twenty hunts. The figures do vary between different species, and at different places, but overall the message is clear – being a hunter is not an easy option.

LOCATING PREY

To find their food, hunters need highly developed sense organs and the ability to use them efficiently. Animals may be able to see, hear or detect faint smells far better than a human. But often a predator will be "tuned in" to particular aspects of the surroundings that betray the presence of prey and may ignore others. Many predators will attack only when they see the prey make a movement.

SIGHT, SMELL OR SOUND?

Some animals react merely to the sight of prey. For example, a praying mantis watches an insect until it is at just the right spot to trigger the mantis to shoot out its front legs and trap it. A chameleon similarly watches with its mobile eyes until the prey is in the right position to be ensnared, this time by shooting out its tongue. Sounds and scents seem to be of little importance to these animals.

For others, however, scent is very important. Wild dogs locate prey in the first place by scent. Snakes follow scent trails by flicking in and out their sensitive forked tongues, "tasting" smells in the air. Some snakes, such as the adder, may pass within sight of their prey but seem to ignore it until the scent trail brings them back to the same spot. It seems that in this situation prey cannot be recognized as such by sight alone.

Other animals use sound as the main information. Some owls are deadly hunters by ear where it is too dark to see. Red foxes and servals may hunt by sound in tall grass, pausing to use their large, spread ears to detect the rustles or squeaks of an otherwise concealed rodent.

"RADAR" SYSTEMS

Sometimes particularly specialized behaviour is used to locate prey. Bats, dolphins and some seals can produce high-pitched sounds and listen for prey by detecting the echoes of these sounds that are bounced back to them. Some fishes generate electric fields in the water. They detect prey by the distortions it produces in these fields. The fishes' behaviour maintains their electric field as constant as possible. They keep the body straight and swim only by gently rippling the fins.

HUNTING TECHNIQUES

Once prey is located close at hand, a predator may simply rush it and hope to outrun it quickly. Cheetahs hunt Thomson's gazelles in this way. They must get quite close before the chase can begin, as they can run fast for only 400m or so. Other species of cat need to be even closer. They stalk prey carefully, keeping low and using any plants or rocks as cover, until they are close enough to make a sudden spring or short rush at the prey. Members

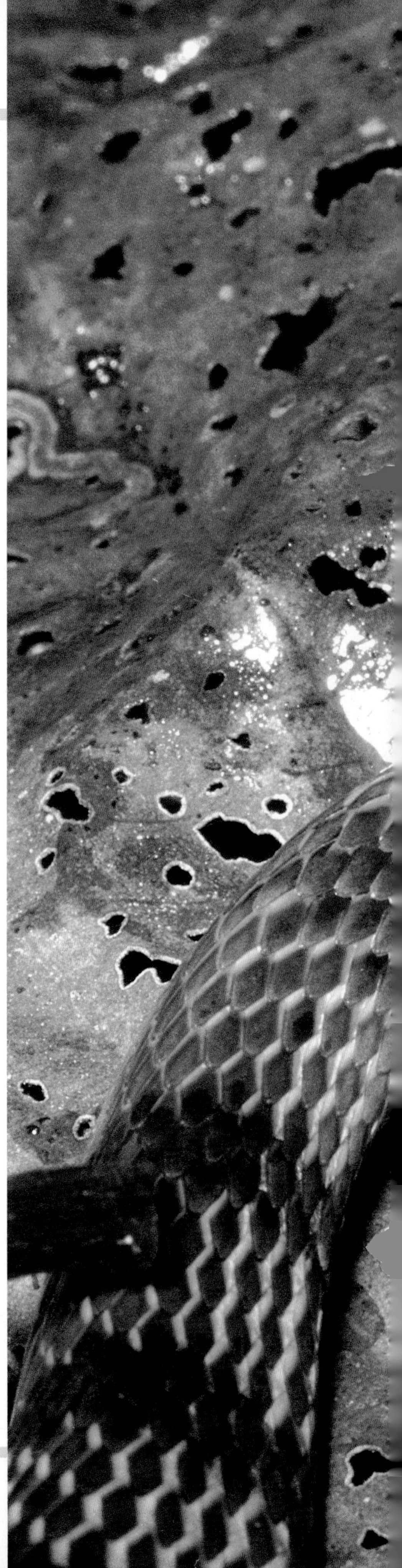

►A Fire-bellied snake eats a harlequin frog. Once they have overpowered prey, snakes manoeuvre it into the best position for swallowing whole – usually head first.

of the dog family often undertake longer chases, relying on superior endurance rather than speed.

Usually, however, hunters employ energy-saving tactics. A predator will use its past experience to increase its chances of successfully catching prey. It may cut corners in a chase. In many cases very old, sick or young animals are singled out for attack because they are easier to catch and less likely to damage the hunter. Lone animals split off from their herd are also preferred victims because it is difficult for a predator to concentrate on a single animal within a large group.

Even so, chasing or stalking prey can take up much time and energy. Some animals cut down on this by simply waiting in ambush for prey to come by – some snakes do this – or even by building traps. The antlion larva makes a slippery-sided pit in sand and lies in wait buried at the bottom ready to kill insect prey that falls in. Many spiders build webs that snare insects. Some fishes and turtles use their mouths as traps, luring fishes within range by means of a brightly coloured tongue or mobile flap of skin on the snout or the chin.

Other animals employ more speculative techniques. Some octopuses, for example, close the web between their tentacles from time to time as they move over rocks and seaweed, and check to see if they have caught anything within.

▼Methods of detecting prey Using heat-sensitive pits near the eyes some snakes **(1)** can detect a temperature rise as small as 0.005°C; this enables them to locate a mouse 15cm away in the dark. Bats **(2)** make high-pitched squeaks and listen to echoes returning from the surroundings, so finding flying insects. Barn owls **(3)** can hear a mouse moving and catch it in pitch darkness. Hyenas **(4)** find carrion by smell.

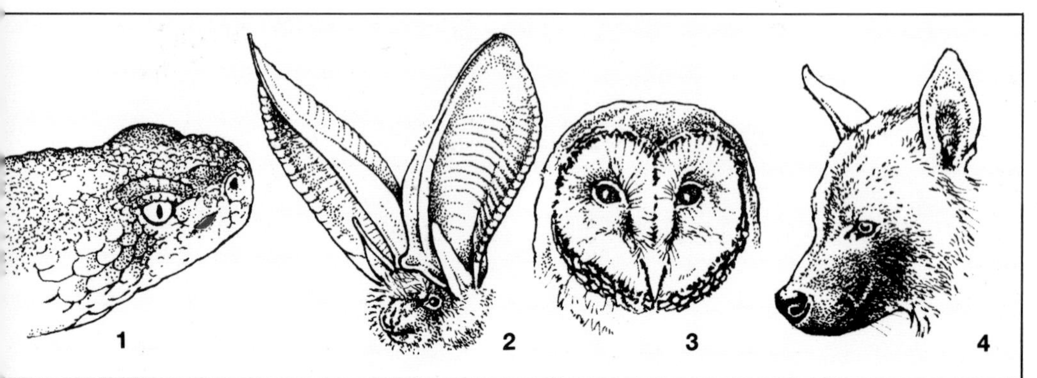

NOT WHAT THEY SEEM

Some predators deceive prey by mimicking the appearance and initial behaviour of harmless species. On the coral reef there are small predatory fish that resemble cleaner fish and imitate their behaviour (see page 96). When an unsuspecting fish comes up to be cleaned the predator dashes in and bites off a chunk of flesh.

The Zone-tailed hawk of North America uses a similar deception. It often soars in the company of vultures. Small mammals feel no danger from vultures, and remain unaware of the hawk until it is too late.

DEAD EASY

Not all flesh-eaters hunt living prey. Some, such as vultures, hyenas, jackals, crows and sometimes even lions, avoid the effort by feeding on carrion – animals that have died or been killed by other predators. Seeking them out, by smell or other means, may still be important. Also useful is the ability to interpret the behaviour of other animals. If a vulture or jackal sees lions hunting it keeps watch for the kill.

KILLING PREY

Once a predator has captured its prey it needs to subdue it ready for eating. A fox or coyote will pin down a small mammal then aim a killing bite at the head and neck. Violent side-to-side shaking of the head by the attacker helps break the victim's neck and deepen the bite into blood vessels and nerves. Big cats may break a victim's neck with a blow from a paw or may grasp the throat of the prey in their jaws and rapidly suffocate it.

Snakes lack limbs to help overcome prey. Some use their whole body to pin prey down or, as in boas, tightly coil themselves round it to suffocate it. Others have apparently more casual behaviour. Lunging at a cornered victim, they inject it with a powerful venom through specialized teeth and then leave it to wander off and die before following its trail and swallowing the victim. Spiders may wrap prey in silk to stop it moving once it has blundered into a web, after first subduing it with a poisonous bite.

▼Predators and their prey An aardvark (*Orycteropus afer*) **(1)** licks up termites. A Red-backed shrike (*Lanius collurio*) **(2)** impales a dead lizard on a thorn. A Grey seal (*Halichoerus grypus*) **(3)** chases fish. A Herring gull (*Larus argentatus*) **(4)** chases a Black-headed gull (*Larus ridibundus*) **(5)** to make it release food which it has taken from a rubbish dump. A Noctule bat (*Nyctalus noctula*) **(6)** homes in on a moth which it has detected by echoes reflected off it.

Most predators kill their prey before eating it – it usually causes less trouble that way – but some may start to feed on prey that is still alive. Some insects do this, and a pack of wild dogs will start to tear at a victim before it has stopped struggling.

SUCCESS RATES

Despite all their physical adaptations and their specialized behaviour, the predators are by no means always successful in the hunt. Studies have shown that ospreys swooping to the water to catch fish do rather well, with success on 9 out of 10 occasions. A number of predatory fish are equally efficient but for most animals the success rate is much less. At their best, cheetahs and wild dogs may be successful in two out of every three attempts, while kestrels and hyenas may achieve only half this score. Wolves hunting moose were seen to fail 19 times out of 20 – but when they were successful there was plenty for all. All these figures are liable to change at different times and under different conditions. Some individuals are better hunters than others.

Whatever the actual percentage of successful hunts, the behaviour of predators usually ensures that enough survive and reproduce. Enough prey survive too for the balance between hunter and hunted to be maintained.

When capturing prey is made artificially easy, a predator's behaviour may seem to become extreme. A fox that gets into a chicken roost will kill far more than it is able to eat. Under wild

▼When wolves hunt, one of the pack may work its way round to the front of a herd of caribou while others drive the herd forward to the ambush. The wolves may also try to split one animal from the herd. A sheepdog being worked by a shepherd uses just the same techniques in the service of its master.

▲▶**Cooperative killers** While one Spotted hyena is chased off by a mother wildebeest, other members of the group chase easier prey – her newly born calf. African hunting dogs chase prey until it is exhausted. Pack members take turns to lead, and through persistence can wear down animals as large as zebra.

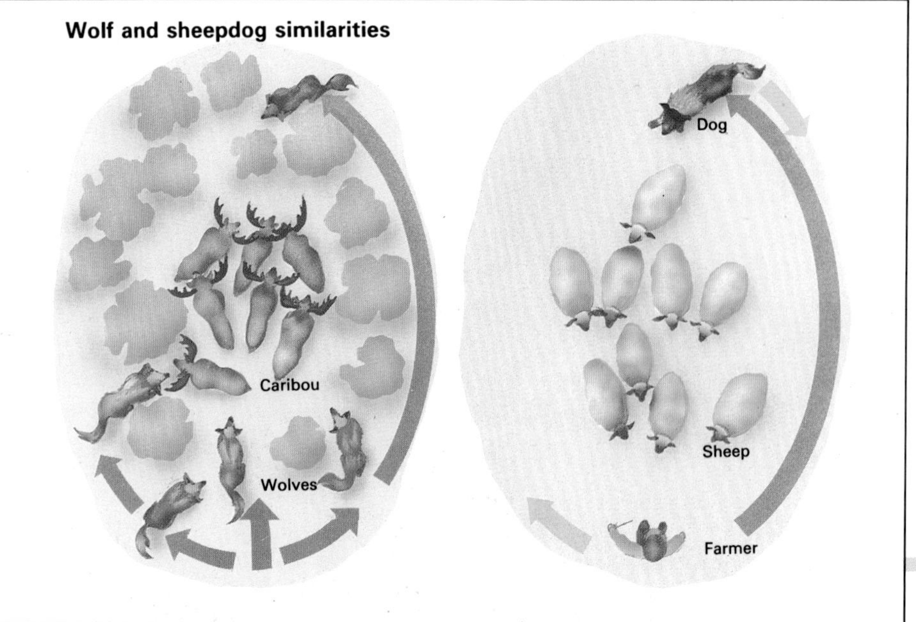

conditions such apparently wanton slaughter rarely takes place. Some predators, however, do encounter situations which allow them to catch more meat than they require for their immediate needs. They can then store (cache) the food and return later to continue the feast. A tiger may drag the remains of a carcass into cover and come back for it the next night. If an Arctic fox is able to kill surplus birds it may bury them in the snow. Sometimes they remain in their natural deep-freeze for a long time before the fox needs to dig them out.

FINDING FOOD TOGETHER
Hunting success may increase if the predators get together in groups, even if the individuals are not actively cooperating. A vulture follows others down to the ground because this is a good sign of food being available, but all members of the group have not worked together in getting it.

COOPERATING IN CAPTURE
Some animals, however, show great cooperation when hunting as a group. The members of a pack of wolves work together to achieve a killing. The group spreads out. The individuals chasing the prey in the middle of the group travel more slowly than those on the outside. In this way the prey can be surrounded, making escape difficult. Mammals from wolves to the Killer whale work this way, as do some birds such as pelicans.

Sometimes cleverer tactics are used. Wild dogs and wolves allow one animal to do all the close chasing. It twists and turns after the prey while the rest of the group lopes along on a straighter, shorter path, saving energy. After a spell the lead animal is changed. These tactics can wear down even animals that are faster runners than their hunters. Driving prey towards an ambush is another tactic used by group hunters.

Though some predators hunt in packs others, like the leopard, work alone, relying on cunning. Some species, however, vary their behaviour according to the prey. Spotted hyenas may hunt singly, or in twos and threes, for Thomson's gazelles and young wildebeest, but cooperate in a pack of a dozen or more when hunting the much bigger zebra.

Studies show that cooperation greatly increases hunting success. A jackal hunting on its own can catch a Thomson's gazelle – but only once in six attempts. A pair of jackals working together, however, are successful four times out of six.

COMMUNICATION

It is early morning in a Central American forest. From the distance comes a sound like rumbling thunder. But this sound is produced by a small troop of Howler monkeys high in the trees. They are signalling their presence to others in the forest. Soon the members of a troop a kilometre away cry back in answer.

For many wild animals, as for humans, sound is a very important means of communication. But there are other forms of "language" too. Some of our own communication is by sight. We take note of the expressions on people's faces, their gestures and the way they stand. Even though our noses are not highly efficient there is evidence that we also respond to scents produced by other people.

Other animals, too, can react to all these types of communication. Some may be able to communicate by yet other means. Some fishes, for example, respond to electrical signals. The signals that are important vary among species, according to their senses and the places they live.

SIGNALS BETWEEN SPECIES

We think of communication as taking place mainly between individuals of the same species, but sometimes different species need to "talk" to each other as well. The warning coloration of venomous animals is an example of one species getting a message across to another. You do not have to be another dog to know that a growling, snarling dog is best avoided. Warning growls and the baring of teeth are common expressions of aggressive behaviour among mammals, and are understood across the species divide.

Warning displays are used as "keep off" notices by some nesting birds. These can communicate a deceptive message. The Cut-throat finch of Africa is small and harmless, but if disturbed on its nest it will open its mouth and writhe its neck about in an intimidating, snake-like display which is usually enough to put off any curious intruder.

GENERAL ALARM

Alarm calls are another type of signal that often works across the species barrier. Many birds have rather similar alarm calls – thin, high-pitched and difficult to locate. Other kinds of bird may react to them. Among species that associate together, the alarm call of one may alert the others. Indeed, for some this may be the main advantage of the association.

SIGNALLING YOUR SPECIES

The sole function of some animal communication is to allow different

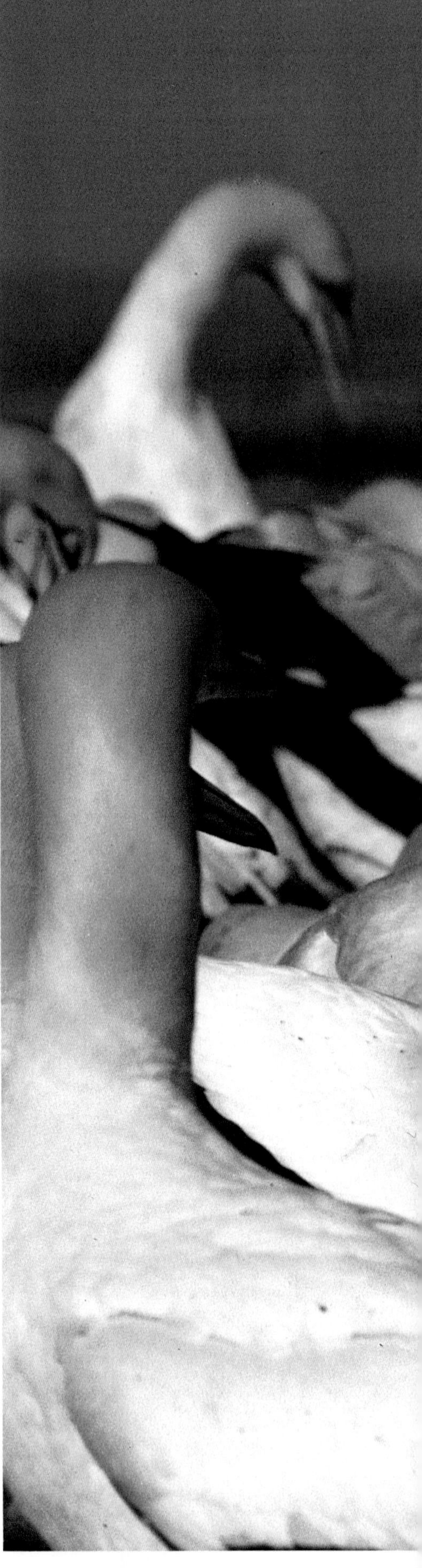

►Gannets live in packed colonies and need clear signals to communicate and maintain order. In the background, behind bickering neighbours, two pairs stretch their necks in greeting.

▲A klipspringer marks the boundary of his territory with secretions from a gland in front of the eye. The black blob of secretion shows this twig has been used many times before.

Scent communication The skunk **(1)** uses scent to ward off predators. Male Ring-tailed lemurs **(2)** smear the tail with a gland on the forearm, then wave it to drive scent at rival males. Ants **(3)** lay scent trails to food for others to follow. Rhinos **(4)** mark their territory with dung, and foxes **(5)** use urine. Special scent glands may be near the anus, as in the Tasmanian devil **(6)**, or between the toes, as in the hyena **(7)**. A Bighorn sheep **(8)** sniffs the mixture of smells on the rump of a companion.

individuals to recognize one another as the same species. Many birds can tell their own kind by the colour and pattern of their feathers. Different fish species of similar shape and size may have easily recognized colours.

Sometimes the recognition signals are confined to small areas of the body. A penguin swims low in the water, so most of its body cannot be seen by others swimming with it. Its species "badge" is therefore restricted to the only really visible parts – the head and neck. An orange collar, a yellow crest, different face markings – all are used as distinguishing features between the various species.

Most of the species of guenon monkey in Africa are rather similar, but each one has a characteristically different face, either in colour or in adornment with special features such as moustaches or nose spots.

"TALKING" TOGETHER

Most other animals communicate general messages rather than precise words and sentences as we do. They may signal their mood, their sex, their readiness to mate, and so on. Many of the signals are very stereotyped and cannot contain shades of meaning. A male stickleback in mating condition keeps his red belly through the breeding season, sending out a constant generalized message that proclaims simply his sex and maturity.

There are many species in which the sexes are different colours. This is a common phenomenon in birds, where the female is often camouflaged for protection, but males may be quite gaudy, as in the Common pheasant. Even where sexes are patterned alike, the male bird will often be brighter than the female.

Among the mammals it is more unusual for the sexes to be differently coloured. Some monkeys, however, do use this form of communication – the male mandrill, with his bright blue and red nose, is a good example.

▲Many whales communicate by sound. It travels well through the water, and keeps whales in touch over thousands of kilometres. Humpback whales have a long complex "song", made up of chirps, groans, snores, ees and yups.

▼The Plainfin midshipman is a fish from the Pacific Ocean. By day it burrows in mud on the bottom. Its repertoire of signals includes grunts, growls and whistles, as well as the luminous spots which form a pattern in its skin.

MULTI-PURPOSE SIGNALS

The same signal can mean different things to different listeners. Although it may be identical every time, the song of a male bird can be interpreted in a number of ways depending on who hears it. It tells the species of bird. It signals that the bird is male. It may have a personal touch that identifies the bird as a particular individual. A neighbouring male reads the signal as "please keep away" but a female may read it as an invitation to mate.

GROUP COMMUNICATION

Animals that live in social groups need signals that help to keep the group together, or to coordinate their movements. Many deer have light-coloured rump patches – an easy feature for other group members to follow. Many antelope have pale rumps or tails that are picked out in white and black. Again, these are easy to see at comparatively short range, and an antelope with its face to the ground feeding is still able to keep track of other members of its group out of the corner of its eye. Many birds have white bars on the wings or tail which are easy for their fellows to notice and recognize, even at a distance.

Sounds can also be used to maintain contact. Feeding parties of birds twitter to keep in touch as they forage through the trees. The "stomach rumble" of elephants is also thought to be a contact call between members of a group, signalling the individual's presence and well-being. A herd of wildebeest contentedly grazing keeps up a continual mutter of the sound "gnu, gnu" that has given them their alternative name.

CRESTS AND SPOTS

Some markings emphasize the parts of the body that an animal uses for signalling. Lions show their mood by the disposition of ears and tail. When annoyed, a lion puts its ears back and swishes its tail. Unlike the rest of the

body, which is camouflaged brown, the back of the ears and the tip of the tail have black fur to reinforce the visibility of the signals. Other members of the cat family have ear spots or tufts for the same reason.

Cockatoos use head movements as signals. These are emphasized by crests that can be raised when the birds are excited. Cranes dance to one another, bowing their heads and holding out the wings. These parts of the body are often specially coloured for emphasis. The Crowned crane has white underwings, and a coloured and crested head that contrast with the grey body. The eyelids and brows of some monkeys are coloured to emphasize facial expressions.

IMPORTANT INFORMATION

As well as communicating to describe mood or status, some animals can also relate specific information about the world around them to others of their kind. The alarm calls of birds say "predator about" to other birds. Some kinds of fishes produce an alarm substance – a chemical that they release into the water when they are hurt or badly frightened – that alerts other fish in the school to possible danger. Mammals too may produce scents when they are frightened.

There are also calls that mean "food is here". For many animals this information is best kept to themselves, but for those that live in groups there may be advantage in directing all group members to a supply.

WAYS OF SENDING MESSAGES

Most animals communicate by sight, sound or smell. Each way has its own merits. Sound radiates in all directions and it can be heard a long way off. It performs even better in water. The song of a Humpback whale can be heard at least 1,200km away. Its properties make sound a good signal for "advertising" for a mate. The croaking of frogs, the chirping of grasshoppers, and the song of birds are examples. Alarm messages also can be given efficiently using sound, such as the thump of a rabbit's foot, or the alarm bark of a deer.

Visual signals travel even faster than sounds, but obstacles can get in the way. Sight may not be effective for long-distance communication but is good for "private" communication at short range, as in courtship displays.

The last of the three main senses, smell, might seem to us a poor means of communication. But, by producing some special chemicals known as pheromones, animals can give quite complicated messages in smells. In mongooses, and probably many other mammals too, each individual has its own scent by which others can recognize it. Some individual fish signal how aggressive they are by their scent. Moths use pheromones to advertise for mates. A tiny amount of scent is released by a female in mating condition. Males of the same species are sensitive to as little as a few molecules of the chemical and can follow the wind-borne trail over long distances

▲The communication signal of the male Great frigatebird is a startling red pouch which can be blown out with air.

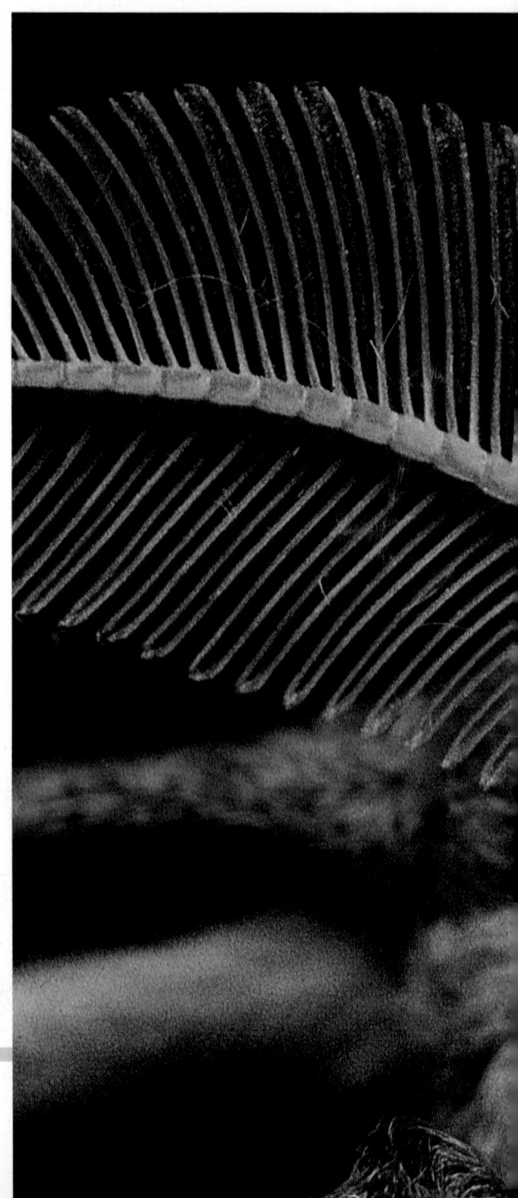

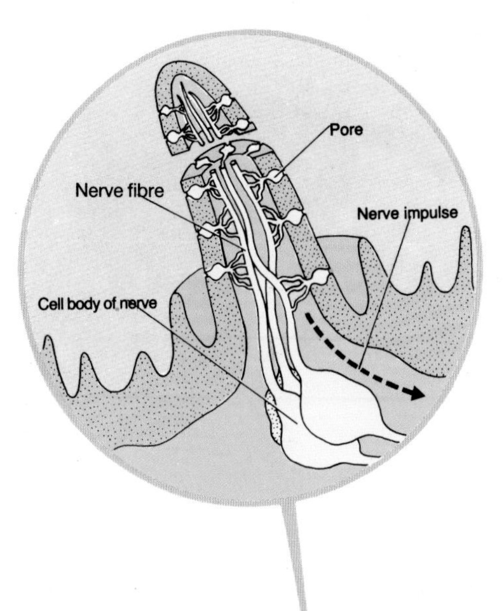

back to its source. This means of communication has a far greater range than any sound or visual signal that such a small animal might be able to produce or display.

LIMITED LANGUAGE

Although other animals use many different signalling systems none can communicate the kind of complex information which is encoded in human language. Those animals that come closest, as might be expected, are the ones which have a complex social organization. Monkeys and apes have an extensive repertoire of facial expressions, grunts and calls, but nothing like speech. However, they may be able to communicate more detailed information to one another than most animals can. Bird alarm calls contain just a general warning, but the Vervet monkey gives a different call for a leopard, an eagle or a snake, and the other Vervets in the group take appropriate evasive action. Some social insects, such as bees, are also able to pass on precise information to their fellows by means of elaborate body movements.

▼The use of scent is very important for communication in some moths. The female African silkworm moth produces scent which the male can detect from several kilometres away. The feathery antennae detect the scent. The inset photos and diagram show the sensory hairs on the antennae greatly magnified.

TERRITORY

A male fish swims above a nest hollow in the lake floor. Another male approaches and suddenly there is a flash of fins as the first one chases the intruder. But then the second fish turns on its pursuer, for it is now close to its own nest. Then the two fish face one another, motionless, across an invisible barrier. Each is at the limit of its territory.

▼Female kob antelope move across a river floodplain. In the breeding season the horned males establish mating territories (called "leks", see inset map) in the areas most used by females. They compete for the females' attention.

A territory is an area defended against intruders of the same species by an individual or a group. Animals may defend their territories by fighting or by chasing intruders away. Often, though, a simple signal that they are in occupation is enough to make other members of the species avoid the area. Signals for this purpose may include visual displays, but scents or sounds, such as the songs of birds or the cries of howler monkeys, are often more important.

WHY HAVE A TERRITORY?

Owning a territory gives an animal the exclusive use of some important resource within it. This may be a food supply, it may be a partner with which

to mate, or it may be a suitable site for a nest or a burrow. In many birds, such as the Blue tit and the European robin, the male takes up his possession of a territory by early spring. He entices a mate into it, and the area he defends provides sufficient space for nesting and for finding the food needed to bring up a family.

Groups of Vervet monkeys on the African savannah are territorial. For them, one of the most important features that a territory must have is a reliable waterhole.

Some animals, such as the hartebeest and kob antelope, use territory just for the purpose of mating. During the breeding season males defend pieces of ground that are too small to

▲A confrontation in a tropical forest Two groups of African Redtail monkeys (*Cercopithecus ascanius*) meet at the edge of their adjoining territories. The adult females and juveniles **(1)** cluster together to face and threaten members of a neighbouring troop **(2)**. During the tension, group members often take time out to groom one another **(3)**, perhaps helping individuals to feel closer and more secure. Although threat gestures are intense and the monkeys make a lot of noise, physical contact between the groups is rare. An adult male **(4)** may stay well away from the squabble.

▲A group of male cheetahs attack a wandering male that has trespassed into their territory on the Serengeti plains in Tanzania. Outsiders intruding in this way can expect to be attacked and driven away or even killed.

◀The Painted snipe is an unusual bird in that the female mates with several males. She establishes a territory and makes hooting calls to attract males. Rival females are frightened away by this extended wing display.

▶Cape gannets live in colonies of up to 100,000 individuals, but each pair holds a small territory around its nest. Here the pair on the right defend their nest against an intruder. Pairs are so densely packed that there is a constant hubbub of such squabbles.

feed even a single adult, but they get exclusive mating rights to any female entering them. Other animals have movable territories. Impala antelope males change their territories as the herds change their grazing grounds, and so do other migratory species such as wildebeest.

VARIABLE SIZES

The size of a territory depends on what it is needed for and where it is. A kob holds a small area. Other species that use territory just for mating also defend relatively small areas. That of the male Sage grouse of America, for example, is a circle only 5 to 10m in diameter on a display ground used by several birds.

A territory that contains all the food necessary for a pair to rear young may be large, particularly if the food is difficult to find. So a pair of eagles or a pack of wolves range over an area of many square kilometres that they try to keep for their exclusive use. Even a small bird like a nuthatch requires a feeding territory up to 200m across. In poor habitats territories need to be bigger than in rich ones. The dunlin, a small wading bird, can manage in southern Alaska with a territory as small as 300 sq m, whereas high in the Arctic it may need one five times this area if it is to survive.

Thus territory sizes vary from a single puddle, in the case of some male frogs, to over 100 sq km in the case of some of the big cats. Even within a species there is variation according to the conditions. Some representative territory sizes are listed below (all areas are given in square kilometres):

Dabchick	0.003
Gibbon (group of 4)	0.16
Tawny owl	0.3
Mountain gorilla (group of 17)	16
Golden eagle	70
Tiger	130
African bushman (group of 20)	708

GETTING A TERRITORY...

Acquiring a territory is sometimes a case of first come, first served. Those migratory birds that return first to the breeding grounds are able to stake their claim easily. Latecomers may have to move on to another area or else try to take ground from earlier residents. Bigger, stronger and more vigorous animals have an advantage if it comes to a fight. Males in possession of a territory are often bigger than those who are not. But being territorial takes its toll, whether it is from constant fighting, or simply from constant display or singing. In some species territorial males gradually lose weight and condition and are ousted from their position later in the season.

...AND KEEPING IT

For most territory owners, though, possession is a very potent weapon. Animals usually respect territorial boundaries. If one does stray into a neighbour's ground it rarely remains long if it is challenged. The owner has a psychological advantage and may drive off even a stronger opponent. Away from their own home ground most animals feel insecure. Many are reluctant to cross over the territorial markers laid down by the owners. A pack of wolves hunts over a huge area and is unlikely to see every potential rival that approaches the edges of the territory. By marking the boundaries with strongly scented urine, though, it can keep any would-be intruders away. Animals as diverse as rhinoceroses and mongooses use dung and urine for this purpose.

FIGHTING AND WEAPONS

Two male Northern fur seals square up to one another on a beach in the north Pacific. Neither backs down. Suddenly one lunges forward, striking towards the maned neck of his opponent. The battle begins to rage, each animal trying to inflict enough injury on his opponent to make him give up the fight. For many minutes they struggle in combat. Then one gives in and turns tail, pursued by the winner.

Animals may fight others of their species over territory, food or mates. Even those that are not equipped for fighting may take part in contests that to them are very important. Chameleons move slowly and are not really built for hurting opponents. But they do take part in ferocious contests in which the loser, though largely undamaged, nonetheless appears to be thoroughly cowed and frightened.

WEAPONS

Some animals, though, are equipped with lethal weapons. The big canine teeth of many meat-eaters are as capable of giving a killing bite to one of their own species as they are to a prey animal. Even many plant-eaters have claws or horns that make good weapons. In most cases these are used against a predator only as a last resort when all other means of defence have failed. But plant-eaters are often ready to use their weapons against their own kind.

Some of these weapons are of gigantic size. The tusks of male African elephants, for example, can weigh 50kg each, and the horns of the Siberian ibex can be up to 1.4m long. The rapier-like horns of an antelope such as an oryx, or the massive spiral horns of some wild sheep, can cause enormous damage. Even though they possess such lethal weapons, however, many species have developed structures or behaviour that, for the sake of survival of the species, minimize the risks of serious fighting while still posing a threat.

DAMAGE LIMITATION

Species like baboons and sea lions, that fight by stabbing and slashing with their canine teeth, have necks and shoulders that are protected by long fur capes or thickened skin. This takes the worst of the blows and protects the internal organs. Some deer also have protective manes on their necks, as do male lions, and during fights they are careful to keep the best protected areas facing the opponent. Bison, which clash head to head, have thick skulls and huge shoulders to absorb the impact.

LOCKED IN COMBAT

Some animal weapons, although they look fearsome, are actually structured to minimize damage. The massive ridged horns of some goats provide

◄The vast yawn of a hippopotamus is a threatening gesture which shows off its main weapons – the huge canine teeth at the front corners of the jaw.

good non-slip surfaces, so that when they crash together they lock rather than slip onto vulnerable parts of the skull. Though sharply pointed and potentially damaging, the branched shape of deer antlers allows them to be used not so much for stabbing but for grappling. Two combatants lock antlers together and push back and forward in a harmless, but effective, trial of strength. Some antelope too have horns that fit together in non-injurious wrestling matches.

THREATS

Despite all the safeguards, occasionally rivals may indeed fight until one is fatally injured. This can happen in some confrontations between male Red deer, but usually, in almost all species, a fight to the death is very much the exception. In a fatal combat even the victor is likely to be hurt and so it is in the species' interest to settle disputes with minimum harm.

Many animals manage to win fights without striking a single blow simply

▲Two massive Southern elephant seals fight for mating territory on a beach. They lunge with open mouths at the neck of an opponent, and may wound deeply. The scars of many former battles are clearly visible on these animals.

▼**Contrasting fighting styles** Muntjac deer males **(1)** have very small antlers which are of little use in fighting, but they do have sharp canine teeth that they can use for slashing at an opponent. The klipspringer **(2)** has short horns, but they are sharply pointed, and can be used for jabbing a rival.

by showing they are bigger and stronger, thus intimidating a rival. Rival male baboons "yawn" at each other, displaying the ferocious canine teeth. Sometimes they also use vocal threats, and even staring hard is often threatening enough, as it is in many other species. Other ploys used to intimidate include roaring, as in Red deer. Because larger, and therefore stronger, individuals usually have a deeper roar, the use of vocal threats provides a means by which rivals can gauge their relative strengths. Raising the fur to appear larger is also a useful technique that is commonly used by rival dogs and cats. Often antagonists will stand in a way that makes them look as tall as possible.

GIVING IN

To reduce the risk of damage in a fight even further, it is important for the losing animal to acknowledge defeat so that the fighting stops. Sometimes losers just turn and run away but often, especially in species that live in groups, they use a special signal called a submissive posture. A wolf or dog that gives in to another will present its throat to the victor or even roll on to its back with its legs pointing upwards. Either of these postures makes it very vulnerable. The opponent could then easily bite it but the submissive posture seems to switch off the aggressive feelings of the winner, who seems to be satisfied by this acknowledgement of his superiority.

Losers of monkey fights will cringe with a special scream or turn their rumps to the victor. Again this stops further aggression, and the winner may touch or even groom the loser to cement the new relationship.

SEX AND AGGRESSION

In most species it is the males that have to hold territories or compete for mates. In consequence they are larger and more aggressive than the females. In those species where the males maintain harems of females, as in baboons, elephant seals or goats, the size difference is particularly marked. In a very small number of species, however. this characteristic is reversed. Among the birds, the phalaropes and painted snipes are two groups in which the female has several mates and tends to be larger and more aggressive than the male.

◀Silverbacked jackals fight over a kill. With lips drawn back into a snarl they show sharp teeth, but the fight is more ritual than actual biting.

▼Two Senegal chameleons fight on a branch. The green, puffed-up one is winning, while the other turns pale in acknowledgement of defeat.

COURTSHIP

A male spider arrives at a female's web. He is smaller than she is and moves towards her with caution. A fly lands on the web. Before the female reaches it, the male parcels up the fly in silk strands. He holds it out as a gift to the female. She takes it and begins to feed. While she is busy the male mates with her. This is just one of a number of ways in which spider males go about their dangerous courtships.

Courtship is the behaviour that takes place before, during and just after the act of mating. It takes an enormous variety of forms in different groups of animals. At times it is very elaborate, but if it ensures that mating and subsequent breeding both take place successfully, it does its job.

WHY IS COURTSHIP NEEDED?

Courtship can help animals find one another. Because each species has its own pattern of courtship, an animal can identify a potential mate and reject those of other species with the "wrong" pattern. In many animals the mates are initially strangers and courtship can help them become less nervous of one another. Courtship may also trigger an animal's body to complete the process of becoming ready to mate. In some animals, even if all other conditions are satisfactory for mating, eggs mature only after a period of courtship.

LOCATING A MATE

For small animals, especially those species in which individuals live far apart, finding a mate can present great difficulties. Some solve the problem by both sexes congregating at a particular site. Male and female dungflies are attracted to fresh cowpats. Here they meet, mate, and lay their eggs. Some birds have traditional breeding

▲▶ Ways of courting The male mandrill (*Papio sphinx*) **(1)** is large and brightly patterned to impress the female. A drake mallard (*Anas platyrhynchos*) **(2)** attracts a mate by ritual preening. Courting Black-headed gulls (*Larus ridibundus*) **(3)** face away from one another so as not to look aggressive. A male Sage grouse (*Centrocercus urophasianus*) **(4)** displays to the smaller females on a communal mating site.

◀▶ **Courtship among fish and amphibians** The male stickleback (*Gasterosteus aculeatus*) **(1a)**, with red belly, dances in front of a female. A male European tree frog (*Hyla arborea*) **(2a)** calls by using an enlarged vocal sac.

grounds. Sage grouse, for example, return each year to the same sites, called leks, where the males display to attract onlooking females to mate.

Amphibians such as toads and newts also return to traditional sites to breed, typically the ponds in which they themselves hatched. Turtles and seals return year after year to the same breeding beaches, sometimes many kilometres from their usual haunts.

ADVERTISING FOR A MATE

Birds are not the only animals capable of attracting a mate by singing. In many frogs and insects the males make calls that can be heard over hundreds of metres. The voices of frogs are often amplified by inflatable sacs in the throat. Insects such as grasshoppers and crickets produce sounds by stridulation – rubbing one part of the body against another. Mole crickets call from the safety of a burrow which is specially shaped to increase the sound-level.

Among animals that use chirps in courtship, such as grasshoppers and frogs, the sound receptors ("ears") of the females are often sensitive only to the particular frequencies used by males of their own species. They may be effectively deaf to sounds, however loud or numerous, made by other kinds of animal.

Some animals even use flashing lights to attract a mate. Fireflies are beetles that are active at night. They have light-producing organs. Males fly around making distinctive sequences of flashes. Females stay on the ground but respond to males of their own species by flashing back. The wingless female glow-worm, a European beetle, produces a greenish-blue light from the underside of its abdomen. At dusk it sits in the grass with its tail turned up and light on to attract a winged male to mate. Some of the deep sea fishes and squids also have light organs that can be used for identification or attraction.

SIGNALLING READINESS

In social animals, where locating a potential mate is not so much a problem, it may be useful nonetheless for females to use signals that show they are ready for mating. In baboons, for example, the female has an area of skin on her rump that swells and reddens when she is in breeding condition. Female chimpanzees also have sexual swellings to show their readiness to mate.

REDUCING AGGRESSION

For mating to take place it may be necessary to defuse the normal wariness or aggression between two animals. Often the female is the smaller, weaker sex, and the male is careful not to alarm her. In leopards the male gently nuzzles and caresses the female as they get to know one another. In giraffes the male rubs the neck of a female in order to reassure her during courtship.

Courting birds are also careful to avoid signalling aggression and may conspicuously look away from a prospective partner rather than risk

►Two Western grebes court by running on the water. Ritualized sequences like this are typical of bird courtship.

▼The Great crested grebe has some of the most elaborate courtship displays. Headshaking with crests raised (1). One dives, while the other puffs up in display (2). One displays, the other rises out of the water (3). Dancing upright and showing nest material to each other (4).

giving what could be interpreted as a hostile stare. One or both partners may take up a submissive posture to avoid provoking aggression.

The members of a pair of courting animals may initially be in a state of internal conflict, both perhaps torn between mating, fighting or running away. It is not surprising that courtship is often stopped in its early stages.

DISPLACED BEHAVIOUR

When animals are in such a state of conflict some strange, apparently irrelevant, behaviour can occur. A courting male will suddenly break off to scratch or preen. These so-called displacement activities can be seen in birds such as ducks. In this group these actions have actually become ritualized and fixed so that they now form part of the display.

During the courtship of mallard ducks the male performs a display in which he turns his head as though to preen a distinctively coloured patch of feathers on the wing, but instead merely touches it.

SUICIDE MISSIONS

For the males of a few kinds of animal, courtship can be a very dangerous activity. In spiders the female is usually larger than the male, sometimes very much so. A female spider is likely to regard a smaller one as potential dinner, so the males have a variety of courtship techniques to help them overcome this problem. Among the web-spinners males may pluck and vibrate the threads of the female's web in a pattern that she recognizes as that of a mate rather than a catch. Among the wolf spiders, that have no web, the male may display by waving his mouthparts and drumming them on the ground. Other spiders perform ritualized dances or leg-wavings. The displays quieten a female long enough for mating to take place, but it is wise for the male to leave straight after. By using these ploys few get eaten.

Female Praying mantises too are larger than the males. In these insects the male's courtship technique is not always good enough for him to avoid being eaten by his mate, but a male may be able to complete mating by reflex actions even after the female has bitten off his head.

RITUAL CHASES

The courtship behaviour of some mammals can be seen as an extension of the male chasing the female. The courtship of the hare, in which chases are interrupted by ritual boxing matches and leaps, is a good example.

▲In the male Domestic fowl (1) and in the Common pheasant (2) the male displays his bright colours to the female during courtship. In other pheasants, such as the impeyan (3) and the peacock-pheasant (4), a spreading tail is added to the display. In the peafowl (5) the male spreads a huge tail covered with dazzling eye markings to attract and impress the female.

In some antelopes, too, courtship is ritualized pursuit, the male parading stiff-legged after the female, sometimes flapping his ears or lifting his neck as added elements of attraction in the display.

BIZARRE RITES

Some of the oddest formalized displays are found among the birds. Many of them are fairly simple to understand. That of a finch dancing up and down in front of his hen with a grass stalk in his beak can be seen as having a direct connection with nestbuilding. On the other hand, though a bird-of-paradise hanging upside down and showing off the brilliant collection of feathers on his under-side to a hen is undoubtedly very spectacular, it is not so easy to understand how such a display, and the equipment for it, ever arose.

It may be a case of "the bigger the better". This would account for the peacock's tail train which can be erected into a splendidly eyecatching display. But there must be a point when such highly over-developed equipment becomes a disadvantage in everyday life. Usually it is hard to show whether females do actually prefer the biggest displays, but this has been shown to be the case with East African widowbirds. In this species the males have long black ribbon-like tails. In an experiment, those of some males were cut short and the removed sections were used to lengthen the tails of other males. These "extra good" males attracted more females than the normal widowbirds.

CORRECTLY TIMED

One of the most important purposes of courtship is to synchronize the behaviour of male and female so that they are ready for breeding in the same place, at the same time, and in the right position. This may be especially important for the species which simply shed eggs and sperm

▼A male giraffe, having won the right to mate with the females in a herd, proceeds to court one of them. The males engage in mock fights to determine which is the most dominant.

into the water, such as many fishes. The dance of the sticklebacks or the manoeuvres of salmon on the stream bed ensure that egg and sperm release is simultaneous.

FINAL PREPARATIONS

Some animals, including humans and monkeys, produce eggs in regular cycles. But many others come into breeding condition for only a short period during the year. Temperature, daylength, abundance of food and other factors in the surroundings may influence when this takes place. But the females may not actually produce eggs until very precise conditions are met. For example, Green lizards do not produce mature eggs unless males display to them first. Female canaries come into breeding condition much more quickly if they hear the song of a male. Female pigeons too need the bowing and cooing display of the male before they can produce eggs. Some animal species, such as the stoat even need to mate before they are able to produce eggs.

▲Courtship in newts and salamanders Special chemicals made by the males' chin glands stimulate the females to position themselves for mating. In the Two-lined salamander (*Eurycea bislineata*) **(1)** the male covers the female's neck with secretions, then scratches her skin with sharp teeth **(1a)**. The male Jordan's salamander (*Plethodon jordani*) **(2)** leads the female, often turning to slap his gland against her snout. In the Redbelly newt (*Taricha rivularis*) **(3)** the male rubs his gland on the female's snout. The male Smooth newt (*Triturus vulgaris*) **(4)** uses his long tail to waft odours secreted from his glands towards a nearby female.

PARENTS AND YOUNG

A mother rat has been out looking for food for herself. Now she is returning to feed her babies in their nest. They are newborn and need her milk at regular intervals. As she nears the nest she hears a high-pitched squeaking. One of the babies, still so young it can only wriggle, has tumbled from the warmth of the nest. Immediately she goes to pick it up, then returns to the nest and suckles all the babies.

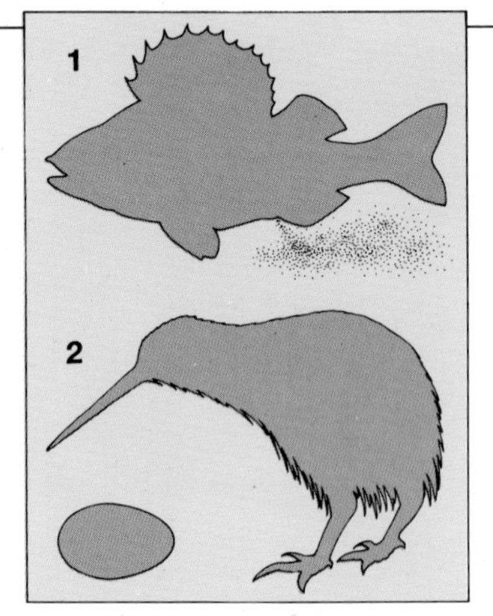

The perch **(1)** takes no care of its eggs. It may lay 200,000 of them each under 1mm across. The kiwi **(2)** lays the largest egg for its size of any bird: a 1.8kg female lays an egg 13cm long weighing 0.45kg. The wolf spider female **(3)** carries young on her back for a few days after they hatch. Many scorpions also protect their young like this.

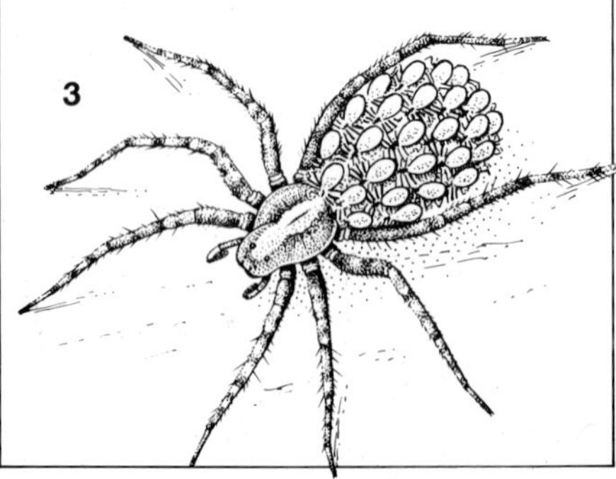

We humans are mammals and tend to assume that parents will look after their babies. But most members of the animal kingdom take no care at all of their offspring. They make up for this apparent neglect by producing such large numbers of eggs that even though most will die before maturity, at least a few will survive to carry on the species. Some of the most successful animals, however, are those that invest effort in caring for their young. They may produce fewer offspring, but each one stands a greater chance of becoming an adult.

EGG CARE

Some animals put a large amount of yolk into their eggs to serve as food for the young during their early development. When fish fry hatch from the egg they still carry the yolk sac with them and can live on this for days. The yolk is very large in the eggs of reptiles such as crocodiles and turtles, and of course in birds' eggs.

A typical fish or amphibian takes little notice of its eggs. A reptile may take care to bury them in an appropriate place, but only a tiny number guard their nests. Only in birds do the parents typically sit on the eggs to incubate them, and then spend some time feeding the young and keeping them warm after they hatch. But in many other animal groups there are some species that, exceptionally, tend their eggs. Some millipedes guard them and there are spiders that weave a special web for eggs and hatchlings to live in. Other spiders, and many scorpions, carry their young for a time after they hatch.

CARING FISH

Among the fishes, some cichlids excavate a nest hollow and then guard the eggs laid in it. Others, like the Egyptian mouthbrooder, gather the eggs into their mouths to protect them until they hatch. This may take 1 to 2 weeks, during which time the mother cannot feed. Some cichlids protect the young after they hatch, taking them into the mouth when danger threatens.

GIVING BIRTH

Although some lizards and snakes bear so-called live young, they simply retain their eggs inside their bodies until it is time for hatching. During this time the embryo feeds only on the yolk in the egg. Some fishes, such as guppies and some sharks, have similar "live births". All these animals ignore their offspring after they are born.

►A cuckoo chick stimulates the parental behaviour of its foster parent, which in this case is a Reed warbler.

▼A baby Olive baboon sucks milk from its mother. Only mammals feed their babies in this way.

It is among the mammals that the most advanced system of birth and baby care is found. A mammal grows inside its mother's body, nourished through the placenta, a structure that brings it in close contact with the mother's blood system. When it has developed enough to lead a more independent life, it is born. The mother continues to feed the baby on milk produced by areas of special skin glands, and typically takes great care of the young, cleaning it, protecting it and keeping it warm.

FEEDING BABIES

Mammal mothers need a huge amount of energy to produce their milk. A Bank vole has to eat twice as much as usual when she is feeding young. A Grey seal mother feeds her baby for less than 3 weeks but in this time the pup may put on over 30kg. The mother loses much more than this, as she has no chance to feed during the suckling period.

Bird parents must gather food for their young, and they too expend a lot

▲A lion cub takes its first solid meal. The process of weaning – changing from a diet of milk to adult food – is one which every baby mammal must go through.

►Babies of mammals such as the Brown rat are born blind, naked and helpless. The mother must take care of all their needs until they can leave the nest.

▼A Chinstrap penguin, feeding its chick with krill brought back from the sea, fights off scavenging sheathbills. Most birds fiercely protect their young.

of energy in the process. Many birds must feed their young as often as ten times an hour throughout the day to satisfy the nestlings' appetites.

Some invertebrates also take care of the food needs of their offspring but in less demanding ways. Butterflies, moths and many other insects lay their eggs on plants which will be food for the larvae. Some solitary wasps lay their eggs in a burrow, having first filled it with another insect. Alive but unable to move because it has been paralyzed by the wasp's sting, the insect will become fresh food for the mass of grubs when they hatch.

HOW BIG A FAMILY?

In animals that care for their young there is a limit to the number that can be raised successfully. Female swifts usually lay three eggs in a clutch. Why not lay more? Swifts that were given artificially large broods had great difficulty finding enough food for all the young, and as a result many died. On average, three babies seems to be the optimum number for this species. In others, however, the number may be different. For animals that invest a lot of care in their young, such as elephants, monkeys or humans, the usual number of offspring they raise at a time is just one.

RECOGNIZING BABY

Baby mammals, and birds too, have characteristics which seem to make them attractive to adults. They have rounder faces and bigger eyes than adults, and this seems to stimulate caring behaviour. Sometimes they may be differently coloured too, as in many birds and monkeys. Baby baboons are black and pink, for example, whereas the adults are olive. Such babies may be attractive not only to their mothers, but also, to other adult and adolescent females, who may try to pick them up.

BONDING

In some species frequent separation between mother and her young is routine. Nestling birds or rats get used to parents disappearing and returning. In other species the young become quite distressed if they are separated from their mother. This might be the case even in species whose young seem to be less reliant on a parent in that they move around soon after birth, such as goslings and ducklings, or sheep and antelopes. But such offspring form a close bond with the mother. When a sheep is born its mother cleans and smells it. After this mother and offspring recognize each other and the parent sheep will not accept a lamb with a different smell. If they are separated the lamb bleats in distress until the ewe, recognizing its offspring's cries, finds it again.

In monkeys too a baby will cry for its mother if left behind. Usually this results in her return. If the mother does not come back for some reason the baby may pine and die, even if other members of the group are willing to look after it.

FAMILY LIFE

It is a sunny day in summer. Deep in a wood three fox cubs are playing near a burrow. Their mother sits above them, keeping watch. A male fox comes trotting up the valley with a rabbit in his mouth. He greets the vixen. She feeds while the father takes his turn watching the cubs. Then the pair rest in the Sun, still watchful, and the tired cubs sleep snuggled up to them.

Mammals such as the beaver and the gibbons are unusual in that they form families consisting of one male, one female and their young. This arrangement is common in birds too, but for most animals that take care of their young the family is quite a different kind of unit.

A MOTHER'S WORK

In many mammals, from rodents to tigers and bears, the male and female have very little more to do with one another after they have mated. In fact, in species such as the tiger it is safer for the young if they do not see their father, because he is as likely to attack them as help with their upbringing.

Even in those species where males and females live together in a herd for much of the time, such as the Blackbuck antelope, the males never show any interest in the young. All care is by the mother. In such cases the family unit is simply a mother and her current young.

LONG-TERM FAMILIES

The chimpanzee is one of the animals whose young stay with their mother for some years. Young males may be up to 7 or 8 years old before they become independent. Young females sometimes stay even longer and may still move around with their mother when they are adult and have babies of their own to look after.

In the African elephant, the adult males are often solitary, but females and young live in groups that are extended families. Cow elephants commonly stay with their mother from the time they are born until she dies. As cows are able to breed at 12 years old and live to be 60, an elephant can spend up to 50 years in a stable family unit.

HELPING MOTHER

In those families that stay together for long periods a mother often gets help from older young in caring for the smallest one in the family. Elephant females may care for their young relatives, and the same is also true of the Rhesus monkey and all meerkats, where babies are groomed, watched over or carried by older sisters. In a few birds, such as the House martin, older young help in feeding nestlings.

BIRD FAMILIES

The young of many birds are raised in a nest, and even after they have all

►Family arrangements More than one female ostrich (*Struthio camelus*) **(1)** may lay her eggs in the nest scrape made by a male, but a single pair do the work of incubation and early chick care. In the Cotton-top tamarin (*Sanguinus oedipus*) **(2)** the older offspring help their parents look after the twin babies. Savannah baboons (*Papio cynocephalus*) **(3)** live in troops of several family groups.

►The inhabitants of a Black-tailed prairie dog burrow will all be members of the same family group.

1
2
3

►**Sex differences** Males and females are often of a similar size in species, like the Moloch gibbon (*Hylobates moloch*) **(1)**, in which a male mates with a single female. When males mate with many females there is often a size difference between the sexes, as in the Northern elephant seal (*Mirounga anguistirostris*) **(2)**, the capercaillie (*Tetrao urogallus*) **(3)** and the Black howler monkey (*Alouatta caraya*) **(4)**. The male is much larger.

◀A gorilla group is based on a large family consisting of one fully adult silver-backed male together with several females and their young.

fledged parents help them for a while by providing food. Soon, however, the families break up and the young go their own way. Some of the best examples of birds that move around as families can be found among those that leave the nest soon after hatching. Ducklings keep together with their mother, following her wherever they can. This behaviour is very strongly developed because it increases the young's chances of finding food and avoiding enemies.

Baby ostriches are obviously much smaller and more vulnerable than the adults, though they can walk and run at a very early age. At this stage the parents protectively shepherd them about, fiercely guarding them from predators. Later, several groups of young from different parents come together and are tended by one or two adults as though they were all members of one very large family.

WHEN DAD IS MUM

In the other large, flightless birds – emu, rhea, and cassowary – it is the job of the male to incubate the eggs. Unusually, the female plays no further part after laying them. The male also protects and moves about with the young after they hatch. Male emus and rheas with chicks are very fierce defenders of their family. Emu fathers look after the young for up to about 7 months and cassowary families stay together for as long as a year.

HITCHING A LIFT

Some animal mothers carry their young about if there is a hint of danger. A nursing rat, if disturbed, will move to another nest, carrying its babies one by one in its mouth. Many carnivores, from weasels to lions, also carry their young in this way.

But some babies are carried about by the mother most of the time, making the family a mobile one. A koala mother carries her baby on her back once it has left the pouch. Opossums too carry their babies on their backs. Very young baboons and chimpanzees cling firmly under their mother's belly as she walks on all fours, but when they are older they ride on her back, jockey-fashion.

GROWING UP

As young animals grow older and their abilities develop, so they need less attention from their parents. There comes a time when they leave their families or are driven from them. The parents may need to concentrate on breeding again, or simply on winter survival.

In many meat-eaters the period of care in the family can be quite long because hunting is a difficult way of obtaining food and learning how to do it takes time. The mother has to show the young suitable prey and teach them how to catch it.

For monkeys and apes the process of becoming independent is often very gradual even though it may begin at an early stage. When their babies are as young as 2 weeks, mother baboons play games in which they place the youngsters on the ground, walk away a few paces, then turn back with a gesture of reassurance. Later the mothers tend to leave the babies more often and will reject many of their attempts to suckle. Even when they no longer feed from her, the young may still be cuddled by the mother. Eventually the adult's attention turns to mating and bringing up another baby. She becomes quite intolerant of older young being close to her for much of the time, but by now they are no longer physically or emotionally dependent on her.

GROUPS AND TROOPS

A big troop of baboons moves across the savannah. Around the edges are alert young males, the eyes and ears of the group. Within this ring of guards are the females and their young. A huge adult male, the father of many of the babies, stays in the middle of the troop, close to the adult females. All the animals in the group know all the others, and their place in the troop.

Many animal species live in groups: the hives of bees, the schools of fishes, the herds of deer, the flocks of birds. Some groups form simply because the food is concentrated in a small area where individuals must congregate in order to feed. The individuals in a large flock of starlings or within a big shoal of sardines do not know one another and have no special roles. But many groups are not just masses of independent individuals. Especially in social insects and the mammals, animals which show the most highly developed instances of group-living, different individuals may have their separate roles. This increases the efficiency of the group's activities.

INSECT SOCIETIES

Group living is practiced by two main types of insect: the termites, and some of the bees, wasps and ants. In the bumblebee a fertilized female survives the winter. In the spring she makes an underground nest and raises young. The next generation join her in care of young and nest. Here the society is fairly simple and lasts only the one season. In some social wasps and bees it is much more complex and sometimes, as in the honeybee, it is long-lasting.

In a honeybee hive there is only one fertile female, the queen. Other females are workers and do not reproduce. They have four main duties which they perform in sequence as they get older. First they clean cells; then they build combs and feed larvae; next they receive nectar and pollen, remove debris and guard the hive; finally they go out foraging. The queen produces a special chemical, called a pheromone, that is spread through the colony by the workers as they communicate by touching antennae. The pheromone stops the production of any new queens. If the queen dies, or the hive becomes very big and the pheromone too thinly spread, then the workers' behaviour is changed. They take some of the queen's eggs and start to rear them in the special way that will produce new queens. One new queen takes over the hive and the old one leaves, taking some of the workers with her, to form a new colony.

A termite colony has a king and queen at its centre. There is a worker caste, made up of "immature" termites whose development has been prevented, and a soldier caste which defends the colony. Soldiers have large heads and either big jaws to bite with or a snout which can shoot sticky, poisonous substances. Once again there is a division of tasks and regulation of individual behaviour.

INSECT-LIKE MAMMAL

Only one species of mammal is known to run a caste system with an insect-like division of labour. This is the strange Naked mole-rat, an almost hairless species from east Africa. It lives in an underground colony with a tunnel system up to as much as 4km long. At the heart is a nest chamber where the only breeding female produces her 40 or more pups a year. Successive litters become the workers that dig tunnels and find food. Some grow larger than others and seem to

▲▶Some animals, like the Muntjac deer from Asia, spend nearly all their lives alone. Others live permanently in groups or, like this huge herd of Subantarctic fur seals, for part of every year.

become a guard caste. Only if the breeding female dies will another develop the ability to reproduce.

WHY FORM GROUPS?

Living in a group can help animals to avoid predators, to find a mate and rear offspring more efficiently, or to find food more effectively. White-fronted geese in a small flock spend more of their time looking out for predators than do those in a large one. The bigger the flock, the more time there is to devote to feeding.

It may be that an animal in a group also does better at finding food. But there can be some disadvantages to group living as well. Food may well be found more easily, but individuals may get less because they have to share with others. Competition for valuable resources within a group is not uncommon. Chickens jostle for grains of wheat, and baboons squabble over the best and safest ledges on which to sleep.

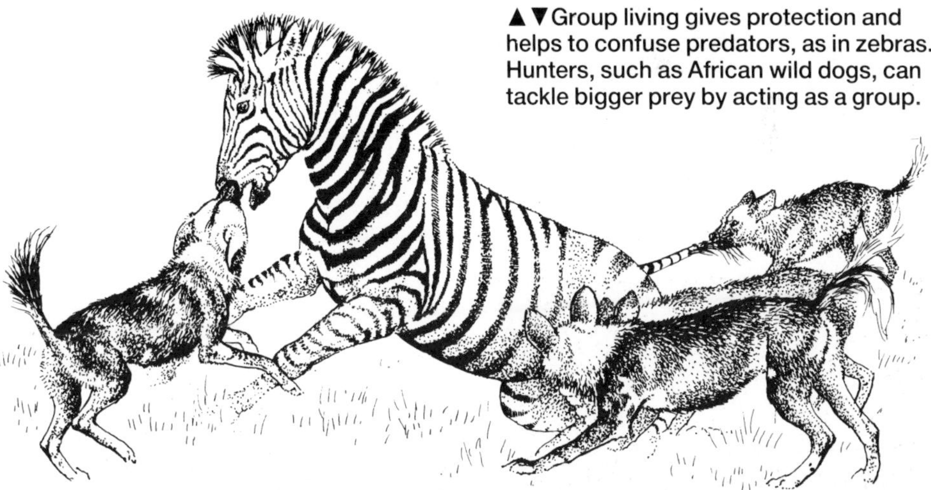

▲▼Group living gives protection and helps to confuse predators, as in zebras. Hunters, such as African wild dogs, can tackle bigger prey by acting as a group.

SORTED INTO ORDER

In order to minimize constant fighting, many groups develop a ranking system so that individuals "know their place". This was first observed in chickens and the arrangement is therefore often known as a "pecking order". When a number of hens first meet they fight over which will have precedence. One emerges as the most dominant (the boss) and it will peck at all the others and push them aside. The next strongest will give way to the boss but will push the others around; and so on down to the last hen that gets chased by all the others. Once the birds have learnt their place in the group there may be very little actual fighting. Pecking orders (also known as dominance hierarchies) are

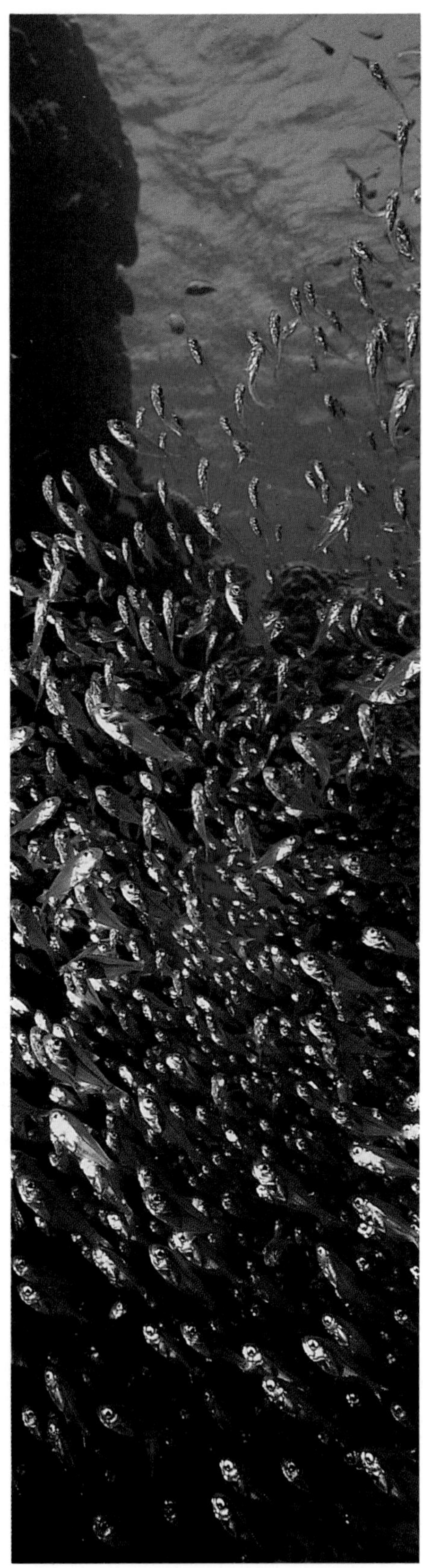

found in mammals as well as in birds. There are some obvious advantages to being high in the pecking order, such as having the first choice of food or mates. High ranking animals often have more success at breeding than do lower ones.

FOLLOW MY LEADER

Animals living in a group must have a way of staying together. The group may have a leader that the others all follow. This is clearly the arrangement among cattle and sheep. In elephants and lions an adult male may be the biggest and strongest animal in the group at any one time, but he often remains aloof from all of the other members, who usually follow the lead of an old, experienced female.

At breeding time some groups are kept together by the adult male. A Red deer stag rounds up any of his females that try to stray and so maintains the integrity of the group. The same is true of baboons such as the Hamadryas, or some kinds of fur seal which, by possessively herding their females, manage to create some semblance of order out of the apparent chaos of a teeming breeding beach.

Some of the most spectacular examples of groups keeping together are provided by big shoals of fishes. Hundreds or thousands of individuals swim together side by side. They turn, accelerate or slow down, all in perfect unison. Keeping together is partly a matter of watching the neighbours but, surprisingly, fishes may do almost as well with their eyes covered. The lateral line that runs down the side of the animal is a sense organ that can feel disturbances in the water, including those made by other fishes. This information is enough to keep a fish in a shoal "on station".

◀Many fishes form large shoals in which individuals seem to act in perfect unison. As the fishes twist and turn their silvery flashes and the shoal's changing shape probably serve to confuse enemies.

GROOMING COUNTS

Grooming can be an important factor in keeping some kinds of group together. Many monkeys and apes spend a large part of their "leisure" time picking through one another's fur. They spend far more time on this than would be necessary for simply removing dirt and parasites. The explanation seems to be that this is an activity which gives pleasure to both groomer and the animal being groomed. The latter may find the experience so relaxing that it actually goes off to sleep. This apparently pleasurable activity has become a bond that helps keep the group together. Grooming may also be used to pacify another animal after a squabble, or to establish a friendly relationship between two strangers. Mutual grooming has been observed in many other species, ranging from horses to lovebirds.

CHANGING GROUPS

Although some animals never leave the same group, many individuals

do change groups in their lifetime. Adolescent male lions are driven out by the adult males. These outcasts usually join an all-male bachelor group. Young male antelope and deer also commonly spend some time in a male herd until they are sufficiently old and strong to battle for females. Bachelor herds like these are usually relaxed about letting new members join. The same is not true, however, if a young male is rash enough to try joining a breeding group.

▲A Kloss gibbon calls from a branch, while his mate and baby search for food. These animals live in small and stable family groups. A distant male (top left) answers, his family clustered near him.

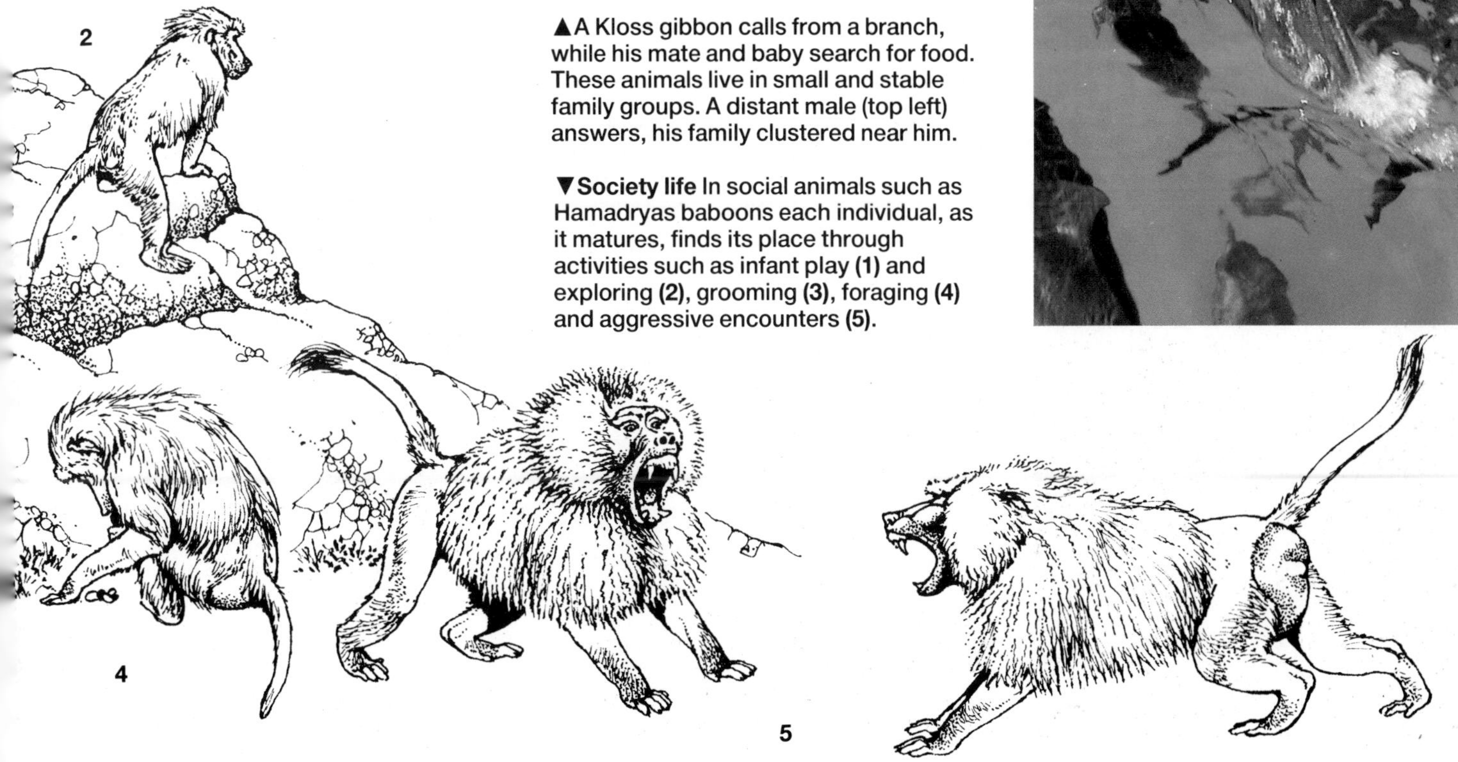

▼**Society life** In social animals such as Hamadryas baboons each individual, as it matures, finds its place through activities such as infant play **(1)** and exploring **(2)**, grooming **(3)**, foraging **(4)** and aggressive encounters **(5)**.

2

4

5

▼Spinner dolphins ride a bow wave. These animals live in social groups of up to 100 during the day but spread out at night to feed. They may join together in different groups next day.

UNSELFISH BEHAVIOUR

A fox prowls near the shore through a colony of nesting plovers. One of the birds begins to shuffle along the ground in front of the fox, with its wing held out as though it is injured. The fox notices the bird and begins to follow it, for it may be easy prey. The bird allows the fox to get quite close before making its escape. It has done its job of leading the fox away from its chicks.

Much of the behaviour we see in animals can be regarded as "selfish", in the sense that it seems to be designed to help the individual survive and do as well as possible for itself, even if this is at the expense of others of its own kind. But in some animals we see examples of behaviour which seems unselfish in that it appears to bring no immediate reward to the individual performing it. Indeed, it may bring the animal discomfort or even death. But it must always be remembered that such self-sacrifice may help others, and in nature the survival of the species is considerably more important than the survival of the individual.

HEROIC PARENTS

Many animals which normally avoid trouble will turn and fight enemies in defence of their young. Blackbirds usually call in alarm and flee at the sight of a cat; but when they have young nearby they will pursue the cat and dive at it, even though this may mean endangering themselves.

There are many other examples where parental devotion to duty is of obvious use to the offspring but is dangerous or debilitating for the parent. The Emperor penguin's care

▼A living zip. Green tree ant workers show selfless service as they draw two sides of a leaf together to form a nest.

▲A single sentinel stands guard in an exposed position to warn a Long-tailed marmot colony of approaching danger.

of its egg is a spectacular case. The father stands through 6 weeks of the Antarctic winter incubating the egg on his feet. He must regularly endure strong winds and blizzards in temperatures as low as −40°C. He cannot feed during this time and loses an enormous amount of weight. Not until the egg hatches and his mate returns from the sea to take over can he make his way over the ice for up to 100km to reach the sea and find food. This behaviour may well be advantageous to the species as a whole in that it enables the Emperor penguin pairs to breed successfully almost every year, but it is a tremendous ordeal to the males as individuals.

INSECT SACRIFICE

Social insects provide many instances where the individual sacrifices itself to the colony. When a worker honeybee stings an intruder, the barbed sting is often torn out of the defender's body, leaving it fatally injured. The bee dies but its death is useful to the hive.

Ant workers too fight fiercely in defence of their colony and many die, even though, as individuals, they could have avoided the danger. Some also make "living bridges" so that other workers may cross water or other obstacles. Some of those that form the bridge may perish.

MAKING ALLIANCES

Sometimes mammals form alliances in which one is apparently acting unselfishly on behalf of another. A male baboon may enlist the aid of another to distract a big male away from a female that is ready to mate. The first one sneaks in to grab the female, while the other may have nothing to show for helping out except the discomfort of a fight. But often these alliances seem to work on a "you scratch my back, I'll scratch yours" basis. The one who gives the favour may expect one back later.

▼A meerkat acts as a babysitter to its young brothers and sisters while their mother hunts with the pack.

▼Banded mongooses will aid their companions. A pack can chase off a jackal. A Martial eagle was once seen to catch a mongoose and carry it to the fork of a tree . The other mongooses climbed the tree and lunged at the eagle, which dropped its catch unhurt.

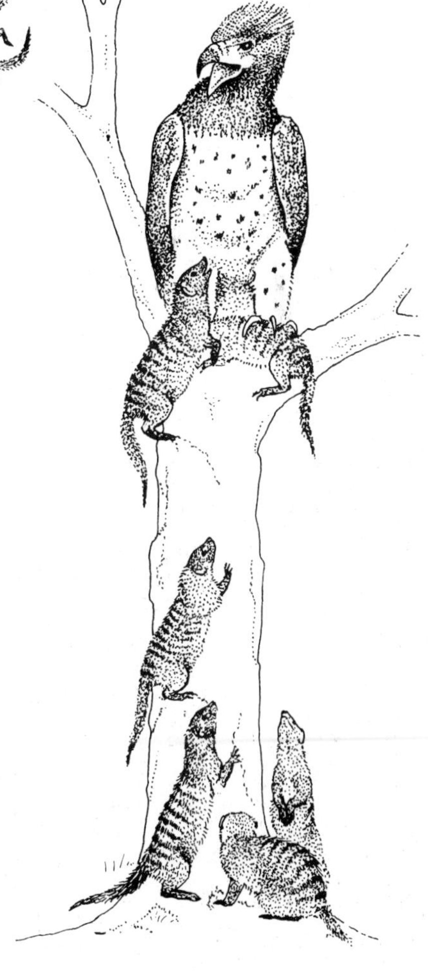

ANIMAL BUILDERS

A weaverbird bends twigs to form a loop hanging below a branch. Now he brings strips of grass and, sitting in the centre, sews them into the loop and around himself to make the beginnings of a nest. With hundreds more strips, he completes an enclosed nest chamber, complete with entrance tunnel.

▲A beaver's dam about 2m high holds back water to form a pond. It is solidly constructed, with mud, stones, and interwoven sticks and branches.

►An underside view of the nest of a social wasp, *Polybia occidentalis*. The papery nest is made of wood fibres, which the wasps chew into a pulp.

Many species of animal can build very impressive structures. The most skilled groups are the birds, spiders and insects, but even some of the simplest animals are able to build surprisingly well. Some tiny amoebas build intricate sand-grain cases. Just single-celled and lacking a nervous system, they pick up minute sand grains of the right size and store them inside the cell. When the cell divides, the sand grains come to the surface of the new cells and are arranged with different sized grains in different places, to give the standard shaped case for that species.

BURROWS

Some mammals are accomplished underground architects. Badgers can build setts made up of several sleeping chambers and connecting tunnels which, in an old sett, can be hundreds of metres long. Many rodents are good burrowers. Some, like the mole-rats, live an underground life most of the time, finding roots to feed on as they move through their tunnels. Moles too are well-adapted for living underground. They hunt worms in their tunnels. Both moles and mole-rats may build nest-mounds which are raised above the ground surface, but their complexity is seen only if they are dug out.

The only mammal that makes much of a "building" above ground is the beaver. It constructs log dams which may be many metres long and up to 3m high. These dams create lagoons in which the beaver builds a "lodge" for the family to live in.

VENTILATION ENGINEERS

Some apparently simple mammal tunnels are quite sophisticated in operation. The Black-tailed prairie

▼►Each Ehrenberg's mole-rat makes its own system of tunnels up to 350m long. A breeding mound contains food stores as well as a nest chamber.

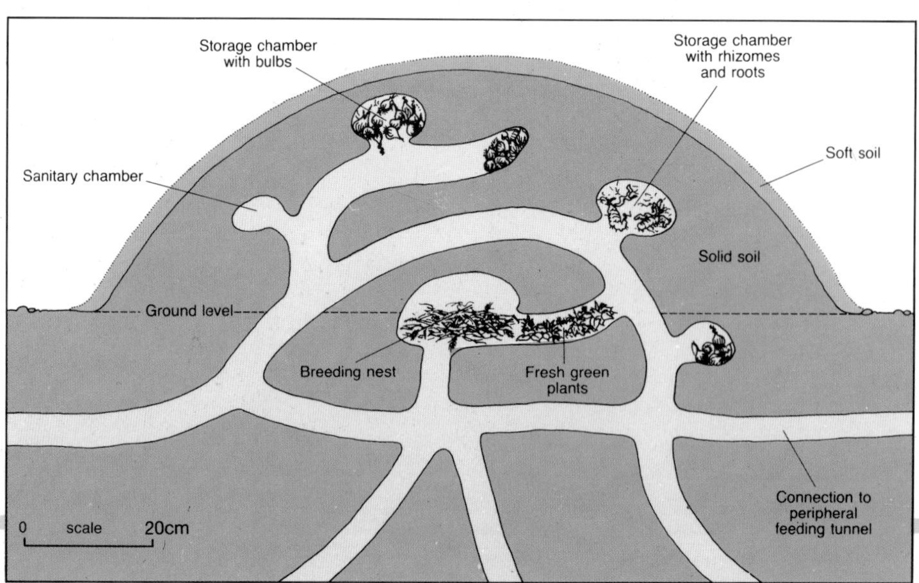

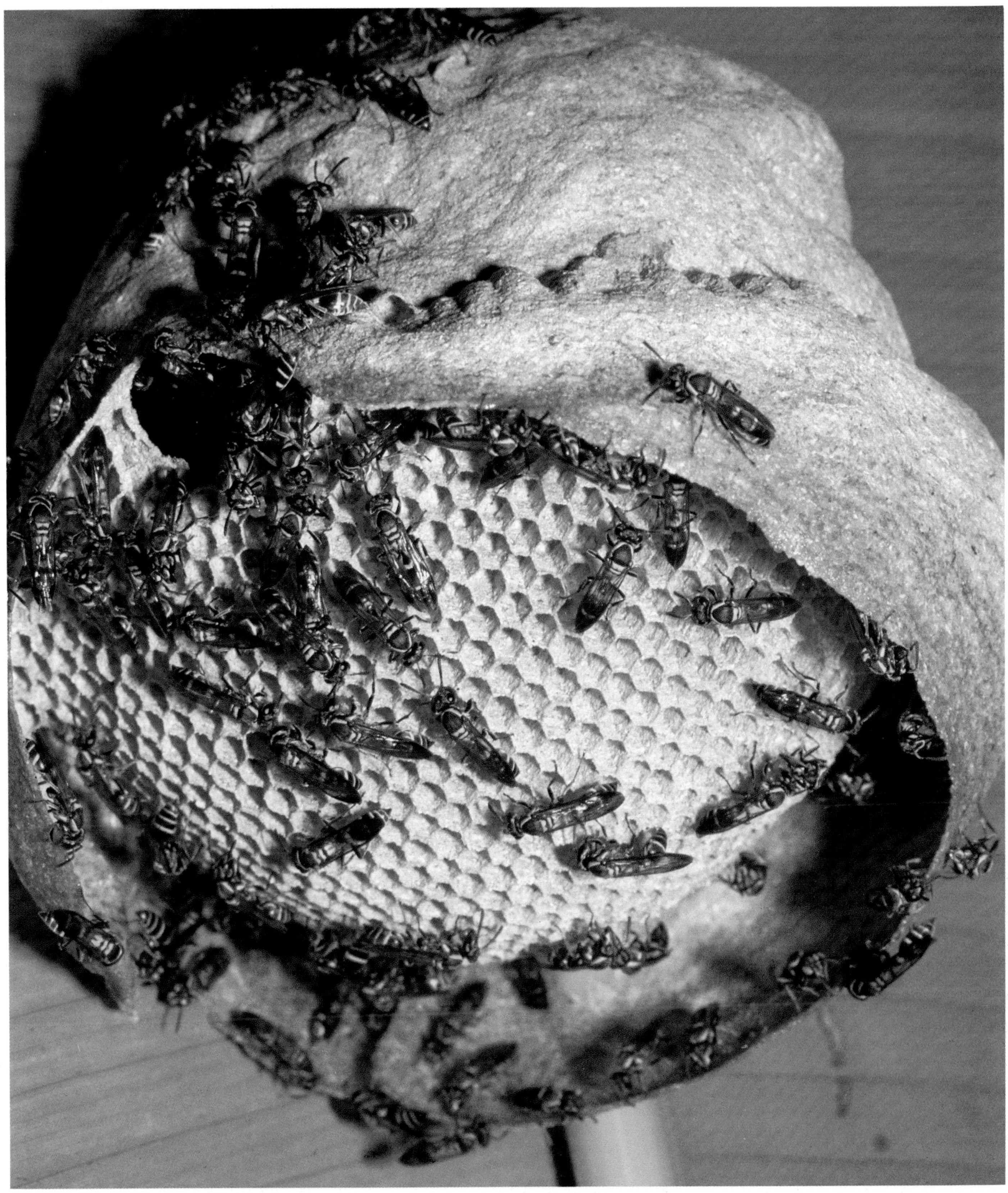

dog makes one with a mound round the entrance to prevent flooding when it rains. But the animals show even more engineering ingenuity than that. One end of a tunnel is encircled by a low ring of earth, while the other is surrounded by a more volcano-like ring. When wind blows across the prairie the air speed is greater over the higher cone, making the pressure at that point lower than at the other end of the tunnel. Thus air is drawn through the entire system to provide very effective ventilation.

Perhaps the best nest ventilation and air conditioning, however, is achieved by the termites. Those of the African genus *Macrotermes* live in tall mound nests with outer walls 50cm thick. Within these walls the termites build air-carrying channels that connect up with "cellars" excavated in the damp ground below the nest. Air warmed by the insects' activities rises from the living area and fungus gardens, and then passes down the outer channels, cooling as it descends into the ground. There its humidity increases as it is circulated through the moist cellar before rising again to the living area. The nest-building behaviour of these tiny insects creates a huge structure that is more efficiently "air-conditioned" than many of the buildings that we humans live in.

INSECT NESTS

Like termites, the other social insects – the ants, bees and wasps – are also accomplished builders. The different kinds of ant show a variety of nest-building behaviour. Some build below ground, like the Black garden ant. Others make a mound of earth, like the Yellow meadow ant, or a nest covered with a pile of twigs and pine needles, like the Wood ant. Some ants make their nests in trees, or even in galls that sometimes form on twigs.

Wasp and bee nests are notable for the arrangement of cells in the comb that the workers build. Each cell is six-sided, an arrangement which is strong and allows the maximum number to be packed into the available space. But the animals have no knowledge of geometry – they build this way purely by instinct. Wasp nests are made of a papery substance, produced by chewing up plant fibres. Bees make their nests using wax secreted by the bees themselves to construct the intricate comb.

COCOONS

Except for the social groups the only other "builders" among the insects are the butterflies, moths and caddisflies, all of which can secrete silk. Caddisfly larvae use silk as a cement to hold sand grains and fragments of plants together in the form of a protective case around the animal's body. Silk can also be used on its own to make a cocoon in which to pupate, as in some moths. The silk worm is a moth

▼An orb-web spider sits at the centre of its web waiting for an insect to blunder into the sticky threads. They are made of silk spun by the spider.

▲The Penduline tit builds a hanging nest shaped like a purse. Although it is made of delicate materials, these are skilfully woven together to give a very strong structure which has a felt-like texture.

▼To build its domed nest, the Rufous hornero uses up to 2,500 pellets of clay, strengthened with hairs and other fibres. A narrow entrance leads to a grass-lined chamber about 20cm across.

caterpillar that is farmed in the Far East because of its ability to spin a cocoon made of high quality silk. The silk strands are unwound from the cocoons by machine and woven into expensive fabrics.

WEBS

Another important group of animals – the spiders – also use silk as a building material. Some secrete a silk thread to act merely as a safety drag line or a parachute, but many spiders spin complicated webs which act as traps for insects. The purse-web spider lives in a burrow, above which it spins a finger-like silk sleeve. When prey walks over this, the spider rushes up and bites it through the silk, before pulling it into its lair.

The best-known type of web, however, is the orb-web. This is built to a fixed plan typical of the particular species. Radial threads are made first, then the spider travels round these in a spiral, making the sticky silk net which will trap insects.

BIRDS' NESTS

Though some make no nest, birds as a group do build an incredible variety of structures in which to lay their eggs. They may be little more than a pile of sticks, as in crows or some eagles. They can be made of mud, or can include fur, feathers and plants in their construction. Some, such as the nests of hummingbirds, which are built of lichens, down and spider silk, are amazingly small and delicate. The basic ability to build these nests is part of a bird's instinctive behaviour, though they do seem to get better at construction with practice.

Weaverbirds make some of the most complex nests. They are roofed, hanging basketwork structures, made from strips of grass and palm leaves. Weaverbirds are able to make a variety of loops and stitches to hold their nests together. They really sew with their beak rather than weave.

SLEEP AND OTHER RHYTHMS

It is ten minutes after sunset. A bat emerges from the eaves of a house and flies off into the night. Then, faster and faster, more bats leave the roost. After a while all have gone. But before dawn all the bats return. They find nooks among the roof timbers, hang head downwards, and settle for a good day's sleep.

Almost all animals live in an environment in which some of the events that affect their lives are rhythmic. Night and day, the tides, the phases of the Moon, the seasons of the year – all these can have effects on behaviour.

DAILY RHYTHMS

Animals have strong internal rhythms that keep their bodies in step with their surroundings. Humans have a daily cycle of changes in body temperature and alertness. Other animals have their "internal clocks" too. They are important to all creatures but can perhaps be seen most readily in our pets. A dog will turn up for its meal at the exact time every day without being able to read a watch.

Many vertebrates spend part of every day sleeping, and these periods are usually closely synchronized with the intervals of darkness or light.

IN STEP WITH THE MOON

Some animal rhythms are in phase with the Moon. The Moon influences the height of tides, and many aquatic organisms, including some fishes and also invertebrates such as king crabs, time their spawning to coincide with the highest tides. Even for annual breeders the Moon may be important. The marine Palolo worm forms vast mating swarms during the last quarter Moon in October and November.

ANNUAL RHYTHMS

Animals characteristically breed at a certain optimum time of year in temperate regions, usually in the spring or summer. In both birds and mammals the increase in day length at this time of year is often the stimulus that brings them into breeding condition. Some, such as ptarmigans and stoats, also change the colour of their coat in response to the annual cycle. In many birds, and some mammals the urge to migrate is governed by an annual rhythm.

TORPOR AND HIBERNATION

When some animals sleep their body temperature falls and all body processes slow down. This is a special kind of sleep known as torpor. Hummingbirds become torpid at night, thereby saving energy. Insect-eating bats in temperate regions have the opposite rhythm, becoming torpid during the day.

A seasonal – winter – rhythm of torpor and wakefulness is known as hibernation. Many animals, such as hedgehogs, spend much of the winter in this state. During such hibernation, with a body temperature only a little above the surroundings, a small mammal needs only one seventieth of the energy it would have used had it remained active. But it does need some body fat – its energy store – left at the end of hibernation to burn up to raise itself to normal operating temperature. A small mammal like a bat may be able to warm itself up in about half an hour. A larger one such as a marmot may take many hours.

Hibernation is a way of surviving periods of food scarcity but some animals become seasonally torpid to avoid the worst conditions in desert regions. This is called aestivation.

▲Spawning grunions deposit eggs high on the beach during spring tides when the Moon is full. Hatchling grunions swim off at the next spring tide.

►This hibernating Daubenton's bat is covered with dew. Its body temperature has dropped to that of its surroundings in a cold, damp cave.

▼Penguins in vast numbers exploit the abundance of krill in the Antarctic summer. Their internal clock tells these Adelie penguins when to head north to their breeding grounds before winter.

MIGRATION

Somewhere in southern Britain a radar operator watches the screen in front of him. As the radar sweeps a circle in the sky the man can see blips of light showing thousands of invaders coming from the skies of continental Europe. But he knows they are completely harmless. They are radar images of starlings migrating west in autumn.

Most animals move about during their lifetime. Some spend their whole lives within a small area. A shrew may be constantly on the move, but never leaves an area larger than a few tens of square metres. Other animals travel hundreds or even many thousands of kilometres during their lifetime in movements we call migrations.

WHAT IS MIGRATION?
Several different kinds of animal journey are sometimes called migration. Some of these journeys are one-way movements. Many scientists prefer to use the term migration only for long-distance seasonal movements to different feeding grounds, or between breeding and wintering areas.

ONE-WAY TICKETS
Overpopulation, causing lack of food or breeding space, is one of the reasons for mass movements. Locusts may be relatively harmless animals, but the build-up of young ones in an area can sometimes act as a trigger that starts the swarming behaviour. Then huge masses of adult locusts take to the wing, moving across a whole continent and destroying crops as they go. Lemmings often march in

►Even a large river is not enough to deter a herd of wildebeest on migration. Each year, herds many thousands strong move regularly with the seasons to take advantage of the growth of grasses in the different parts of their range.

hordes in those years when they have a sudden population explosion.

Some birds from Northern Asia, such as waxwings, crossbills and Siberian jays, also have exceptional years in which the enlarged population spreads from its normal area. Birds from Siberia may even end up in Western Europe. Some may return, but others colonize new areas or die out. Such movements are usually known as "irruptions", and this is probably a better term than migration for these one-way movements.

ROUND TRIPS

In East Africa millions of wildebeest make a huge circular trip each year round the grasslands of the Serengeti plains. Although close to the equator, the area experiences seasonal changes in rainfall which result in a flush of new grass at different times in different areas. The wildebeest keep on the move to make the best use of the new grass as it appears.

In Canada, great herds of caribou move up into the Arctic tundra in the summer, then travel back more than 800km to the south as winter starts. Once again, they are making use of the seasonal wealth of food.

On a smaller scale, many amphibians such as newts and frogs migrate. They move from winter quarters on the land to their breeding ponds.

▼Some Humpback whales (like those photographed here off the Alaskan shore) spend the summer months feeding in the far north of the Pacific and Atlantic Oceans. In the northern winter they migrate to equatorial regions where they breed. Others occupy the Southern hemisphere and undertake a similar migration (map). Because the hemispheres have opposite seasons, the two populations never mix.

Though of short duration the migrations may be spectacular because of the sheer numbers involved. A few species travel several kilometres, a surprising distance for such small, slow-moving creatures. In some places in Britain tunnels have been built as "underpasses" for toads, to help them cross busy roads safely.

The spectacular migrations that salmon undertake are also linked to their reproduction. The eggs must be laid in the well-oxygenated, clean water of the upper parts of rivers. As the salmon grow, however, they migrate downstream. They move far out to sea where they feed for up to 10 years. When they are ready to breed large mature adults find their way back, nearly always to their birthplace, continuing up-river past waterfalls and other difficult obstacles.

FOLLOWING FOOD

How far a species migrates often depends on the availability of its food. A seed-eating bird may need to migrate only a short way to find conditions where it can survive the winter. An insect eater, though, needs to be in a climate where it can rely on its food. So a swallow or swift may migrate from northern Europe all the way to southern Africa in the winter when insects in its breeding area are scarce. Hummingbirds can live in the northern USA in summer but falling temperature and lack of flowers with nectar force them to fly many kilometres south for winter.

Many long-distance migrants take advantage of the local summers of each hemisphere in turn. The Arctic tern lives and breeds within the Arctic circle in the northern summer, then goes south as far as the Antarctic coasts for the southern summer. This regime allows it to enjoy long days and an abundant food supply throughout most of the year.

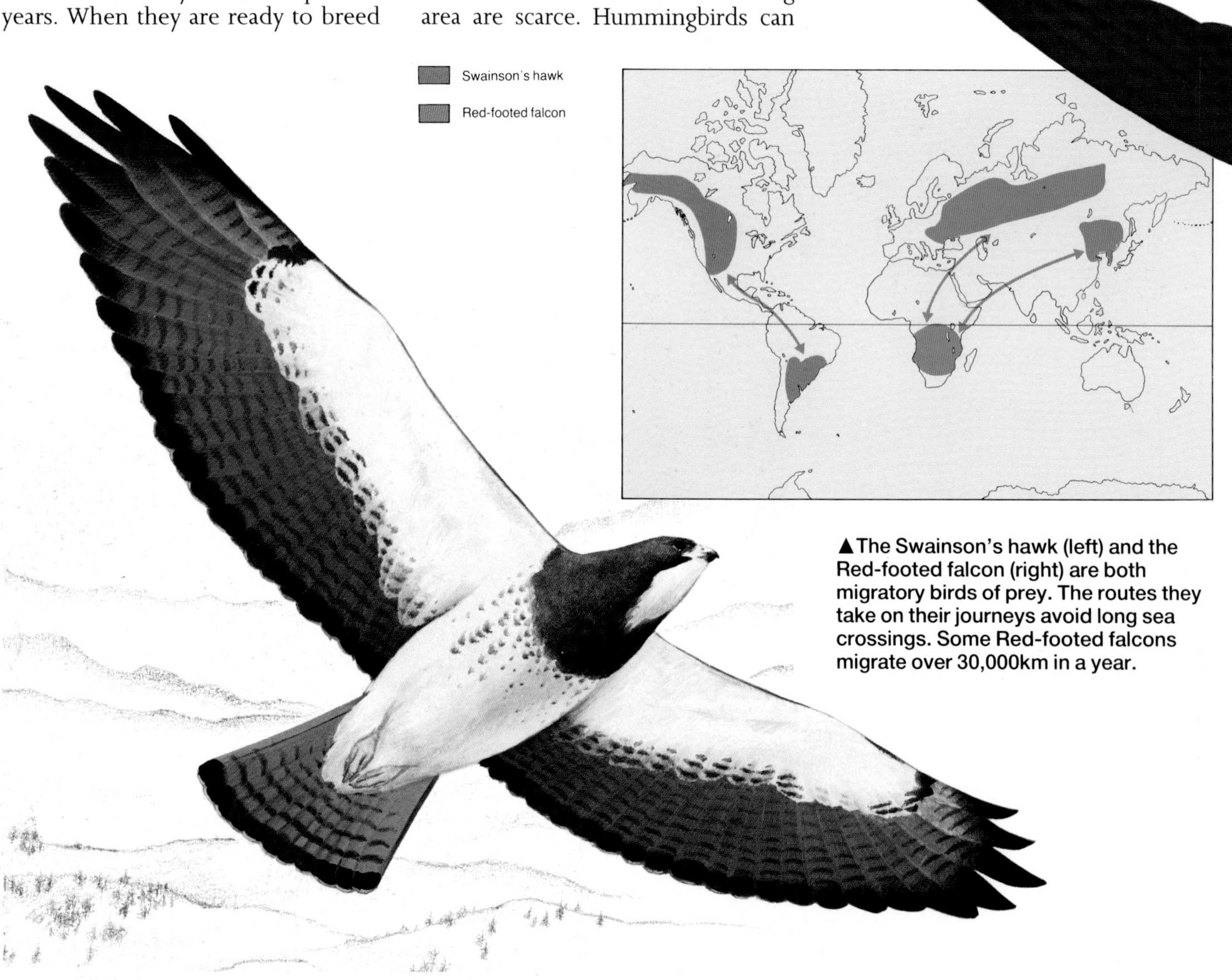

▲The Swainson's hawk (left) and the Red-footed falcon (right) are both migratory birds of prey. The routes they take on their journeys avoid long sea crossings. Some Red-footed falcons migrate over 30,000km in a year.

MYSTERY MIGRATIONS

European eels start life in the Sargasso Sea in the western Atlantic. The larvae develop as they move across the Atlantic and after 3 years they all reach European rivers. They swim up the rivers and spend several years feeding and growing. Then they reach breeding condition and begin the migration back. But it has never been proved that these adults complete the crossing, against the North Atlantic Drift, back to the breeding grounds. Some people believe that all the breeding adults in the Sargasso Sea come from the American continent.

Another mystery migration is that of the Green turtles of Ascension Island in the middle of the South Atlantic. The turtles breed on the island but they feed off the coast of Brazil. How they travel between these two areas is completely unknown. In one direction they would be swimming against ocean currents which exceed the turtle's swimming speed. Perhaps they take a roundabout route, but nobody knows.

▲North American Monarch butterflies fly thousands of kilometres south and overwinter in masses in valleys in Mexico, Florida and California.

▼These transparent eel larvae ready to swim up a European river, took several years to cross the Atlantic since hatching in the Sargasso Sea (map).

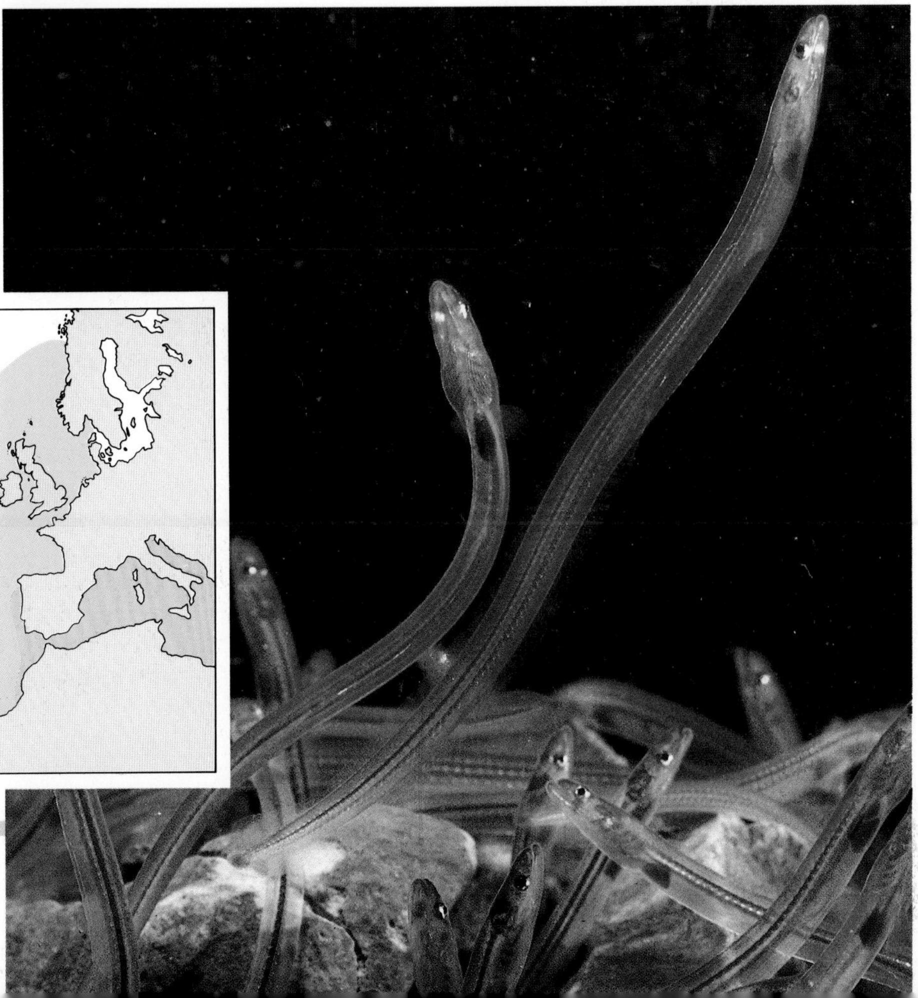

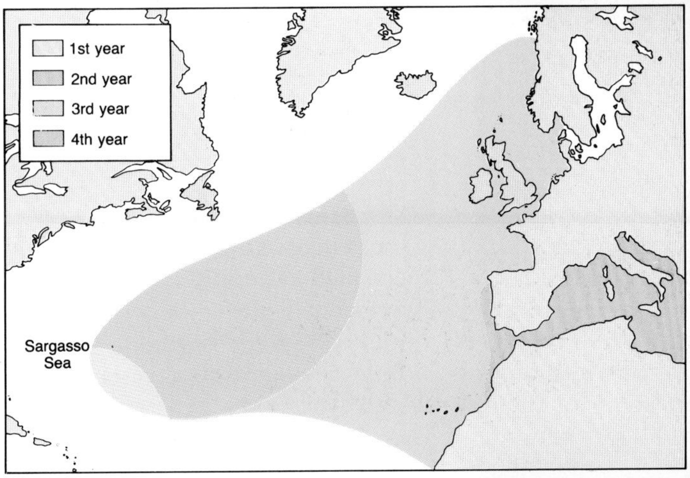

NAVIGATION

A lorry draws up. The back is full of baskets of pigeons. The driver releases the birds. They take off and climb fast. They circle briefly, then, with scarcely a pause, set off purposefully in the direction of home. Before the lorry has time to complete the return journey all the racing pigeons have covered the 200km to their home lofts.

Homing pigeons provide one of the most spectacular examples of navigational ability among animals, but they are not unique. Most animals, even some of the simplest, possess some ability to find "home" or steer about their familiar surroundings.

KEEPING IT DARK

Some animals can find their way by responding very simply to changes in their surroundings. Woodlice instinctively move away from light. By doing this they end up in crevices or under stones which form a moist, protective home. Worms too may move away from light, a reaction that sends them back in the right direction if they become exposed on the surface of the ground. Even some complex animals find this sort of simple response useful in their orientation. Turtles hatch at night and find the safety of the sea by heading off towards the brighter part of their surroundings (see page 151).

In some cases much more complicated reactions guide animals in their movements or their return to a base. A limpet returns to its own particular home spot on a rock after a feeding expedition. A badger returns to its sett after a night of foraging that may cover hundreds of metres. A whole combination of factors helps such animals to reach home. The familiar smell of home may play a part, and animals such as badgers leave their scent marks at intervals so they can find their way back along their own trail. Wild animals, like people, may also develop a mental "map" of their surroundings. This gives them a good idea where they are at any one time.

Many animals also seem to have the ability to memorize, unconsciously, the movements they have made during an expedition, so they can retrace their footsteps to get back to a place they recognize. Some people too have this same ability to navigate by recognizing the direction and the distance travelled, while in others this sense is poorly developed.

▲Planetaria can be used to expose birds to the night-time sky patterns seen at different places or times of year. This may show when the migratory instinct is strongest or whether birds could compensate if blown off course.

LANDMARKS

Sometimes other animals seem to navigate in the most common way that we use – by sight. We recognize particular features of the surroundings and take our directions from them. Birds use the same ability when in a familiar area. Many insects, including bees and digger wasps (see page 150), may also use visual landmarks to recognize their own nest entrances. Patterns in the terrain help animals such as elephants and antelopes on the plains of Africa to find their way about, even though their surroundings may seem featureless to us.

EXPERIENCE TELLS

Experience is a major factor in becoming skilled at finding your way about. An area will never become familiar until you have explored it. A young honeybee taken a short distance from its hive becomes lost but an older, more experienced bee can get back from several kilometres away.

▲▼Racing pigeons can find their way home over long distances. There is evidence that they can navigate using a combination of any of the following methods: the Sun (1); remembering the route on the outward journey (2); smells (3); the Earth's magnetic field (4); and familiar landmarks near home (5). Which sense is most important at any one time seems to differ according to the conditions, but for successful navigation more than one is used.

Experiments have revealed that migratory birds can also improve their navigational performance with experience. Birds flying just south of west through Holland on autumn migration from eastern Europe were caught. They were taken south to Switzerland and released. The young birds in the group, who were on their first migration, carried on in the original direction and ended up in Spain. The older birds readjusted their direction of flight and successfully arrived at their normal wintering areas in France and England.

BUILT-IN MAPS

Experiments such as this show that a young migratory bird carries some sort of built-in information that enables it to make its first long migration. This has to be so, because in many bird species such as swallows the adults start their migration earlier than do their young. With no parental example to guide them, how do the juveniles know where to go?

If we accept that the young birds somehow possess information on the distance and direction of their destination, even though they have never been there before, how do they put it into effect on the journey? In their first weeks of life, before the compulsion to migrate arises, they pick up information that orientates them in their daily lives. They acquire the ability to "know" which is north and which is south. An appreciation of direction similar to our own understanding of the points of the compass is clearly important because the actual line of the migration is not necessarily straight. For example, for a young Garden warbler, hatched in central Europe and migrating via Spain to central Africa, the necessary flight plan might be "fly 6 weeks south-west, then 8 weeks south-south-east".

GETTING YOUR BEARINGS

Experiments with young birds raised without seeing the sky have shown that some at least can use the Earth's magnetic field as a reference system for directions. But many night-time migrants can use information from star positions as well. Just as we can find north by the Pole star and its nearby constellations, so birds seem able to travel in the right direction by reference to the starlit night sky. Birds may be able to use both these types of clue either independently or together.

Some migrants use the Sun to help them orientate, but experiments suggest that for many daytime migrants it is not important. The setting Sun may help to label the west for some night migrants, however.

SUPERSENSES

Some of the navigational ability shown by other animals may depend on senses which we do not possess. The ability to detect magnetic fields, for example – something that we cannot do – has been shown in a range of animals from pigeons to bees. If an animal can detect the Earth's magnetic field it can tell north from south. Also, if it is very sensitive, it may be able to detect the direction of the field in relation to the ground (the "dip") and thereby tell how far north or south of the equator it is at the time. Most animals investigated so far, however, cannot do more than use magnetism as a simple compass.

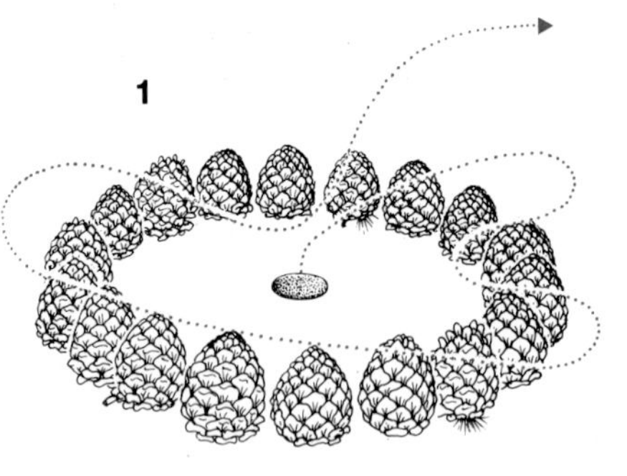

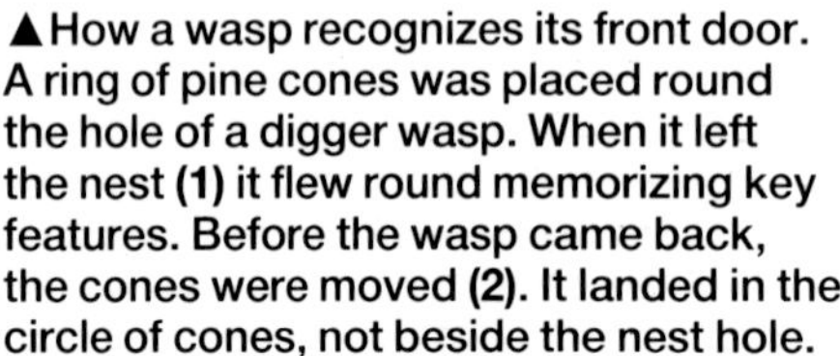

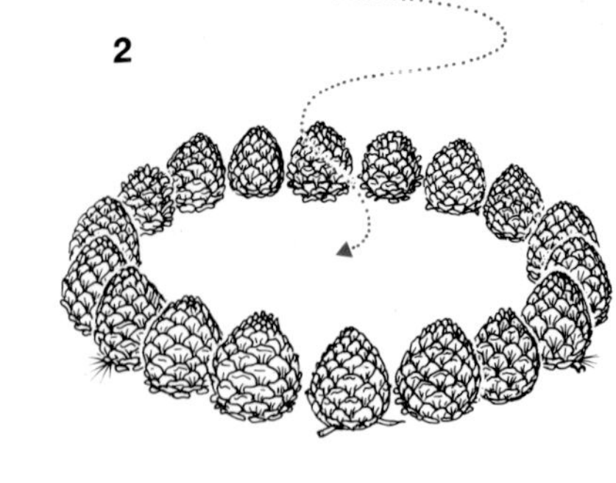

▲How a wasp recognizes its front door. A ring of pine cones was placed round the hole of a digger wasp. When it left the nest (1) it flew round memorizing key features. Before the wasp came back, the cones were moved (2). It landed in the circle of cones, not beside the nest hole.

▼Elephants build up a "map" in their memory that helps them find their way around, even in countryside that to us seems to have few distinctive features.

Another cue that may be used by other animals, but which we cannot detect, is very low-frequency sound. It is believed that some species may be able to detect the whereabouts of particular features such as mountains by the sounds made by wind blowing over them. Noises like these may be detectable from thousands of kilometres away.

Other species use visual cues that we cannot see. Many insects can see ultraviolet light, or are sensitive to polarized light. Bees use the position of the Sun as a reference point when finding their way about. Because their eyes are tuned in a different way to ours, they can "see" where it is in the sky even when it is clouded over.

We know that some animals find their way by smell, and in some this sense is millions of times more sensitive than our own. Salmon find their way back from the ocean to the river where they hatched by detecting the characteristic smell of the water at the river mouth. As they go upriver they can even choose the right feeder stream by its smell.

FAILSAFE SYSTEMS

Some animals often use more than one system to find their way. Many experiments have been done with pigeons because their homing skills are so good and they are easy to work with. Much of their ability is still not properly understood, but they seem to be capable of navigating in several ways. They have a good memory for local features and can also make use of smell, one sense that is generally not well-developed in birds. They sometimes remember the twists and turns of an outward route as well. For long-distance navigation they rely heavily on the Sun and the Earth's magnetic field.

If pigeons are released on a sunny day they soon turn and make for home. If the day is overcast they do the same. But if they are released on an overcast day, and with little magnets attached to them to upset their senses, they are unable to orientate correctly and set off in random directions.

It seems that they can use either the Sun or the magnetic field to work out their orientation, but if they are denied the information from both these sources they are unable to determine which way to go. They fly aimlessly around the release point and usually remain in the area until either the Sun reappears or they are captured and the magnets removed.

LONG-DISTANCE NAVIGATION

Experiments with marked birds have produced some remarkable navigational feats. A Leach's petrel, taken from the coast of Maine in the east of the USA to England, found its way back home. The shortest distance it could have flown was 4,800km, but it made the flight in 2 weeks. Even more impressive were the journeys of the Laysan albatrosses that were taken from Midway Island in the middle of the Pacific Ocean and released 6,500km away. They found their way back to this one tiny dot in the vastness of the Pacific. The birds were artificially moved in these experiments but, of course, comparable feats of navigation are performed by many migratory birds every year.

▲▼▶ When Green turtles hatch on the sandy beaches of Ascension Island, their first challenge is to find their way down to the sea. As they struggle across the moonlit sand many fall prey to predators. They know instinctively which way to head, reacting to the brightness over the sea, which reflects more light than the land behind them. Having paddled wildly to reach the sea they swim out to the relative safety of deep water. Migrating adults (map right) may navigate by taking their bearings from the Sun.

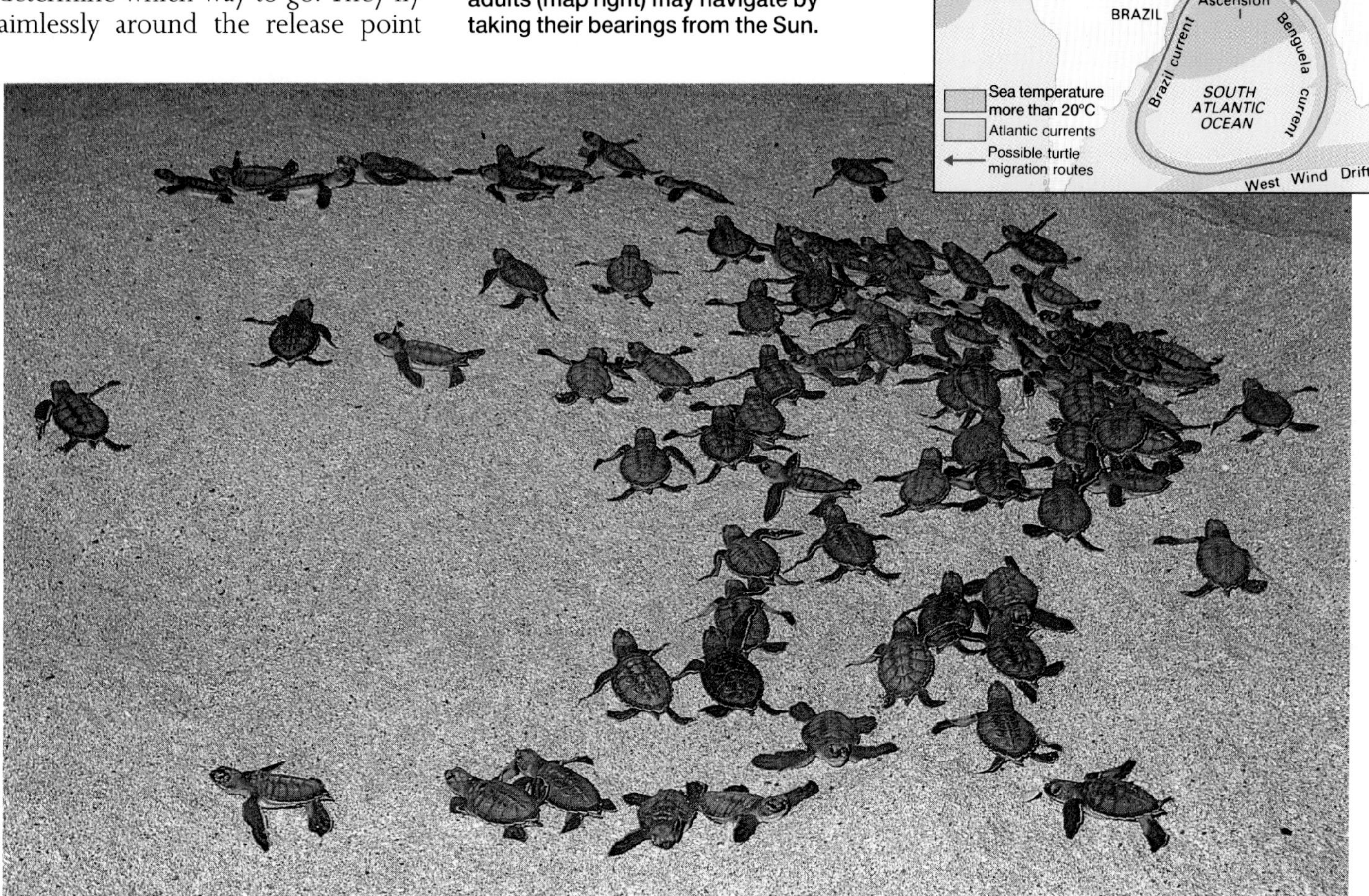

GEOGRAPHY OF ANIMALS

It was their first day of study in the Himalayas in central Asia. The two American field biologists were determined to locate their subjects, a pair of young Snow leopards. For the next month or two, the biologists were to study the behaviour and habits of these big cats. Then they were to journey 3,000km south to Malaysia to study the Clouded leopard. They hoped all this would shed some light on the life-style of the jaguar, a species they were trying to protect back home in Mexico and which is considered to be the American equivalent of the leopard in the Old World.

Few species other than humans and the animals they have introduced can be found all over the world. Each region of the world has its own characteristic, or typical, kinds of plant and animal. For example, only Australia has koalas, and only tropical Africa has gorillas. Only the Arctic has Polar bears; and only South America has capybaras. Why should the plants and animals that live in each region be so different?

One obvious reason is climate. Gorillas, for example, are used to an easy life in the hot, humid, tropical rain forests, where there is plenty of vegetation for them to eat. They could not survive on the Arctic tundra, where the climate gets bitterly cold and vegetation of any kind is hard to come by. On the other hand, the Polar bear has a thick coat and layers of insulating fat to help it combat sub-zero temperatures. This bear could not tolerate the tropical heat and humidity of the African rain forests.

But climate cannot be the only factor determining the distribution of animals around the globe, otherwise animals would live wherever the climate suited them. There would be Polar bears in Antarctica and gorillas in South America, India, South-east Asia and northern Australia. There would also be koalas in North America and Europe and capybaras in India.

ON THE MOVE

Clearly, other factors must affect the distribution of animals. The most important of these is the changing geography of the Earth. The shape and position of the great land masses are very different today from what they were in the past. The major force that has shaped the Earth's surface has been the gradual movement, or drifting, of the continents.

Continental drift over millions of years has pushed some continents apart and prevented recent species of plants and animals moving from one continent to another. Other continents have moved together, allowing animal species to move between them. By studying the way in which the continents have drifted over the ages, scientists can trace how the present distribution of animals across the globe has come about.

Another name for continental drift is plate tectonics. The process occurs because the Earth's crust is not one continuous layer, but is split up into a number of separate giant segments, or plates.

The land masses we call the continents sit on these plates. They are solid, but the rock beneath them is partly molten, and this allows them to move apart or together.

SEPARATE REGIONS

Drifting continents is one reason why different regions of the world have their own unique animal species. These species are said to be endemic to the regions, which are referred to as zoogeographic regions.

There are six main zoogeographic regions. Some are made up of a single

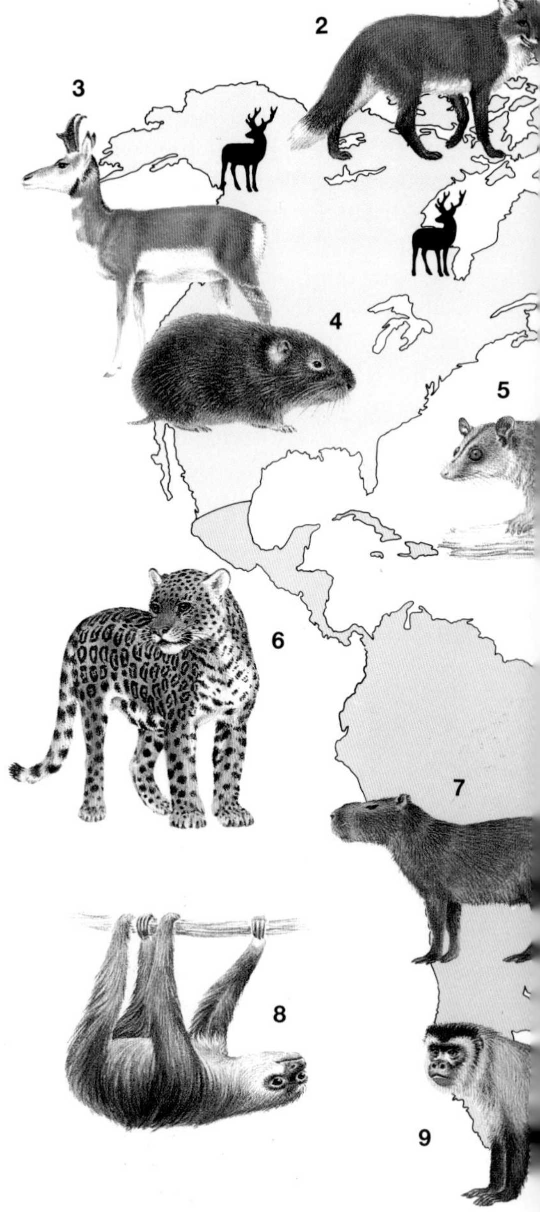

▲Typical animals of the six main zoogeographic regions of the world
Palearctic/Nearctic: Red deer, or wapiti (*Cervus elaphus*) **(1)**; Red fox (*Vulpes vulpes*) **(2)**. Nearctic: pronghorn (*Antilocapra americana*) **(3)**; Mountain beaver (*Aplodontia rufa*) **(4)**. Neotropical: Woolly opossum (*Caluromys lanatus*) **(5)**; jaguar (*Panthera onca*) **(6)**; capybara (*Hydrochoerus hydrochaeris*) **(7)**; Brown-throated three-toed sloth (*Bradypus variegatus*) **(8)**; Brown capuchin (*Cebus apella*) **(9)**. African: gorilla (*Gorilla gorilla*) **(10)**; giraffe (*Giraffa camelopardalis*) **(11)**; Ring-tailed lemur (*Lemur catta*) **(12)**. Australian: Tasmanian

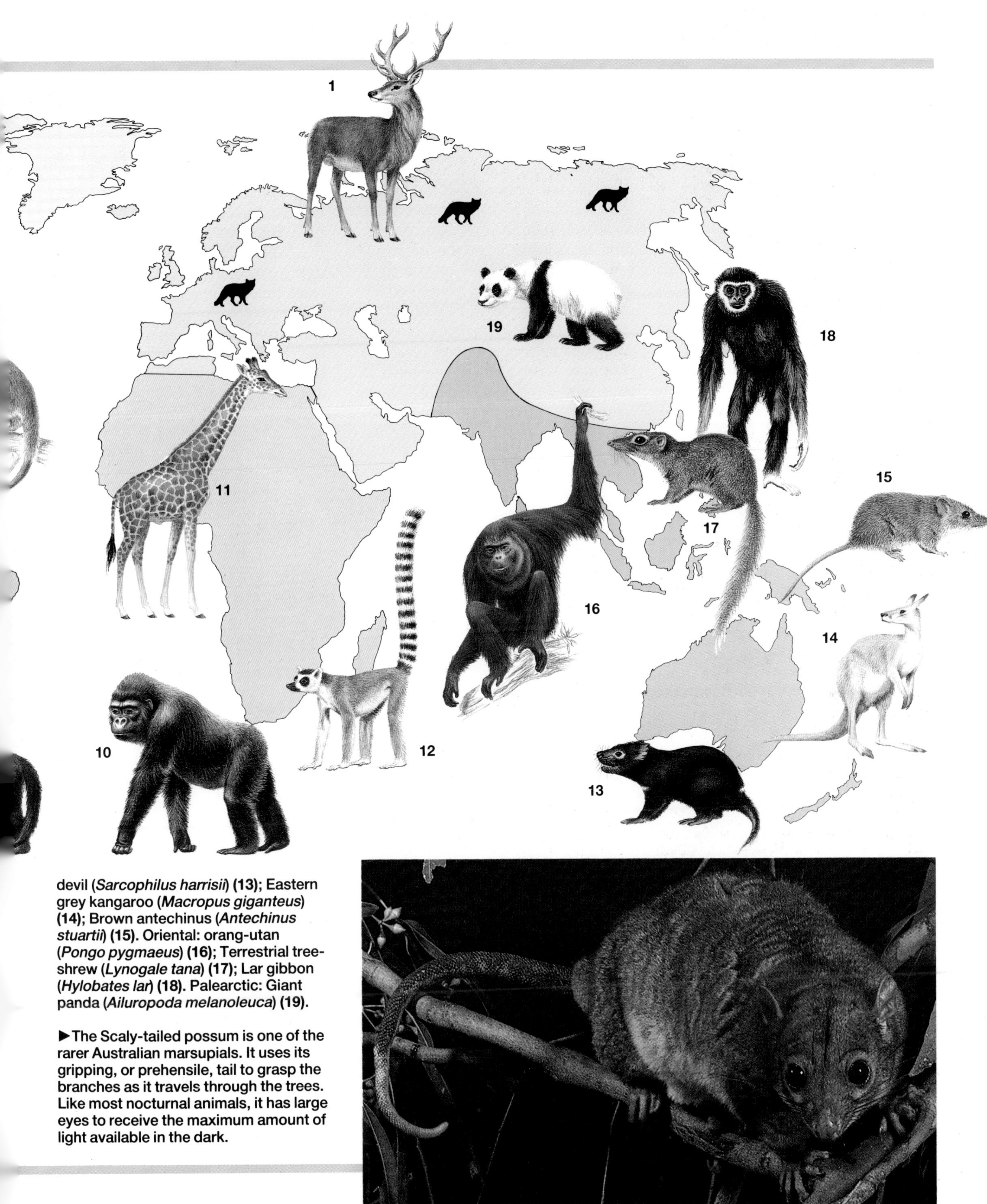

devil (*Sarcophilus harrisii*) **(13)**; Eastern grey kangaroo (*Macropus giganteus*) **(14)**; Brown antechinus (*Antechinus stuartii*) **(15)**. Oriental: orang-utan (*Pongo pygmaeus*) **(16)**; Terrestrial tree-shrew (*Lynogale tana*) **(17)**; Lar gibbon (*Hylobates lar*) **(18)**. Palearctic: Giant panda (*Ailuropoda melanoleuca*) **(19)**.

►The Scaly-tailed possum is one of the rarer Australian marsupials. It uses its gripping, or prehensile, tail to grasp the branches as it travels through the trees. Like most nocturnal animals, it has large eyes to receive the maximum amount of light available in the dark.

continent. North America forms the Nearctic region; South America, the Neotropical region; Australia, the Australian region; and Africa, the African region. At one time or another all these continents have been more or less cut off from other land masses.

The huge continent of Eurasia (Europe and Asia) is split into two zoogeographic regions. The bulk of the continent forms the so-called Palearctic region, while India and South-east Asia together form the separate Oriental region. Deserts and the towering Himalayan mountain chain have isolated this region from the rest of Eurasia.

MARSUPIAL RULE

Australia has been almost totally isolated from other land masses since about 45 million years ago. At that time marsupials were the most advanced mammals. They give birth to small underdeveloped young, which then grow to maturity in a pouch.

In other regions marsupials eventually had to compete with placental mammals – those which give birth to large well-developed young. These are regarded as being more "advanced" because their offspring are able to fend for themselves at a younger age. In Australia, however, there was no such competition, and a great variety of marsupials – kangaroos, koalas, possums, and so on – evolved and flourished. Even more primitive egg-laying mammals survived, such as the Duck-billed platypus and echidnas.

Over 60 million years ago marsupials also lived in South America, the Neotropical region. But they are now represented on that continent only by the opossums.

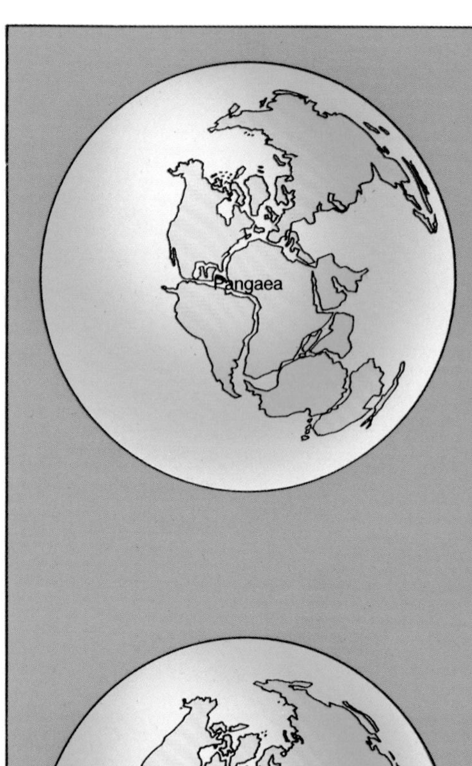

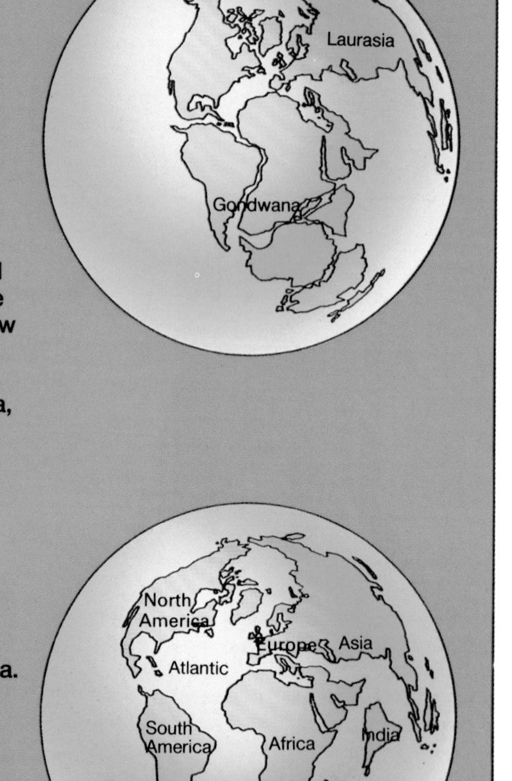

The drifting continents

◀*200 million years ago (mya)*
During the Permian period of Earth's history (286-248 mya), all the land masses of the world came together to form one supercontinent called Pangaea. But about 200 mya, Pangaea was on the verge of breaking up. The land masses that were to become today's continents began to drift apart.

▶*150 million years ago*
The first major split in Pangaea resulted in two main land masses. The one in the north, Laurasia, comprised what are now North America, Europe and Asia. The southern land mass of Gondwana comprised what are now South America, Africa, Australia, Antarctica and India. But by about 150 mya, Gondwana had started to split up.

◀*100 million years ago*
By now the Atlantic was widening, separating South America and Africa. Antarctica, Australia and India had also separated, and India was about to start its long journey northwards towards Asia.

▶*50 million years ago*
By 50 mya, during the Eocene epoch, India was well on its way towards Asia. Antarctica and Australia were still joined, but only for a few million years longer. India finally collided with Asia about 30 million years ago. North and South America were joined on and off as sea levels rose and fell. The present land bridge between them formed about 2 million years ago.

▼A Barrington land iguana suns itself on the rocks. It is one of the unique species endemic to the Galapagos Islands off the west coast of South America, which it colonized many years ago. The islands of Madagascar, Fiji and Tonga similarly have land iguanas found nowhere else in the world.

The marsupials did not evolve or thrive in South America because of competition with placental mammals such as anteaters and armadillos, and later with New World monkeys (howlers, spider monkeys and marmosets). (Historians refer to Eurasia and Africa as the Old World and the Americas as the New World, reflecting the order in which Europeans "discovered" them.) A variety of rodents, including porcupines and cavies (Guinea pigs), also entered South America with the monkeys. They came either from North America or from Africa.

Later still the present bridge of land with North America was formed, and a host of placental mammals, from weasels and foxes to jaguars and bears, flooded in. This led to the extinction of many unique endemic species such as the Giant sloth.

THE ATLANTIC DIVIDE

Many species of placental mammal appear to have evolved in North America, the Nearctic region. They were able at first to spread across Greenland into Europe, but that route became barred as the Atlantic became wider. Nevertheless, these mammals were still able to cross into Asia through Alaska and Siberia until the ice age became increasingly severe a few million years ago.

As a result, the animals of the Nearctic and Eurasia, or the Palearctic, are very much the same. Only the pronghorn and some rodents are unique to the Nearctic region. For the same reason the Palearctic region has only a few types of rodent and the unique Giant panda.

SAME BUT DIFFERENT

Among the early mammals to evolve in Africa – the African or Ethiopian region – were elephants, rhinoceroses and ancestors of the Old World monkeys and apes. These animals spread into the southern Palearctic region and India (the Oriental region). Many species in the Palearctic region eventually died out when the climate cooled down.

A barrier was set up between the African and Oriental regions by the onset of deserts in Arabia and the opening up of the Red Sea. Similar species in the regions have since evolved in a slightly different way.

This shows up, for example, in the differences between the African and the Indian elephant, the African White rhinoceros and the Javan rhinoceros, and the gorilla in Africa and the orang-utan in South-east Asia.

The Oriental region, comprising India and South-east Asia, is separated from the Palearctic by the Himalayas. This mountain range was formed when the plate carrying India collided with the main Eurasian plate about 30 million years ago. These mountains are so high and their climate is so severe, they have formed an effective barrier to the movement of animal species since then.

A LOT OF HOT AIR

Within the various zoogeographic regions of the world, climate is the main factor that affects where particular animals are to be found. Climate is largely produced by different parts of the world receiving different amounts of the Sun's energy. Because the Earth is round, the Sun's energy is concentrated more at the equator than at higher latitudes, that is at greater distances north and south of the equator.

This means that the climate is hottest at the equator and coldest at the poles. The temperature changes gradually from equatorial, to tropical, to warm temperate and cool temperate and then to cold at the poles.

The difference in temperature over the Earth sets the air circulating. As it is heated at the equator it rises. Then as it is cooled at the poles it drops. The hot air at the equator picks up moisture, which it sheds as it rises. So equatorial regions get a heavy rainfall. The now much drier air circulates to the poles and descends. It has little moisture left to shed.

WET AND DRY

Within this overall circulation are other smaller circulations. One of these creates descending dry air currents just north and south of the tropics (latitude about 30°). This often gives very dry, desert-like conditions at the surface. Farther north and south (latitude about 50° to 60°) is a disturbed region of rising and descending air currents, which usually give moist conditions at the surface. These are a feature of the temperate regions mentioned earlier.

▲The elephant evolved into two different species in Africa and Asia. The African species (above) is the larger and has bigger ears and longer, thicker tusks.

►A savannah scene on the Serengeti Plains, Tanzania. This biome has been created by a variety of natural factors. For example, trees are scarce because of browsing by animals and the fires that occur naturally in the long dry seasons.

▼Influencing the climate
A beam of sunlight spreads over a greater area of surface away from the equator than a similar-sized beam on the equator (1). This means that temperatures become lower the farther away you are from the equator. The main air circulation travels at high altitude from the equator to the poles and over the surface in the opposite direction (2). Other circulations take place in between. These circulations create regions of high and low pressure. If other factors except solar energy are ignored, there would be bands of different temperatures going from hot to cold away from the equator (3). Different climates produce a different mix of plant types, for example, rain forests in the tropics and tundra in the Arctic region.

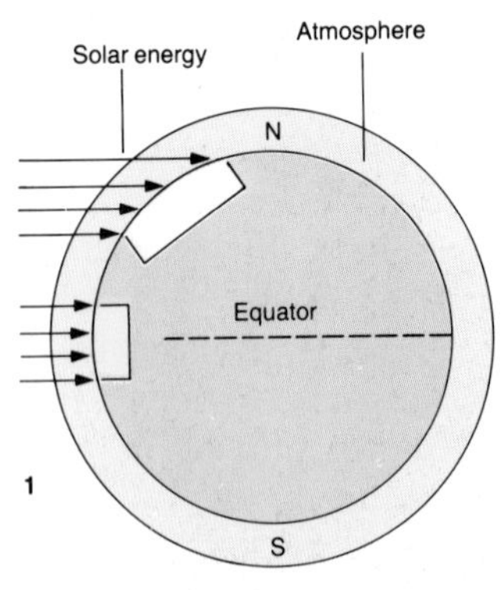

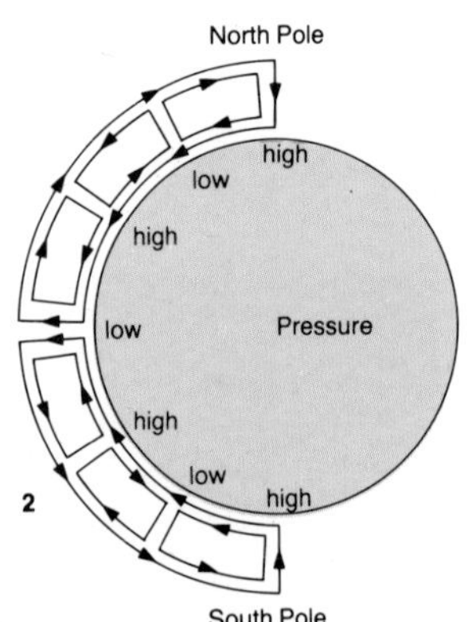

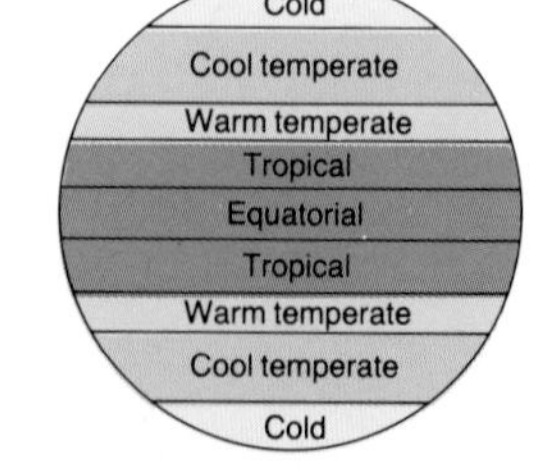

In practice the air circulation is complicated by the spinning of the Earth. This deflects the air currents at the surface – the winds – to the east (right) in the Northern hemisphere and to the west (left) in the Southern.

The direction of the winds blowing over the surface affects climate. When they blow in from the sea, they are usually moist and bring rain. When they blow over large expanses of land, they are usually dry and may give rise to drought conditions.

Among other factors that affect climate, the altitude, or height above sea level, is perhaps the most important. Temperatures fall increasingly the higher one goes above sea level. So cold climates can exist at the equator, if the altitude is high enough.

▼ **Polar bears prey on seals and walrus in the Arctic tundra. They build up layers of fat that carry them through a long winter of hibernation beneath the snow.**

CLIMATE AND PLANT LIFE

The variety of different climates has led to the development of a wide variety of plants which can grow in each climatic region. In turn, these types of vegetation support particular types of animals.

Broadly speaking, there are about 10 different climatic regions, each with its own characteristic flora and fauna, or plant and animal life. The plants and animals form fairly distinct ecological units, called biomes.

The animal species that occupy the same kind of biome in different parts of the world are not necessarily identical. But they are often similar in the way they have learned to live in, or have adapted to, a particular environment. For example, the guanaco that grazes the South American grasslands, or pampas, is a similar kind of beast to the bison that grazes the prairie grasslands of North America.

1 Tropical rain forest
Canopy of several layers of trees
Colombo, Sri Lanka

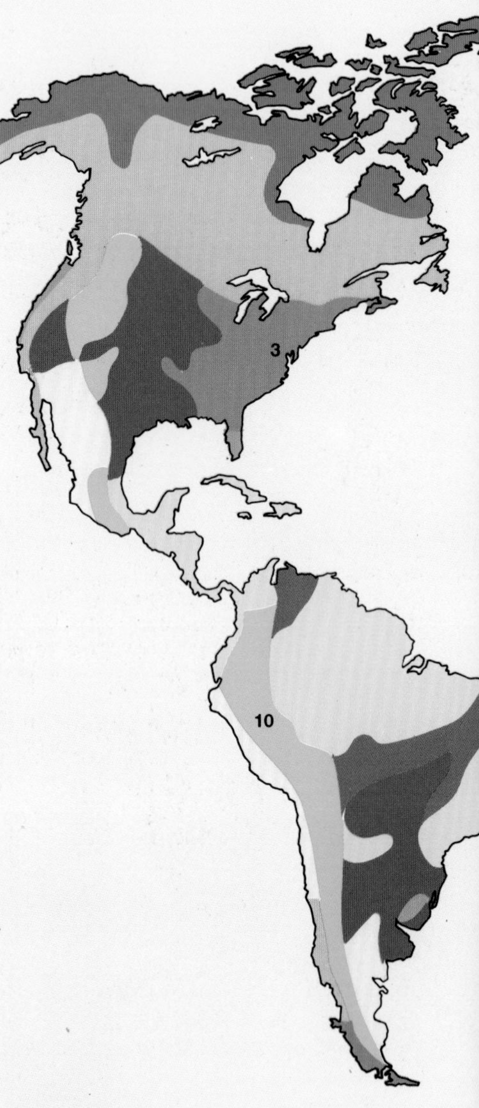

6 Desert
Well-spread low shrubs
Baghdad, Iraq

2 Temperate rain forest
High tree canopy, tree ferns underneath
Hobart, Tasmania

3 Temperate forest
Tree and shrub canopy, herb layer
Washington DC, USA

4 Boreal forest
Snow-shedding evergreen trees, shrubs
Verhoyansk, Siberia

5 Scrub
Evergreen trees/shrubs, or open grassland
Capetown, South Africa

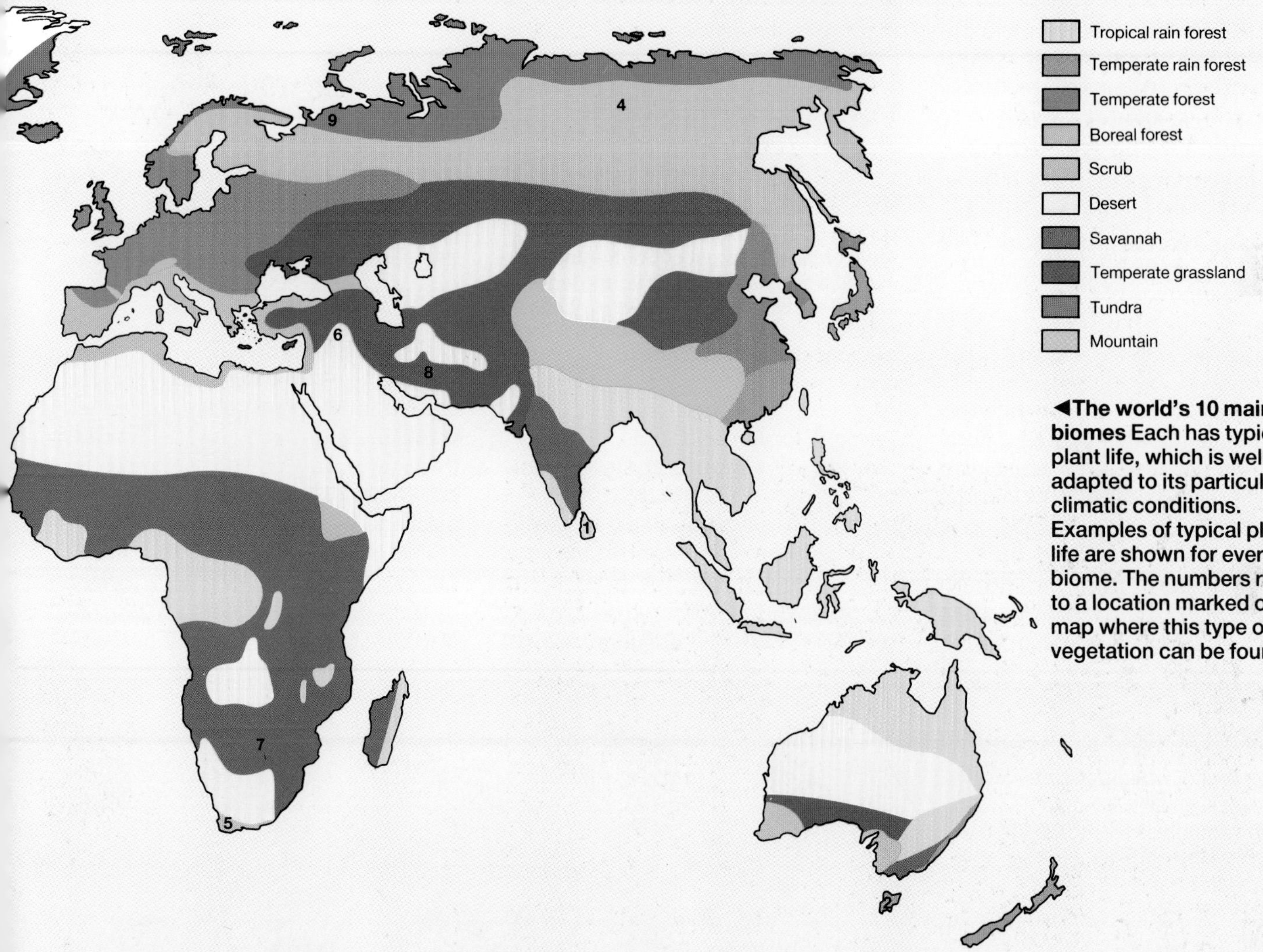

- Tropical rain forest
- Temperate rain forest
- Temperate forest
- Boreal forest
- Scrub
- Desert
- Savannah
- Temperate grassland
- Tundra
- Mountain

◀The world's 10 main biomes Each has typical plant life, which is well adapted to its particular climatic conditions. Examples of typical plant life are shown for every biome. The numbers refer to a location marked on the map where this type of vegetation can be found.

7 Savannah
Scattered trees and tall grass
Harare, Zimbabwe

8 Temperate grassland
Grass canopy
Kabul, Afghanistan

9 Tundra
Low cushion plants and dwarf shrubs
Archangel, Soviet Union

10 Mountains
Cushion plants or dwarf shrubs
Cuenca, South America

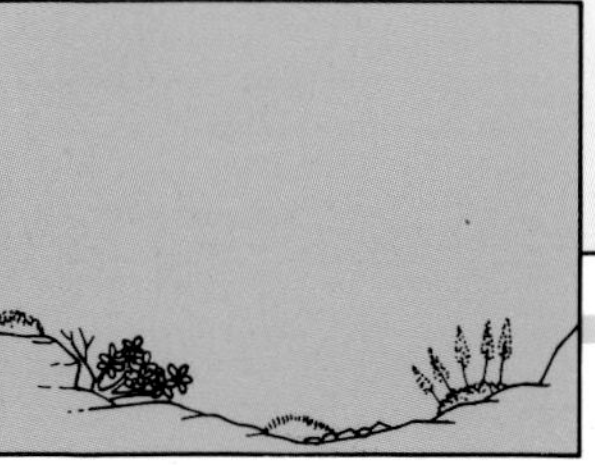

TROPICAL RAIN FOREST

A seething river of insects, up to 20m wide, is scything a path through the leaf litter on the floor of the Amazon rain forest. It is a raiding party of army ants, containing up to 200,000 ferocious worker and soldier ants. It is unstoppable. The marauding ants are flushing out and killing anything that lives in the leaf litter – other ants, centipedes, cockroaches, spiders, even scorpions. The larger animals of the forest are running for their lives. If they get trapped by the ant swarm, they too will be killed.

Straddling the equator in Africa, the Americas and South-east Asia are regions that provide a great richness of plant and animal life. Their natural wealth is unequalled anywhere else in the world. They comprise the tropical rain forests.

The tropical rain forests thrive in equatorial regions, near the equator, and in the tropics, the region between the lines of latitude which are often referred to as the Tropic of Cancer (latitude 23½° north) and the Tropic of Capricorn (23½° south).

▲High up in the dense canopy of the Amazonian rain forest of South America, a howler monkey feeds on young leaves. Like all the New World monkeys, it has a prehensile, or grasping tail, which it uses to anchor itself while feeding.

Rain falls on most days, and averages between 2.5 and 4m each year, depending on the location. Some places have been known to have as much as 10m of rainfall in a year!

►In the rain forest of Panama, in Central America, a Brown-throated three-toed sloth perches in an emergent tree above the dense leafy canopy. The sloth can be thought of as a kind of "tree cow", since, like a cow, it has a many-chambered stomach which breaks down the cellulose in the leaves. Sloths do not extract much energy from this leafy diet, which accounts for their characteristic slowness of movement.

Temperatures in the tropical rain forest are fairly steady throughout the year and are between 20° and 28°C.

There are regions of forest north and south of the tropics that also have high rainfall. But they do not experience such high temperatures. They are called temperate rain forests (see page 164).

THE LAYERED FOREST

The tropical rain forest provides ideal conditions for plant growth – constant warmth and very high humidity (moisture). In undisturbed areas this growth tends to be arranged in a series of layers.

The dominant layer is the canopy. This is a dense mass of foliage formed by trees growing up to about 20m tall. Breaking out of the canopy here and

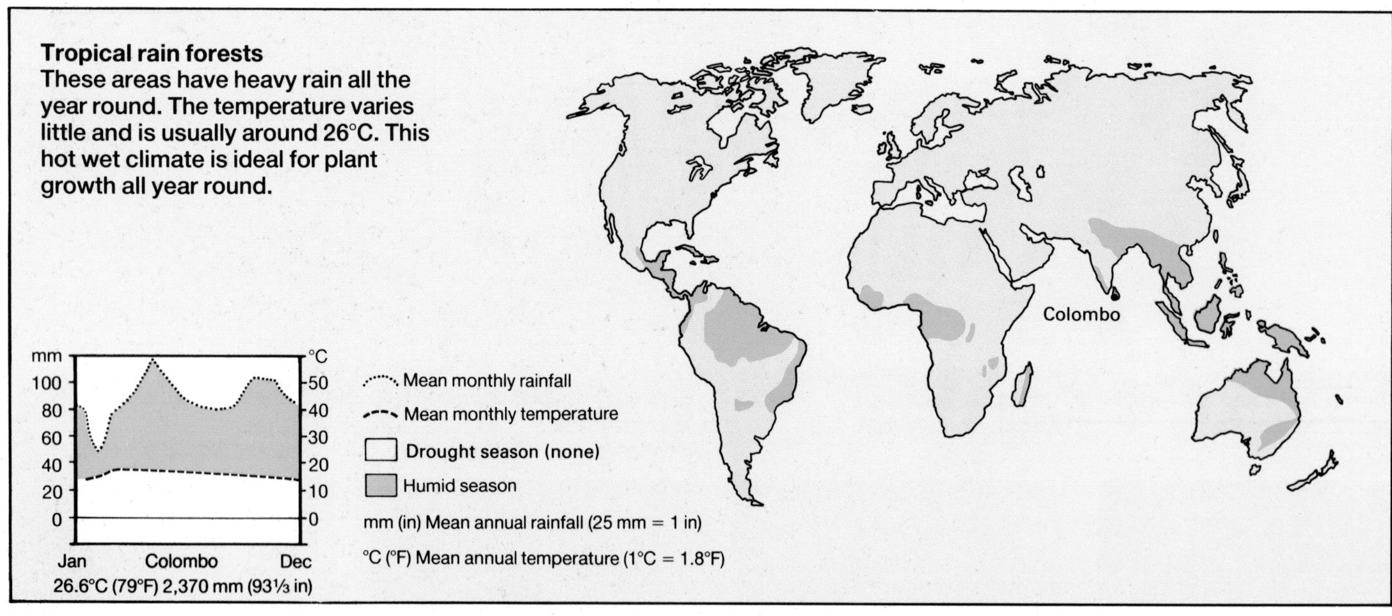

there are the taller emergents, trees up to 40m tall. Beneath the canopy, middle and lower layers of "understorey" vegetation may also be found.

DARK JUNGLE

With such dense vegetation above blocking out the sunlight, the floor of the forest is dark with less growth than might be expected. Creepers abound, climbing the trunks and branches of the trees as they struggle to reach the daylight high above. These plants are epiphytes – they rely on other plants for support. Some epiphytes, including many beautiful orchids, root high up in the tree trunks and branches, taking nourishment from their host and from the air. Other flowering plants are saprophytes – they live on the decaying leaf litter that covers the forest floor in a thick carpet.

Where the forest canopy is broken, more light filters through to ground level, and the vegetation can become very dense. This produces the kind of impenetrable undergrowth usually associated with "jungle".

FOOD FOR ALL

The animal life in the tropical rain forest is rich and varied. There is a plentiful supply of food, as abundant rainfall and consistently high temperatures allow plants to flower, seed and fruit throughout the year. The forest floor and the various layers of foliage provide a wide range of habitats for many different animals.

▲▼Species of bat of the tropical rain forests of Panama They feed on a variety of abundant food. The False vampire bat (*Vampyrum spectrum*) **(1)** is carnivorous. The Fringe-lipped bat (*Trachops cirrhosus*) **(2)** preys on frogs. The Mustache bat (*Pteronotus parnelli*) **(3)** is an insect-eater, while the Fishing bulldog bat (*Noctilio leporinus*) **(4)** catches fish.

The largest animals live on the forest floor. The elephant, tapir and gorilla all feed on the understorey vegetation. Other animals, such as the chevrotain in Africa and Asia and the agouti in South America, feed on the sparse ground cover.

LIFE IN THE UNDERSTOREY

The smaller beasts are preyed on by a variety of big cats, such as the jaguar in South America and the Clouded leopard in South-east Asia. These lithe carnivores climb into the branches of the understorey and pounce on their prey as it passes underneath. The cats also prey on birds and rodents. So do snakes, such as the highly venomous fer de lance and bushmaster.

The understorey supports a wide range of animals. Conditions on the forest floor are so wet that even frogs have taken to the trees. Tree frogs spawn and develop in the water that collects in plants or holes in the trees. Many are very poisonous and advertise this with their brilliant colouring.

Insects are found in vast numbers in the trees. Many have evolved remarkable protective coloration, or camouflage, and look like twigs and leaves. But the most spectacular insects of all are the butterflies, which are often dazzlingly beautiful. The many species of birds, such as parrots and macaws, are amazingly colourful, but they are outshone by the birds of paradise of Papua New Guinea in their stunning courtship display.

IN THE CANOPY

Birds fly in and around the forest canopy, and mammals live there too. Monkeys travel through the canopy, often in noisy troops. Using their long arms and legs to good effect, they can swing along at a remarkable speed. The New World monkeys of South America have a prehensile tail, which they use as an extra limb when moving about and feeding in the branches. In South America the sloth is a canopy dweller too, though it is as slow as the monkeys are quick.

Up in the canopy the monkeys and sloths are out of reach of the big cats that roam far below. But they can be attacked from above by some of the world's largest birds of prey. These include the Harpy eagle in South America and the Crowned eagle in Africa. The eagles live in the emergent trees, swooping down into the canopy when they spot likely prey. Two species of fruit-eating birds with huge brightly coloured beaks also live in the emergent trees of the rain forests – the toucan in South America and the hornbill in Africa and Asia.

►A male Regent bowerbird displays at the elaborate bower it has built to attract the female (shown behind). As in many bird species, the male is brilliantly coloured, while the female is drab. The brilliance of the male helps him to attract a mate; the drabness of the female camouflages her while she is sitting on the nest incubating the eggs.

TEMPERATE RAIN FOREST

At night most of the birds in the New Zealand rain forest have gone to roost. But one, the size of a large chicken, is out foraging for food. It is a kiwi, which is probing into the deep litter with its long bill. Its small eyes are useless in the pitch darkness, and it has to find its prey by smell. A crashing sound in the undergrowth nearby alerts it, and it takes to its heels and runs fast in the opposite direction. It cannot escape by flying, because it has no wings or tail.

The relatively small regions of temperate rain forest, such as the homeland of the kiwi, occur just to the north of the tropics in the Northern hemisphere, and just to the south of the tropics in the Southern hemisphere.

The temperate rain forests have less rainfall than the tropical ones, but still an appreciable amount – between about 1,000mm and 2,000mm a year. The rainfall is much more seasonal than it is in the tropical forests, with most of it falling in winter. The temperature is also lower than in the tropical forests, but there are seldom any winter frosts.

GIANT REDWOODS

The mild damp climate of the temperate rain forests is very favourable for plant growth. The typical trees are broad-leaved evergreens. In the rain forest regions in eastern North America there are evergreen oaks. Evergreen oaks and beeches are common in the temperate forests of Japan. Conifers also feature in Japan's forests, as they do in New Zealand.

By far the most impressive of the rain forest trees, however, are the Californian redwoods, which are among the tallest and oldest living things on Earth. They can reach heights of up to 100m or more.

The temperate rain forests are not as structured, or layered, as the tropical

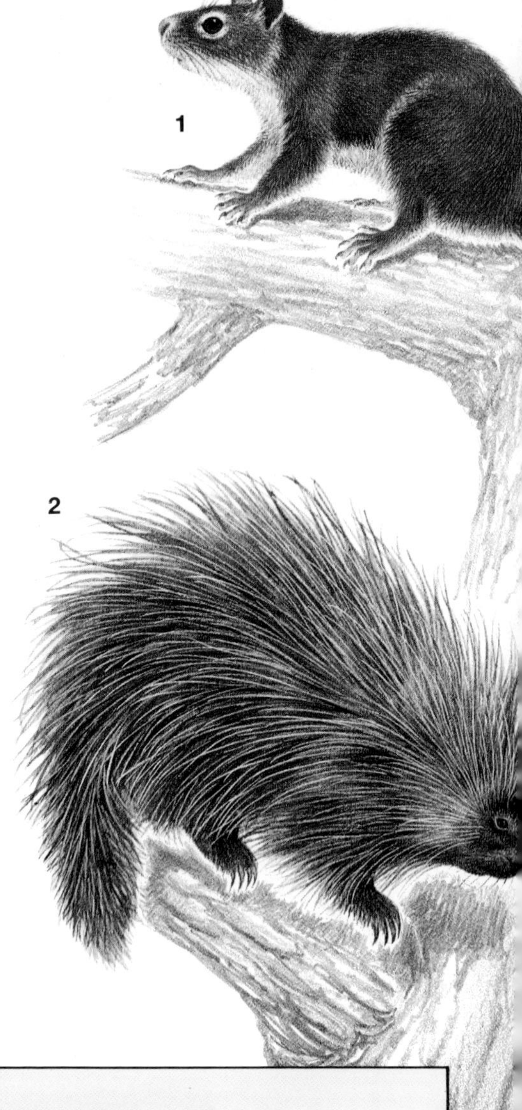

▶Some typical animals of a temperate rain forest in Washington State, USA Douglas squirrel (*Tamiasciurus douglasii*) (1). North American porcupine (*Erethizon dorsatum*) (2). Fisher (*Martes pennanti*) (3). Black-tailed or Mule deer (*Odocoileus hemionus*) (4). American shrew mole (*Neurotrichus gibbsi*) (5). Similar types of animal are found in other temperate rain forest regions.

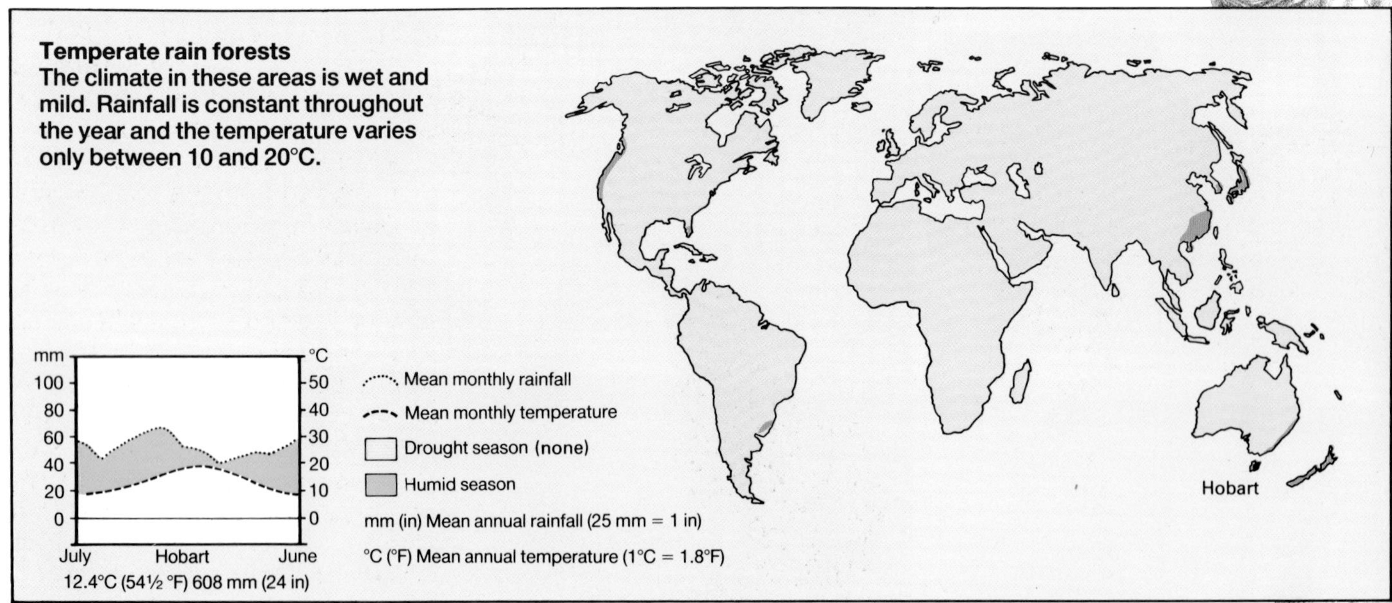

Temperate rain forests
The climate in these areas is wet and mild. Rainfall is constant throughout the year and the temperature varies only between 10 and 20°C.

◀A Great spotted kiwi foraging in the undergrowth of the temperate rain forest in the South Island of New Zealand.

ones, and there is much more leaf litter, dead branches and fallen trees cluttering up the forest floor. This is because the creatures that help decompose the fallen vegetation, such as woodlice and springtails, work more slowly in the cooler climate.

Despite the clutter on the forest floor, several large animals can often be found there. They include, in the North American forests, the Mule deer and the American black bear, which can also climb trees. They share the habitat with other mammals, such as moles and martens.

Similar kinds of animals are found in the temperate rain forests of other regions. For example, there are black bears in South America (where they are called Spectacled bears) and in Japan and China (where they are called Asian black bears).

QUOLLS AND KIWIS

The most unusual animal species of the temperate rain forests are found in New Zealand and Tasmania, where there are several unique marsupials, such as the Tasmanian tiger quoll. This is a carnivore that behaves rather like members of the cat family, climbing trees and preying on roosting birds. In Tasmania too lives the shy Red-bellied pademelon, a kind of wallaby.

The most unusual animal in the New Zealand forests is the country's national bird, the kiwi. There are three species, all of them are unable to fly.

Kiwis have only been able to survive in New Zealand because the islands have long been isolated by the sea, which has prevented invasion by predatory mammals. Only in comparatively recent times have kiwis come under threat, from the destruction of their forest habitat and from predators such as domestic cats, which were introduced by people.

TEMPERATE FOREST

For several weeks since the winter cold set in, the hedgehog has been sleeping in its cosy nest, lined with leaves and grass, in a hole in the side of a canal embankment. Today, however, the weather has turned particularly warm, and the hedgehog has woken up feeling hungry. Cautiously, it peeps out of its hole to see if the area is clear. It makes its way to a spot nearby where plants have started to grow again and where blackbirds are digging for earthworms. When it has eaten its fill of worms and slugs, it returns to the nest and soon sinks back into sleep.

The winter cold that the hedgehog experienced, when temperatures very often fall below freezing, is a feature of the temperate forest regions, which cover much of the eastern half of the United States and most of Europe.

The typical trees of the temperate forests are deciduous, that is, they shed all their leaves when the temperature falls in autumn. They then become dormant. Their tough bark helps them withstand the cold, which would kill anything growing. The buds, the points where new growth will start, are small and well protected. They burst into life in the spring, when the temperature begins to rise.

THE FLOWERS IN SPRING

The structure of the deciduous forest is a simple one. There is a canopy, up to about 30m tall, and a lower shrub layer up to about 10m tall. The canopy is usually relatively open, which lets in much more light than in a rain forest, and allows plenty of growth on the forest floor.

Most growth at ground level takes place in early spring, when the plants take advantage of the period before the leafy canopy of the trees fully develops. At this time many woods are carpeted with spring flowers.

RHYTHM OF THE SEASONS

The seasonal nature of plant growth in deciduous forests means that the supply of food available for animals is seasonal too. So, to survive, animals have to be generalists rather than specialists, which means that they must be able to live on a variety of

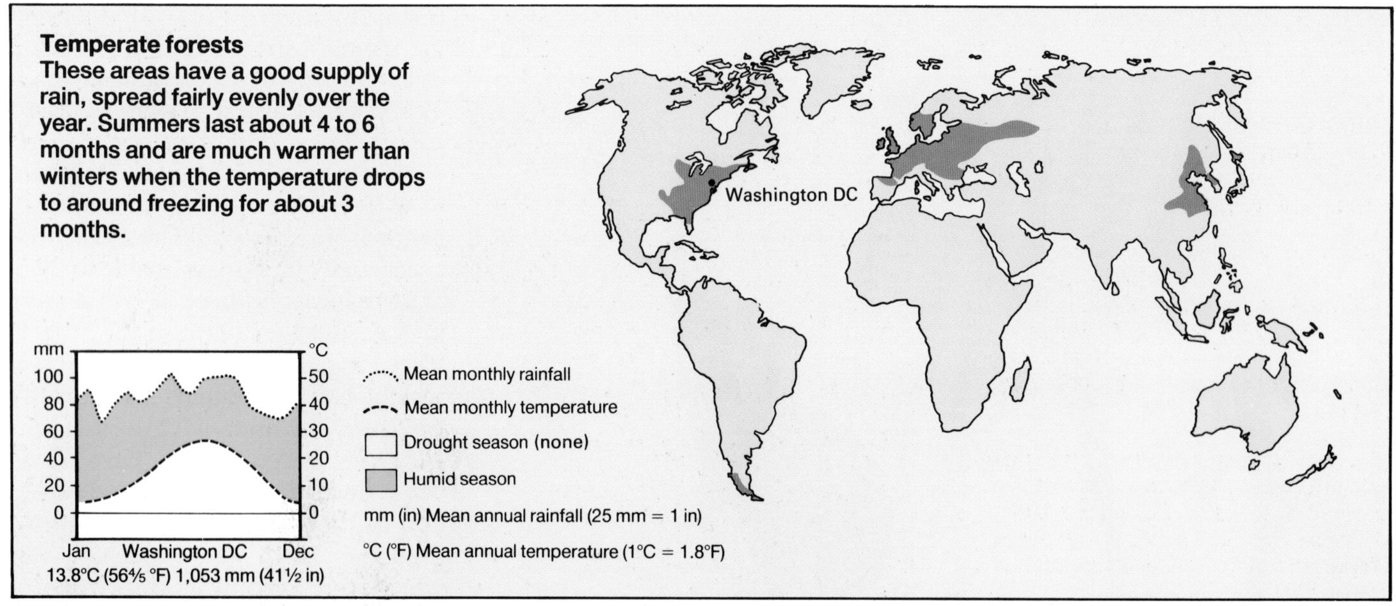

Temperate forests
These areas have a good supply of rain, spread fairly evenly over the year. Summers last about 4 to 6 months and are much warmer than winters when the temperature drops to around freezing for about 3 months.

▲A hungry brood of Coal tits begs for food as a parent returns to the nest. Tits are among the most common birds in deciduous woodland, feeding mainly on insects, but also on seeds and berries. The Coal tit has an extensive range, breeding from the British Isles, across Europe and Asia, to Japan.

▲(Right) A Grey squirrel in its drey, or nest, in an oak tree. The Grey squirrel is a native of North America, and was introduced to Britain in 1876. It has become a major forest pest there, killing saplings and young trees by stripping off the bark.

►Not oak apples but growths known as galls produced by the presence of the larvae of a gall wasp, *Biorrhiza pallida*, which feed inside. The life-cycle of many temperate forest insects includes such a tree-dwelling stage.

foods rather than on just one type. The other factor that limits the number of animal species in the temperate forests is the winter cold. Animals adopt different means of surviving. Some, such as many birds, migrate to warmer climates. The Willow warbler, for example, is a resident of many north European woodlands during spring and summer. But it flies 10,000km to Africa for the winter.

THE WINTER SLEEP

Most animals cannot escape the cold in this way, however. Some, including hedgehogs and dormice, hibernate instead – they go into a deep winter sleep. Their body temperature drops very low and their heart beats only feebly. Like the trees around them they seem dead. For months they remain like this, their body feeding on an internal store of fat.

Squirrels and badgers also fall into a winter sleep, but it is not so deep, and their body temperature does not fall. From time to time they wake up and feed if they can. Squirrels, for example, feed on nuts they have stored during the autumn. They need to have many such stores because they do not remember where they all are.

FIGHT FOR SURVIVAL

The other animals of the forest survive as best they can during winter. Birds like tits search for insects and eggs in the bark of trees. Deer and wild pigs grub around in the leaf litter for roots and any remaining vegetation. They may also browse on bark and branches if no other food is available. A bitter winter will often result in trees being severely damaged or killed by browsing animals.

THE LEAF LITTER

The leaves that fall in abundance in the autumn are a major feature in the ecology of the temperate forest. They act as an insulating blanket for hibernating animals and plants alike. Little breakdown (decomposition) takes place in the leafy layer in the winter. But in the spring woodlice, worms and smaller creatures get to work on the previous year's leaves.

The leaf litter becomes alive not only with the decomposers, but also with the creatures that prey on them, such as beetles and spiders. This varied animal life also makes rich pickings for moles, shrews and birds.

ABUZZ WITH INSECTS

Insect life within the temperate forests is rich and varied too. Moths and butterflies often survive the winter in the bark. Species that eat leaves lay their eggs so that they hatch as the buds begin to burst in the spring.

There are good reasons for doing this. For one thing the fresh leaves are rich in nitrogen, which the insect young need to build up their body proteins. Also, they do not yet contain toxic compounds, which might harm the young. Many old leaves tend to

▲A Eurasian badger foraging in the leaf litter on the forest floor for earthworms, insects and snails. It will also eat voles and mice. It is a nocturnal animal and spends the day in its burrow, called a sett.

►A group of Red deer grazes in a forest glade. The male is distinguished by its fine set of antlers. Among all species of deer except reindeer, only the males have antlers. Every year they shed them, and grow new ones.

be low in nitrogen and high in tannin, which make them not so nice to eat.

The Spangle gall wasp has evolved an ingenious method of surviving the winter. It lays eggs on oak leaves, which causes them to develop galls, or growths. The young develop inside these galls, which fall off the leaf before the leaves themselves fall. The falling leaves then provide a covering layer to protect the young gall wasps.

◀Curled up in its nest, a Common dormouse sleeps throughout the cold winter. By curling up, it reduces the exposed area of its body, and so reduces heat loss.

▼A Japanese macaque foraging in the winter snow for food. The macaque is the only forest-dwelling monkey outside the tropics. It lives in the temperate forests of Japan, keeping mainly to the ground. It survives the winter cold by growing a thick furry coat.

BOREAL FOREST

In a northern pine forest of Canada a family of Red squirrels is sitting in the branches of a tree, feeding on seeds in the pine cones. One of the group sees their arch enemy, the goshawk, some distance away, and makes a chucking call to alert the others. One of the younger squirrels panics and jumps out on an exposed branch. The goshawk sees its chance and swoops down. Within seconds the young squirrel is struggling in the bird's vice-like talons, with no hope of escape. Within an hour it has been torn to pieces and swallowed.

The boreal, or northern pine, forests occupy vast regions of the Northern hemisphere. "Boreal" comes from the name Boreus, god of the north wind in Ancient Greece. No similar forest regions occur in the Southern hemisphere. The boreal forests merge in the south with temperate forests and grasslands, and in the north with the virtually treeless tundra.

▲Beavers build dams with the trunks and branches of trees they cut down with their sharp teeth. They make the dams watertight by adding stones and mud. They also build their lodges of the same materials.

Being at a higher latitude than the temperate forests, boreal forests have a much harsher climate. The summers are shorter and the winters much colder. Only about 2 months of the year are free from frost, and temperatures in some places may fall as low as −60°C at times.

THE CONE-BEARERS

Because the growing season is short, plants of boreal regions must be able to burst quickly into growth when

►A Red squirrel eating a nut, which it holds in its forepaws. It is an attractive creature, with conspicuous ear tufts. It is one of the commonest residents of the boreal forests of Europe and Asia, where it is preyed upon by martens and goshawks.

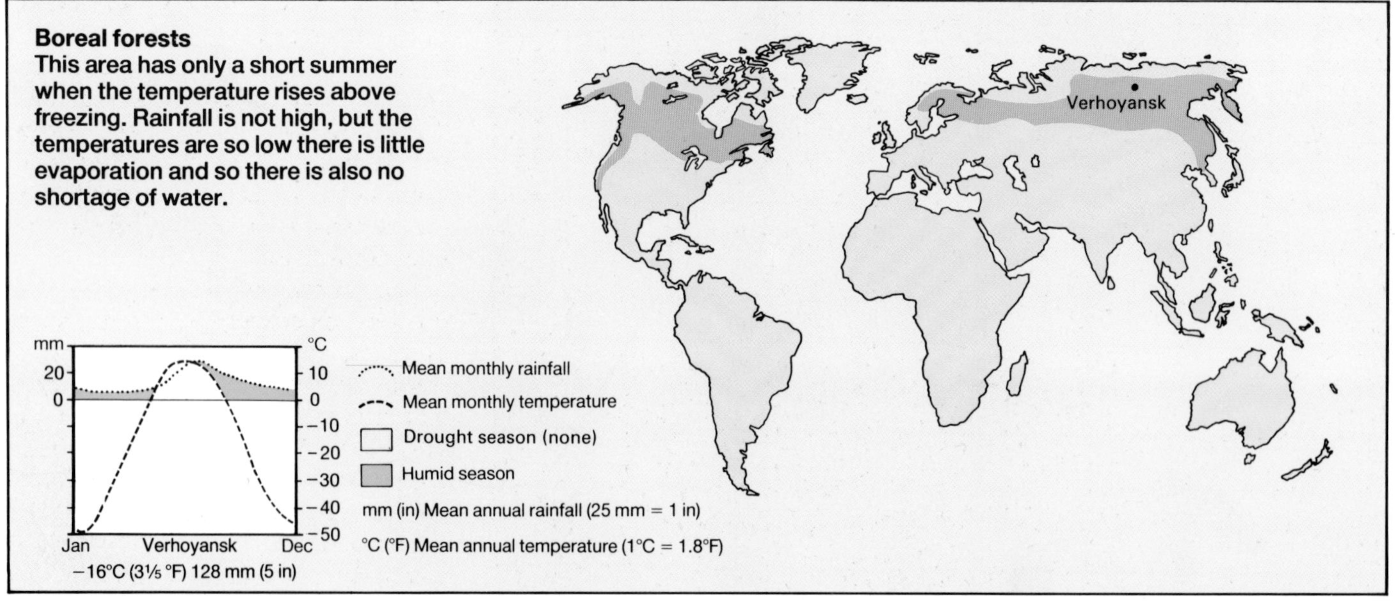

▲A pair of Red crossbills, natives of the boreal forest regions of Europe and Asia. Only the males are red; the females are green. The bill of these birds crosses over at the tip. This enables them to open out the scales of cones and pick out the seeds.

temperatures start to rise in the spring. Evergreen plants with existing leaves can do this better than deciduous ones, which need time to develop their foliage. And that is why evergreens dominate the boreal forests. Among the deciduous trees that do grow in boreal regions are birch, aspen and willow.

The evergreens of the boreal forests are not broad-leaved evergreens like those in the rain forests. Broad leaves would lose too much heat. Boreal evergreens feature thin needle-like leaves, which lie close together and retain more heat.

The majority of the evergreens are conifers, or cone-bearing trees, such as pines, spruces and firs. Another feature of these trees is their shape, which is like a cone pointing upwards. This shape is very effective in shedding snow before it builds up enough weight to break the branches.

Compared with the forests farther south, there is not much variety in the plant life on the floor of boreal forests. This is almost certainly due to the recent geology of the region. The boreal regions occupy areas covered by glaciers until a few thousand years ago. There has not been enough time for a greater variety of plant species to become established since then. Indeed, there are still glaciers at high altitudes in the regions, for example, in North America and Scandinavia.

HUNTERS AND HUNTED

Among the larger animals of the boreal forests are the caribou, reindeer and moose, which graze on any available vegetation. Like most of the other mammals, they tend to remain in the forest during the winter months for protection against the icy winds and bitter cold. The feet of the reindeer and moose are specially adapted for life in the snow. They are splayed out to give a larger area over which to spread their weight.

Big as they are, these beasts are prey for an increasingly rare species, the wolf. Wolves hunt in packs for greater efficiency. They sometimes attack domesticated livestock, which has led to their being hunted by farmers and so to their dwindling number.

The boreal forests are also the home of many other predators, such as lynxes, foxes, martens and goshawks. Their prey includes particularly the Snowshoe hare and the Red squirrel.

BUSY BEAVERS

In the boreal forests in North America the American beaver has a marked effect on the vegetation, particularly around streams and rivers. The beavers feed on the bark of deciduous trees such as birch and aspen. They will often eat right round the trunks of the trees, thereby killing them.

Beavers also deliberately cut down trees, which they use to construct dams and build their lodges, or homes. They dam streams to make a pond with deep water, and then build their lodge

in it. The lodge is built so that the living area is above the water, but the entrance is underwater. This protects the beavers against such predators as the wolverine. In the autumn the beavers store branches at the bottom of the pond, and then feed on these branches during the winter.

THE CROSSBILLS

Most of the birds that live in the boreal forests during the spring and summer migrate south in winter to warmer places where they can still find insects and other food. Exceptions are the birds of prey and the crossbills.

Crossbills are birds of the finch family, which have adapted to feed on conifer seeds, the most plentiful food supply in the boreal forest. They have a bill that crosses over at the tip, and they use this to pry open the tough cones that hold the seeds.

Insects, such as beetles and moths, thrive in the forests in the summer months. Over a period of time insect populations may build up in huge numbers. Their caterpillars, or larvae, feed on the leaves and can completely strip trees of foliage, and so kill them. Among the most destructive species is a moth called the Spruce budworm.

People are also affecting the character of the boreal forests, which are increasingly being harvested for their timber. The evergreen conifers yield softwood, used as sawn timber for construction and to make woodpulp for papermaking. Careful management will be needed in the future to prevent the eventual destruction of this unique biome.

◀Examples of boreal forest animals
The trees of the boreal forest offer animals some protection from the extreme cold of the northern winter. The elk, or wapiti (*Cervus elaphus*) (1), a sub-species of Red deer, is one of the largest animals in boreal forests. The coat of the Snowshoe hare (*Lepus americanus*) (2) turns white in winter, which provides it with camouflage. In summer the coat turns grey-brown. The lynx (*Felis lynx*) (3) preys on the Snowshoe hare, as do foxes, coyotes and martens. In the air the Peregrine falcon (*Falco peregrinus*) (4) is a formidable predator.

SCRUBLAND

In the heart of the Mallee scrubland of southern Australia, the male Mallee fowl has been building a nest for some months. He has been collecting leaves at the nest site, and then covering them with soil. The nest has by now become a huge mound of rotting vegetation, rather like a compost heap, and, like a compost heap, it is warm inside. Now it is egg-laying time. The male scoops out a hollow in the mound, in which the female lays the eggs. She does not need to incubate the eggs – that is brought about by the heat of the mound. Eggs and chicks are then ignored.

▲The puma is sometimes known as a cougar or Mountain lion. It is the largest of the North American cats, with a head-and-body length up to nearly 2m. The puma ranges widely in search of its main prey, which are Mule deer and elk. But it will also take smaller prey, such as rodents. Like the other North American cats, the puma is now an endangered species.

The Australian scrubland, home of the Mallee fowl, covers many thousands of square kilometres. However, the largest area of scrub is found around the Mediterranean Sea, and so the type of climate enjoyed by this biome is often called Mediterranean. It has hot, dry summers and mild, wet winters. During the summer months the average temperature is often more than 20°C. In winter the temperature hardly ever falls to freezing point (0°C) and almost all of the annual rainfall of up to 500mm occurs in the winter.

Low woody shrubs form the typical vegetation of the arid scrubland. The leaves of these plants are small and leathery. They are well adapted to

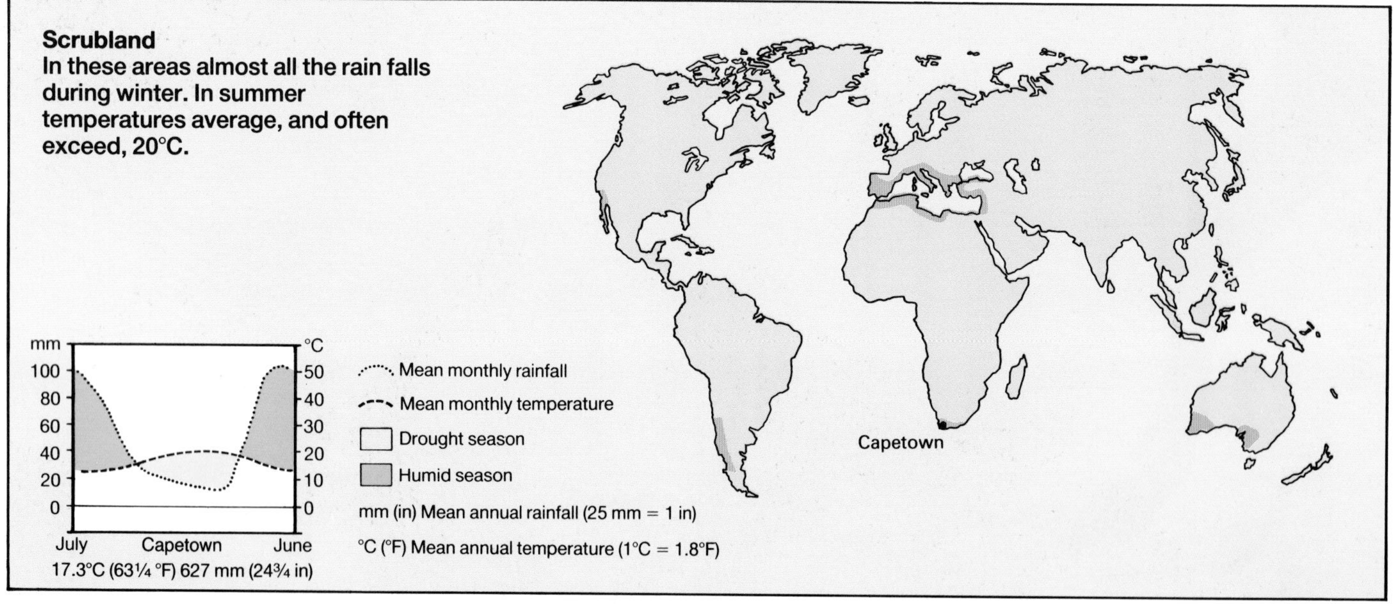

▼Some animals of the Californian chaparral: The Antelope jackrabbit (*Lepus alleni*) **(1)**, noted for its speed; Merriam's kangaroo-rat (*Dipodomys merriomi*) **(2)**; Collared peccary (*Tayassu tajacu*) **(3)**, a small wild pig; the sidewinder (*Crotalus cerastes*) **(4)**; White-tailed antelope-squirrel (*Ammospermaphilus leucurus*) **(5)**; Western collared lizard (*Chrotaphytus collaris*) **(6)**; Road runner (*Geococcyx californianus*) **(7)**, with lizard prey.

withstand the blistering heat and drought conditions of summer. Some shrubs are evergreen and their leaves tend to shrivel in summer due to lack of water. Other shrubs minimize water loss by losing their leaves as the summer drought takes hold.

CHEMICAL WARFARE

Many of the shrubs are rich in strong-smelling oily chemicals, which stop insects and other animals from eating them. The oils also find their way into the surrounding soil, and prevent the growth of competing plant life. The California sagebrush is an example of this kind of shrub. The oils it contains are also inflammable. In the tinder-dry conditions of high summer the sage-brush easily catches fire, and the whole region is swept by fire on average about every 25 years.

Apart from the shrubs, the plant-life consists mainly of annuals and bulb plants. They burst into growth after the annual rains, flower and seed, and then die back during the summer. Interestingly, the seeds of many of the annuals are stimulated into growth by the drop in temperature in the late autumn. This contrasts with the typical seeds of temperate regions, which are triggered into growth by the warmth of spring.

THE WILD WEST

The area of scrubland in California where the sagebush is found is known as the chaparral. It is the home of a fascinating variety of wildlife, despite the harsh summer climate. The top carnivore of the chaparral is the beautiful but deadly puma. It preys on a variety of animals, from small rodents to the large Mule deer. It is active mainly at dusk. In some areas wolves and Grizzly bears are still to be found, although they are becoming scarce, as they increasingly come into conflict with people.

Ground squirrels live in burrows in the ground, as do the smaller kangaroo rats. Both store seeds in their burrows. The seeds probably help to conserve water by absorbing the moisture given out by the animals when they breathe.

Among bird life, the Road runner, or Chaparral cock, is the most distinctive. It does not fly well, but can run remarkably fast, hence its name. It feeds on lizards and small rodents. It is a member of the cuckoo family, but does not have the typical cuckoo habit of laying its eggs in another bird's nest. The chaparral was also part of the original home territory of the wild turkey, from which the domesticated variety descended.

LIFE IN THE MALLEE

Australia has two regions of scrubland, in western Australia and South Australia. In southern Australia it is called mallee. In some areas wallabies rest in the scrub during the daytime, but they feed during the night in more open grassland. Much of the scrubland region, however, is so dense that it is largely impenetrable by the larger mammals.

MATORRAL BURROWERS

The scrubland in Chile, in South America, is known as the matorral. Among this region's most interesting residents is the degu. It is a burrowing rodent about the size of a rat. It uses its sharp claws to dig for roots and tubers. It also eats some grasses and produces an interesting pattern in their distribution. It feeds on grasses that grow around its burrow, but it does not eat sneezeweed. So sneezeweed, which cannot compete with the other more vigorous grasses, thrives and grows only around degus' burrows.

MAQUIS AND GARRIGUE

The scrubland of the Mediterranean region is called maquis when it is thick and garrigue when it is sparse. There is scarcely any undisturbed scrub in this region because of the influence of the human population over thousands of years. Most areas are now cultivated and, with the help of irrigation, profitable crops are grown. Groves of olive trees have replaced scrub in many areas.

The wildlife of the region has also suffered because of human intervention. Herds of domesticated goats, kept for their meat, milk and hides, have been particularly destructive to the ecology of the region. They are able to eat virtually anything that grows, and even climb trees to browse on the leafy branches.

►A male Mallee fowl looks after his incubation mound in which the female will lay her eggs. She lays between 5 and 33 eggs at intervals of several days. Mounds used year after year reach 5m in diameter. The chicks hatch at any time from 50 to 90 days.

DESERT

Darkness has fallen over the sand dunes. The sand is now cool, and the air temperature is falling rapidly. Dotted about here and there are little black Tenebrionid beetles, standing on their head, with their abdomen pointing up in the air. This is not some curious mating ritual but an instinctive habit that enables the beetles to survive. As the air temperature falls further, moisture from the air slowly condenses on the beetles' bodies as dew. The water runs down into their mouths, and they drink.

Deserts are among the most forbidding places on Earth as far as life is concerned. They are hostile for two main reasons: the lack of water and the very high temperatures that last throughout the year.

Deserts are usually defined as places where the annual rainfall is less than 250mm a year. But many deserts have an annual rainfall of less than 50mm, and in some it may not rain for years at a time. In one part of the Atacama Desert in Chile, for example, it has not rained for over 400 years!

The daytime air temperature in the hot deserts rises to 50°C or more in the summer, and at such times the temperature of the surface can rise to 90°C, nearly the boiling point of water. Altogether deserts form one of the largest biomes of the world and occupy about one-eighth of the land surface. The largest desert region is the Sahara Desert of North Africa, which covers an area of over 8 million square kilometres – nearly as much as the United States.

▲A scorpion scurries over the sand in north-east Africa. It uses its large, menacing, pincer-like appendages to capture spiders and other scorpions to eat. Scorpions tend to hide in rock crevices and burrows in the sand.

►A clutch of ostrich eggs starting to hatch in the Namib Desert in Namibia. The clutch will usually include eggs laid by a number of hens, though they will be incubated only by the "major" hen and its mate. The chicks are well developed when they hatch out and are able to run around and follow their parents to food and water shortly afterwards.

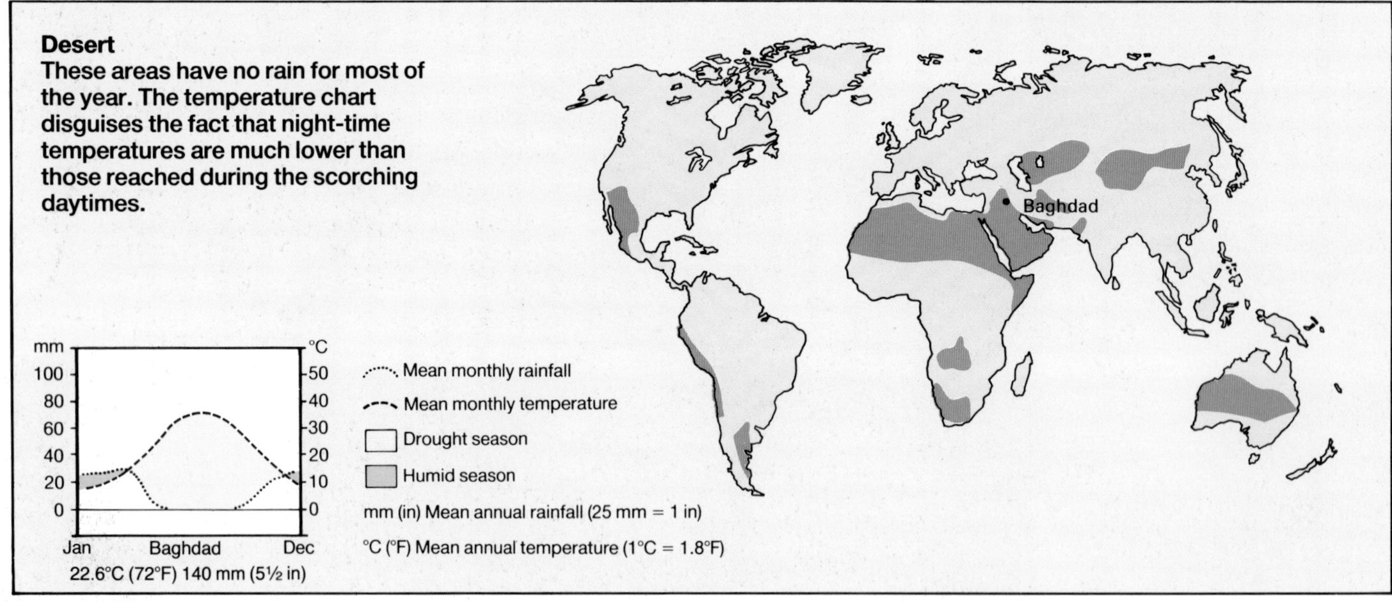

Desert
These areas have no rain for most of the year. The temperature chart disguises the fact that night-time temperatures are much lower than those reached during the scorching daytimes.

▲This gecko in the Namib Desert has webbed feet, which stop it sinking into the sand and help it to dig its burrow. Geckos are a kind of lizard. Most are active at night and feed on insects.

►A cactus plant with flower buds starting to open. Insects pollinate the flowers as they feed on nectar. A number of desert birds, such as owls, nest in holes in the thick stems of old cacti.

There are signs that the area of desert is increasing, partly because of a change in climate and partly because of too much grazing of the marginal areas by the livestock of nomadic farmers. Such desertification is occurring in other parts of the world too as the human population increases.

CACTI AND DESERT BLOOMS

It is astonishing that anything can live in the drought and high-temperature conditions of the hot deserts, but some plants and a surprising number of animals can. Various species of cactus are the typical plants of the deserts of the Americas. In the African deserts their place is taken by members of the euphorbia plant family, which have evolved along similar lines to the cactus.

Cacti are perennial plants that have become specially adapted to drought conditions. Their swollen, succulent stems are able to store water. The surface of these plants is shiny, so that it reflects much of the sunlight that falls on them.

Cacti have no real leaves so photosynthesis to make food takes place mainly in the stems, rather than in the leaves as in other plants. To photosynthesize, plants have to open their pores, or stomata, and take in carbon dioxide. Most plants do this during daytime but many species of cactus open their pores at night when the temperature is lower, and when they will lose less moisture.

Annual plants, those that live for just one season, are common in many deserts. They have evolved in such a way that they can take immediate advantage of any rain that falls. For much of the time they exist as seeds. When the rains come, they spring into rapid growth, flower and seed in just a few weeks before the drought sets in again. The abundant seed produced during this brief "flowering of the desert" is one of the major food sources for desert animal life.

DESERT RATS AND RELATIVES

Among the commonest animals in the deserts are rodents such as gerbils,

▼A deadly predator in the desert is the desert viper. It submerges itself in the sand with only its eyes visible above the surface (below). It digs its way into the sand by means of specially adapted scales on the body (bottom). As it wriggles, the scales scoop out the sand and deposit it over its body. This species is the Common sand viper, pictured in the Negev Desert in Israel.

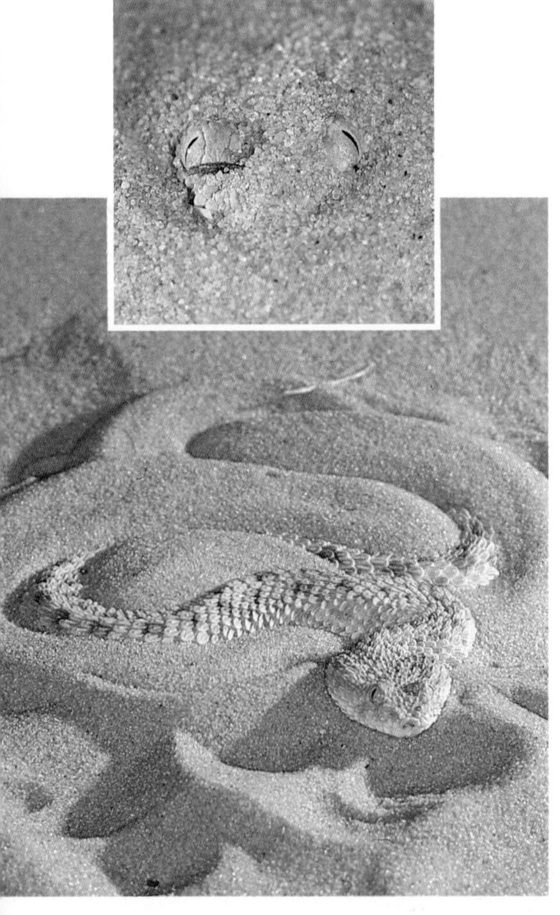

▲A scorpion devouring its grasshopper prey. They usually paralyse their prey by stinging with their tail, which is arched over the body.

▼Some desert mammals The African porcupine (*Hystrix cristata*) (1). The Cape ground squirrel (*Xerus inaurus*) (2), from South Africa. The Marsupial mole (*Notoryctes typhlops*) (3), from Australia. The Fennec fox (*Vulpes zerda*) (4), from North Africa and the Middle East.

kangaroo rats, pocket mice, jerboas and ground squirrels. They feed on seeds and grasses; some eat insects as well. Being small creatures, these animals quickly heat up when they are exposed to the Sun. For this reason most of them spend the daytime in burrows they have dug below the ground where they are protected from the worst heat.

Kangaroo rats, jerboas and some other small rodents never drink water. They get the water they need from the food they eat. It is produced from carbohydrates as their food is digested. Their bodies also reduce the amount of water lost by producing very concentrated urine.

DESERT CARNIVORES

The rodents are important prey for the various carnivores that live in the desert. Among those that live on the edge of the desert are members of the cat family, such as the caracal in Africa and Asia, and the puma in North America; and members of the dog family, for example the Striped hyena in Africa and Asia, and the dingo in Australia.

Among the smaller carnivores are various reptiles, such as lizards and

snakes; and arachnids, such as scorpions and spiders. Many of these animals are venomous. The Gila monster of the western United States and Mexico is a venomous lizard; while the rattlesnake is one of the most dangerous poisonous snakes.

There is a good reason why desert predators should be able to deal a deadly blow. In the desert, food is relatively scarce, so when a predator comes across a suitable prey, it must make sure of killing it quickly. In general the carnivores need little to drink. They get most of the water they need from the bodies of their prey.

BIRD LIFE

Various birds are present in desert regions. Being airborne, they can travel long distances between water holes, roosting places, nests and feeding grounds. Birds in general have a higher body temperature than other animals, and so can tolerate the desert heat better.

Among desert birds are various hawks, eagles and vultures, which feed largely on carrion. Among these predatory birds is the Egyptian vulture, which is well known for its habit of dropping stones onto ostrich eggs to break their thick shells.

The ostrich is probably the best-known bird of the African deserts. It is a huge bird, up to 2.5m high. It can run at speeds of up to 50kph on its long, powerful legs. Its large size is an advantage in the desert because the larger the mass of an animal, the longer it takes to heat up. Large flightless birds similar to the ostrich are found in some other deserts, for example, the emu in Australia.

◄The Shingle-backed lizard of the Australian deserts is slow-moving and cannot escape from predators by running away. Instead it puts on an impressive threat display to frighten them. It opens it mouth wide to show its strong jaws, and pokes out its long blue tongue, hissing all the while. Note how well its body is camouflaged for the desert terrain.

SHIPS OF THE DESERT

The large size of the other well-known desert-dweller, the camel, gives it the same advantage. In addition the camel has adapted to desert life in other ways. It can go for several days without drinking, using water stored in its body.

The camel is able to lose more than a quarter of its body weight of water without coming to any harm. It is also able to drink large quantities of water very quickly to make good this loss – as much as 130 litres in 10 minutes. Donkeys have the same capability of existing for days without water and then drinking rapidly. This is why they are widely used as animals for carrying goods in hot climates.

KEEPING COOL

Camels and donkeys, together with sheep and goats, are to some extent insulated from the heat by their hairy coats. This acts just as well as a barrier against heat as it does against cold.

These animals still need to cool down, however. And they do this partly by radiating heat from the shaded underside of their bodies, where the coat is thin. They also sweat to keep cool. The pores of the skin give off moisture, which evaporates in the air, taking heat from the skin, and so cooling it.

The reason these animals, and indeed all mammals, must keep cool is that they are warm-blooded, and their body can only work within quite a narrow temperature range. A rise of just a few degrees in a human being, for example, can be life-threatening.

But some desert animals, including the camel, are able to let their body temperature rise by as much as 6°C without any danger. This reduces the need for them to sweat so much, which in turn reduces the loss of precious body water.

SAVANNAH

A group of giraffes stretch their long necks to feed on the leaves at the top of one of the trees that are scattered over the African savannah. It is the middle of the dry season and the grasses have already shrivelled up. Many zebras, wildebeest, and other grazing animals are dying through lack of food. The giraffes, however, still look healthy because they can get at food the other animals cannot reach.

▲A zebra tries to escape from a hungry cheetah, but it is hopeless. The cheetah is much too fast for it, being able to reach speeds of over 100 kph.

The vast, grass-covered plains that lie on either side of the tropical rain forests in central Africa support not only giraffes and zebras but many other large animals too. These plains form the largest area of the biome known as the savannah.

There are smaller areas in other parts of the world. In southern Africa they are called the veld. In South America the large region of tropical grassland south of the rain forests is called the llanos. Smaller savannah regions are found in Madagascar and southern Australia.

WET AND DRY

The savannah has quite a plentiful rainfall, up to 1400mm in some parts. But the rain falls only for part of the year, during the wet season. During the rest of the year – the dry season – it does not rain at all. The length of the dry season varies from place to place and from year to year, but is often 6 months or more. The lack of water, coupled with high temperatures (up to 35°C) makes the dry season a testing time for both plant and animal life.

The typical vegetation of the savannah is grassland with scattered clumps of trees. There is a mix of tall and short grasses. Where conditions are favourable, tall grasses like the African Napier grass may even grow several metres high. The trees of the savannah are usually not very tall and have small

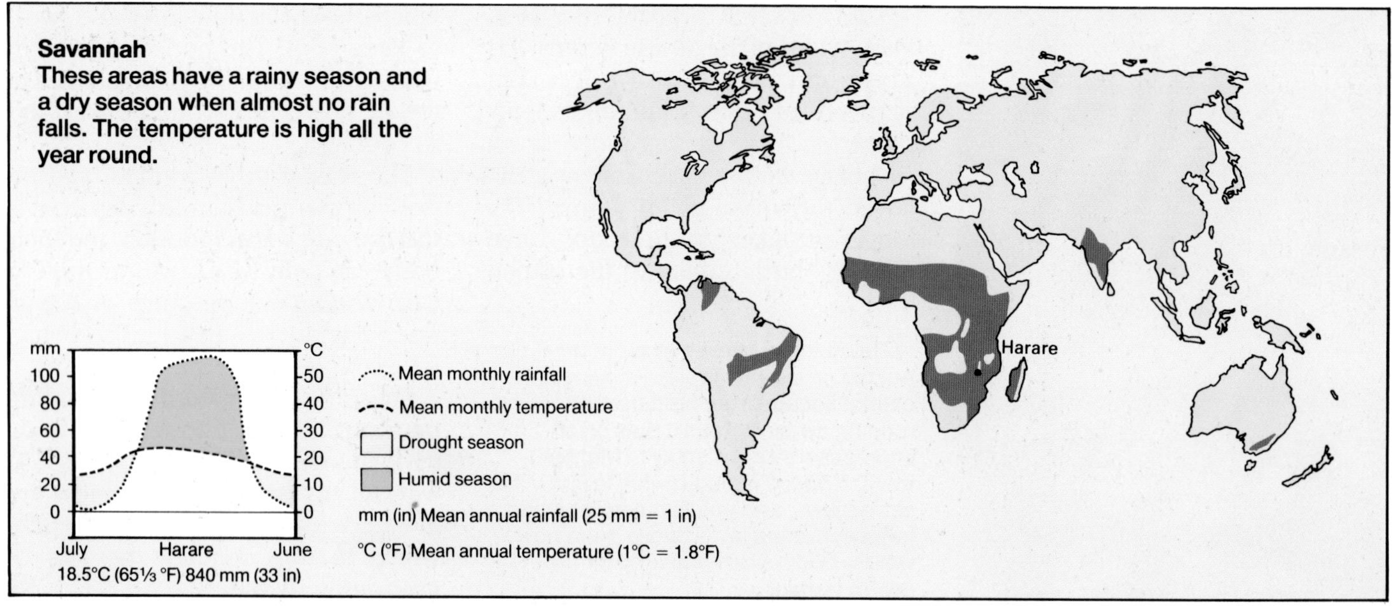

◀A lioness rests am[illegible]uriant vegetation of the Af[illegible] This is the wet season[illegible] and flowers bloo[illegible] grass-eating anima[illegible] from their waterholes. [illegible] hunting in such dense cover.

▼A herd of African elephants makes its way noisily through the tall savannah vegetation. The landscape is covered in flowers, for again this is the wet season. In a few weeks, however, the rains will cease and so will plant growth. The vegetation will soon turn brown in the relentless Sun and the drought. The animals will drift back to the waterholes, which will become the hub of their life until the next rains.

leaves and thorny branches. The acacias of Africa are typical. The most remarkable African tree, however, is the baobab, or bottle tree. It has spindly branches but a thick trunk, in which it stores water to live on during the dry season. In Australia the typical savannah tree is the eucalyptus, which is well-suited to surviving the fires that regularly sweep over the grassland regions.

GRAZERS AND BROWSERS

The African savannah supports vast herds of many species of herbivores, or grazing animals. Prominent among these are zebra, gnu, wildebeest, gazelle, impala and other antelopes. These animals do not all feed in the same way. If they did, the grasslands could not support them.

Some species, such as giraffes, prefer to eat specific plants. Others feed in succession on the grass. The Plains zebra, for example, grazes on tall grass. The Brindled gnu prefers shorter grass, and Thomson's gazelle grazes on the short grass left behind by the zebras and gnu. So herds of these three species tend to follow each other across the savannah.

The biggest herds are often to be seen during the dry season, when animals head for new feeding grounds. Other animals, including the Common eland, browse on the leaves of shrubs and trees in addition to grazing. Elephants feed on a wide range of vegetation, and have a major effect on the landscape by uprooting trees and shrubs.

Any vegetation that the grazers leave provides food for the detritivores – those creatures that live on detritus, or discarded material. The most important are the termites.

▼A flock of Marabou storks roosts as the Sun goes down on the African savannah. These birds are scavengers and feed on carrion. They nest in the dry season when prey is concentrated near the waterholes, and they can find plenty of food for their young.

▼Various species of South American savannah animals The Burrowing owl (*Athene cunicularia*) **(1)** of treeless grassland. The Southern tamandua (*Tamandua tetradactyla*) **(2)** and the Great-banded armadillo (*Dasypus novemcinctus*) **(3)**.

They build nest mounds which are several metres high and form a distinctive feature of the savannah.

PREDATORS AND SCAVENGERS

The wide variety of large herbivores provides rich pickings for many predators, particularly in Africa. Foremost among them is the lion, a majestic creature, well named "king of the beasts". Lions usually need to stalk their prey and surprise it, because they do not have the speed to outrun it. The cheetah, however, can outrun any other animal.

Other major carnivores include the African wild dog, the jackal and the hyena. The wild dogs hunt in packs and can bring down prey as large as zebras. Jackals take smaller prey and also feed on carrion. Hyenas are hunters and scavengers, and they often chase lions away from a kill.

▼Animal dung provides food for the dung beetles. Here two females are feeding. Dung beetles also collect balls of dung and roll them into their burrows. They lay their eggs on these balls, which provides nourishment for the larvae when they hatch.

PRAIRIE

A hungry coyote slinks through the prairie grass, hoping to sneak up on one of the prairie dogs sitting near the entrance to a burrow. Closer and closer the coyote creeps and still its intended victim hasn't seen it. But just as it is about to pounce, one of the prairie dog's neighbours spots it and gives out a warning call. The prairie dog just has time to dive into its burrow. It will remain there until it hears the "all-clear" call.

The prairie dog and its predator, the coyote, are both natives of the American prairies, which form part of the biome of temperate grasslands. These grasslands occupy vast areas of North America and Eurasia. In Asia they are known as the steppes. A much smaller region of temperate grassland, known as the pampas, is found in South America, mainly in Argentina.

Lying in the middle of the continents, these grasslands have a fairly dry climate, with hot summers and cold winters. In the eastern steppes, for example, the daytime temperature averages up to 25°C in the summer while dropping below −15°C in the winter. Rainfall averages only about 60mm every year.

In the western steppes the temperature difference between summer and winter is much less, and up to 400mm of rain falls. This climate provides ideal growing conditions for grass, and also for all the cultivated grasses we know as cereals – wheat, oats and barley. That is why vast regions of the western steppes are given over to agricultural use. The same is true of the North American prairies and the Argentinian pampas.

BISON AND DEER

Farming, therefore, has made the temperate grasslands very much a disturbed habitat for the native wildlife. Naturally, the main native animals of the region are grazers – herbivores. In the past the American prairies were dominated by bison, or American buffalo, which could be numbered in millions. But wholesale slaughter by settlers nearly wiped out the species. It was a very similar story with the

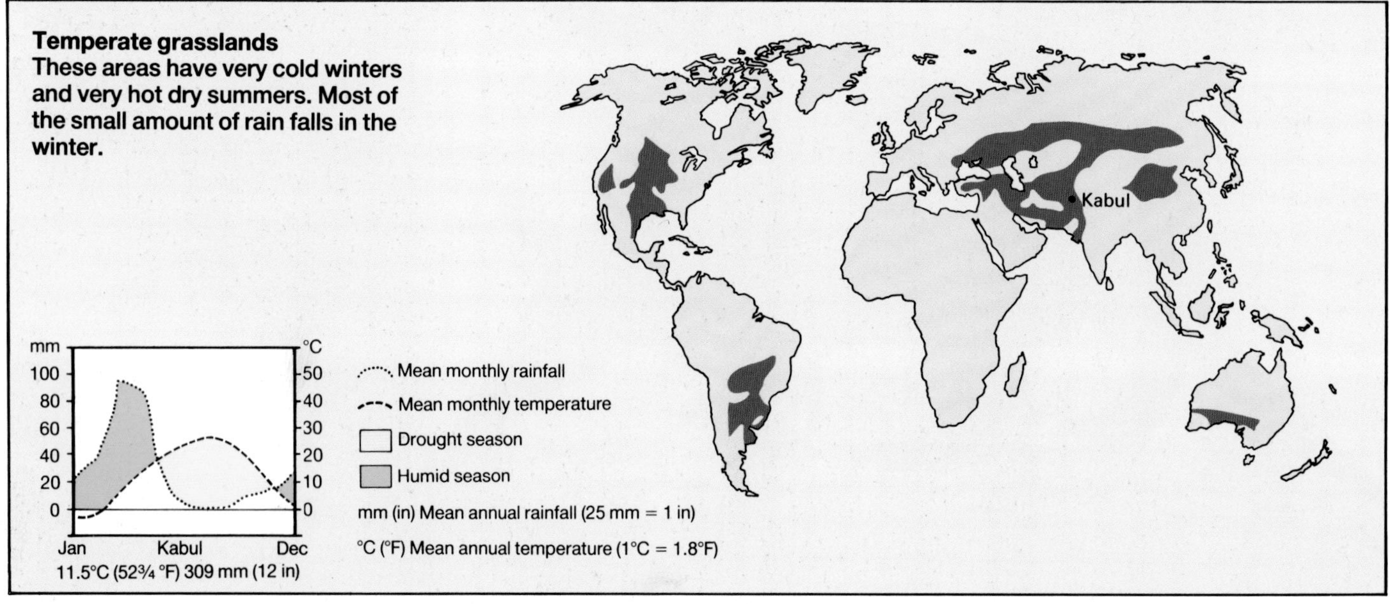

Temperate grasslands
These areas have very cold winters and very hot dry summers. Most of the small amount of rain falls in the winter.

◄A herd of American bison or buffalo grazes on the grasslands of North Dakota. Millions of these large herbivores once roamed the American prairies but buffalo hunting in the 1800s reduced their numbers to just a few hundred. Under protection, they have again increased to over 40,000.

►A group of Roe deer grazing. It is early summer and the deer's grey winter coat has changed to fox-red for the summer.

▼A herd of pronghorns on the prairie in Wyoming, USA. Like the buffalo, the pronghorn was almost hunted to extinction in the 1800s. But under protection its population has increased to several hundred thousand.

European bison, or wisent, which lived on the Eurasian steppes. Protection has helped both species survive.

The other large herbivore of the prairies is the pronghorn, a deer-like animal with distinctive prongs on its horns. On the Eurasian steppes Red and Roe deer occupy this niche.

On the pampas there are no really large herbivores. The largest are the Pampas deer and the guanaco, a relative of the camel. The large flightless birds known as rheas also feed mainly on the grass.

RODENT LIFE

The main animals of the pampas are burrowing rodents. They include the Plains viscacha, the males of which weigh up to 8kg. Other rodents include the mara and the tuco-tuco.

On the prairies, ground squirrels and prairie dogs occupy a similar niche. The prairie dog is a member of the squirrel family and is a very social animal. Large numbers of prairie dogs live together in a social group called a coterie. The animals dig an extensive network of tunnels and chambers for shelter and for raising their young.

Often numerous coteries group together and form a "town" covering as much as 65 hectares. On the steppes the souslik has a similar life-style. Among the other rodents that live there is the Common hamster, familiar to pet lovers.

THE PREDATORS

In all three main temperate grassland regions there are similar predators. The largest are dog-like animals, such as wolves and foxes. They feed mainly on rodents and nesting birds. Other predators include weasels, badgers and birds of prey. On the prairies the American badger is a more determined hunter than the Eurasian species, actively digging out ground squirrels and even taking rattlesnakes.

►▼Prairie dogs pictured on the entrance mound of their burrow. These rodents dig out tunnels and chambers underground for shelter and for raising their young. Other animals, for instance badgers, may invade these tunnels in search of prey or, like the Burrowing owl, take them over after the prairie dogs have left.

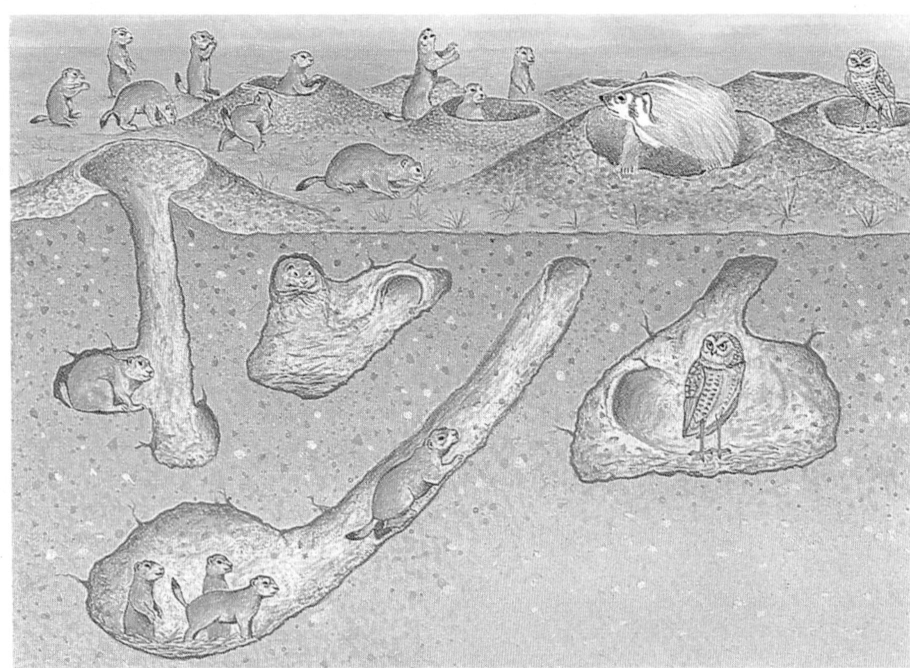

TUNDRA

Driven by instinct, a group of lemmings is migrating. They are moving along a track, which narrows as it winds along the river bank. Another group joins them from another track. Suddenly both groups panic and rush blindly ahead. The track is not wide enough to take all the frantic horde. First one or two, then many get pushed over the edge of the bank into the river. Soon the water is a seething mass of panicking animals trying to swim and fighting for breath. Some make it safely to the river bank, but many drown.

Lemmings survive and multiply in one of the harshest climates on Earth – in part of the region in the extreme north of North America, Europe and Asia called the tundra. In winter the temperature in places may drop to –50°C, and the Sun may not shine for days on end. Frost may occur even in summer. Much of the ground is permanently frozen – it is known as permafrost – and less rain falls here than in some of the deserts.

Yet despite the severity of the climate, plants and animals live in this biome which extends north from the boreal forest regions in Europe, North America and Asia.

Most of the tundra lies around the Arctic Ocean and inside the Arctic Circle (latitude 66½°), but in North America it extends farther south. There is a smaller area of tundra in northern Europe than expected because the land there is warmed by the Gulf Stream ocean current.

In the Southern hemisphere there are only scattered regions of tundra, for example, on the Falkland Islands. Most of the great mass of Antarctica itself is covered in snow and ice the whole year round.

A tundra-type region also exists near the top of high mountains, where the climate is similar. This type of biome is often called alpine tundra.

TUNDRA LANDSCAPE

Perennials – plants that come up year after year – are the commonest plants on the tundra. Among the most successful are the many saxifrage and crowberry species, which have a compact, low-growing form to combat the cold winds.

Other plants include sedge and cotton-grass. A few shrubs and trees are found in some regions, mainly willows and birch. But these grow as dwarfs, only a metre or so high.

Most tundra plants have a very rapid life cycle in order to cope with the limited growing season, which may be as short as just 2 months. They flower a few days after the snows have melted and quickly produce seeds just a month or so later.

As the summer snows melt and the upper soil thaws, much of the ground becomes boggy. This is because the lower soil – the permafrost – remains frozen and so prevents the surface water from draining away.

RESIDENTS AND MIGRANTS

The summer growth of vegetation on the tundra attracts a number of large herbivores, or plant-eaters. From the boreal forests come the caribou and reindeer. They join the herds of Musk oxen, which live on the tundra winter and summer. They can survive the freezing cold winter because of their exceptionally thick coat and thick layers of body fat. Musk oxen often huddle together for warmth and for protection against predators.

Among the other permanent residents of the tundra are the lemmings. Lemming numbers vary wildly from year to year. They are very rapid breeders, the females being able to give birth to their first litter of young when less than 40 days old. Every 4

▲In the short summer, birds flock to the Arctic tundra to breed and feed on the vegetation and the plentiful insect life. These are White-fronted geese.

▲The Musk ox is a large beast, weighing up to 350kg in the wild. Its thick, shaggy coat protects it from the bitter cold of the Arctic winters.

►The Norway lemming, which lives in northern Scandinavia and north-west Russia. It has specially adapted claws for digging in the snow for food.

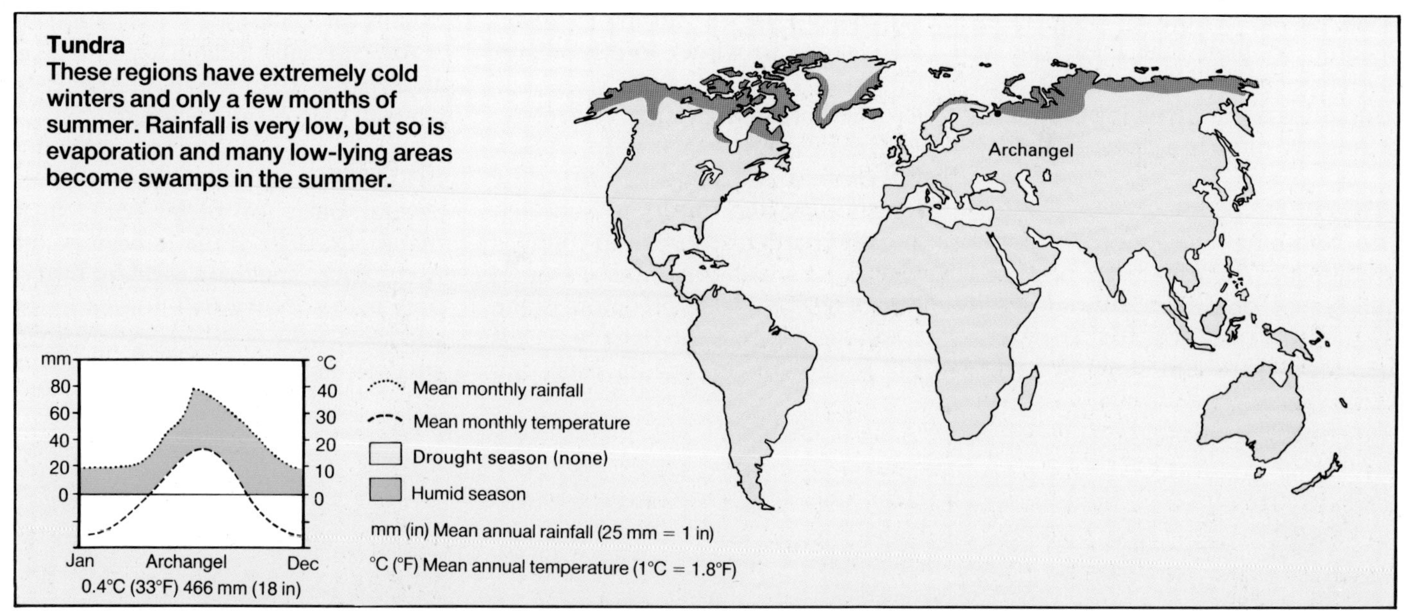
Tundra
These regions have extremely cold winters and only a few months of summer. Rainfall is very low, but so is evaporation and many low-lying areas become swamps in the summer.
Archangel
mm
80
60
40
20
0
°C
40
30
20
10
0
Jan
Archangel
Dec
0.4°C (33°F) 466 mm (18 in)
Mean monthly rainfall
Mean monthly temperature
Drought season (none)
Humid season
mm (in) Mean annual rainfall (25 mm = 1 in)
°C (°F) Mean annual temperature (1°C = 1.8°F)

years or so lemming populations become so high that they have to migrate to new feeding grounds. Mass migrations occur involving thousands of animals, often in a state of panic.

THE PREDATORS

The lemming and another tundra resident, the Arctic hare, are prey for a number of predators. Among them are the stoat and Arctic fox. The Arctic fox, Arctic hare and stoat all have a brownish coat in summer, which turns white in winter to camouflage the animals in the snow.

Other predators, such as wolves, wolverines and Brown bears, follow the caribou and reindeer out of the forests onto the tundra in summer, and prey particularly on their young as well as on smaller mammals. One of the most formidable predators of the north, however, is the Polar bear. It is not found on the tundra itself, but usually on ice floes. It feeds mainly on seals, especially Ringed seals. Wolves and Arctic foxes often follow Polar bears to feed on any leftovers.

BIRD LIFE

Several birds of prey attack small mammals, such as the lemmings and Arctic hare. The main resident bird of prey is the Snowy owl, joined in the summer by buzzards, jaegers (skuas) and falcons.

►An Arctic fox in its white winter coat. This remarkable animal does not start shivering until the temperature drops to below −50°C.

These last two species are attracted by birds like the Arctic warbler, which have migrated to the tundra to feed on the plentiful insect life that thrives in the boggy tundra region. The insects include blackflies and mosquitoes, which attack any warm-blooded animal for a blood meal, making their life a misery. To escape these swarms of irritating insects, caribou and reindeer move away from the low-lying swamps onto higher, drier ground.

Vast flocks of geese also migrate to the tundra in summer to breed. They include the Greylag, White-fronted, Snow and Canada geese. As the summer draws to a close, they wing their way back south to the British Isles, the Mediterranean region or the southern United States.

FROM POLE TO POLE

The greatest migration, however, is made by the Arctic tern. It nests in the tundra in the Arctic summer, then flies more than 6,000km to the Antarctic for its summer before returning once again to the Arctic.

Both the Arctic and Antarctic are in continuous daylight during their summers, so this bird probably enjoys more daylight and less darkness than any other species on Earth. Its twice yearly journey from pole to pole is the longest migration route of any animal.

◄On the Arctic tundra Polar bears are the top carnivores. They feed mainly on seals and walruses, and occasionaly on smaller mammals and birds.

►A Grey wolf, the largest member of the dog family. This is a youngster, which has left the pack in which it was born to seek a mate and set up its own territory.

MOUNTAINS

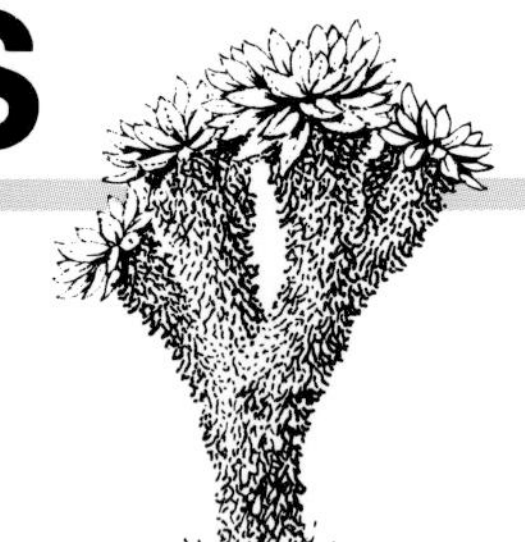

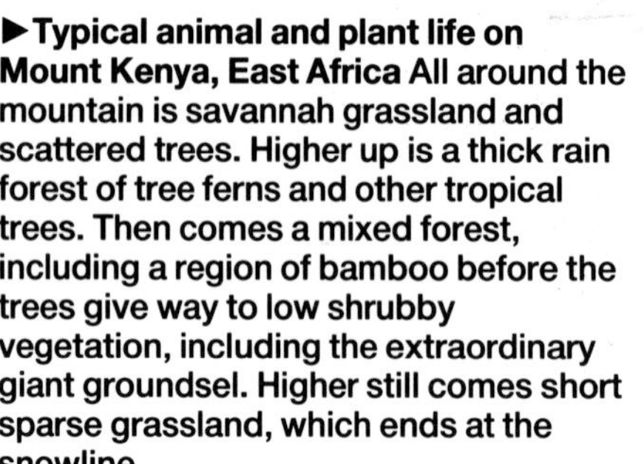

It is late autumn in the Swiss Alps, and the days are drawing in. A plump animal with thick greyish-brown fur is waddling towards its burrow beneath a boulder, carrying dried grass in its mouth. It is an Alpine marmot. It disappears underground to a chamber and spreads out the grass. Later other members of the family group join in. In a few days the chamber has become a cosy den. As the cold sets in, the family retire to the burrow. The last animal in plugs the entrance hole with grass and soil. The time has come for the long winter sleep.

The Alps, the highest mountains in Europe, are just one of the world's great mountain ranges. All mountains have a different kind of climate from that of the land around them. This is mainly because the temperature falls steadily with increasing height, or altitude. On average the temperature drops about half a degree for every 100m rise above sea level.

▶**Typical animal and plant life on Mount Kenya, East Africa** All around the mountain is savannah grassland and scattered trees. Higher up is a thick rain forest of tree ferns and other tropical trees. Then comes a mixed forest, including a region of bamboo before the trees give way to low shrubby vegetation, including the extraordinary giant groundsel. Higher still comes short sparse grassland, which ends at the snowline.

The change in temperature that occurs with increasing altitude is similar to the change in temperature that occurs over increasing latitudes, or increasing distances from the equator.

The temperature change with latitude gives rise to the world climatic zones – equatorial, temperate, and so on. The temperature change with altitude produces the equivalent climatic zones going up a mountain. Each will favour certain types of plants and animals. In other words, a mountain creates its own set of biomes.

UP THE HIMALAYAS

The change in climate with altitude is well illustrated by the Himalayan mountain range. These mountains are located just outside the tropics, and their lower slopes, or foothills, are covered with luxuriant subtropical forest. Above about 1,400m the climate becomes temperate and leads to deciduous forest of oak and rhododendron. From about 2,500m conifers such as deodar, pine and fir take over. This zone is equivalent to the boreal forest region of the high northern latitudes.

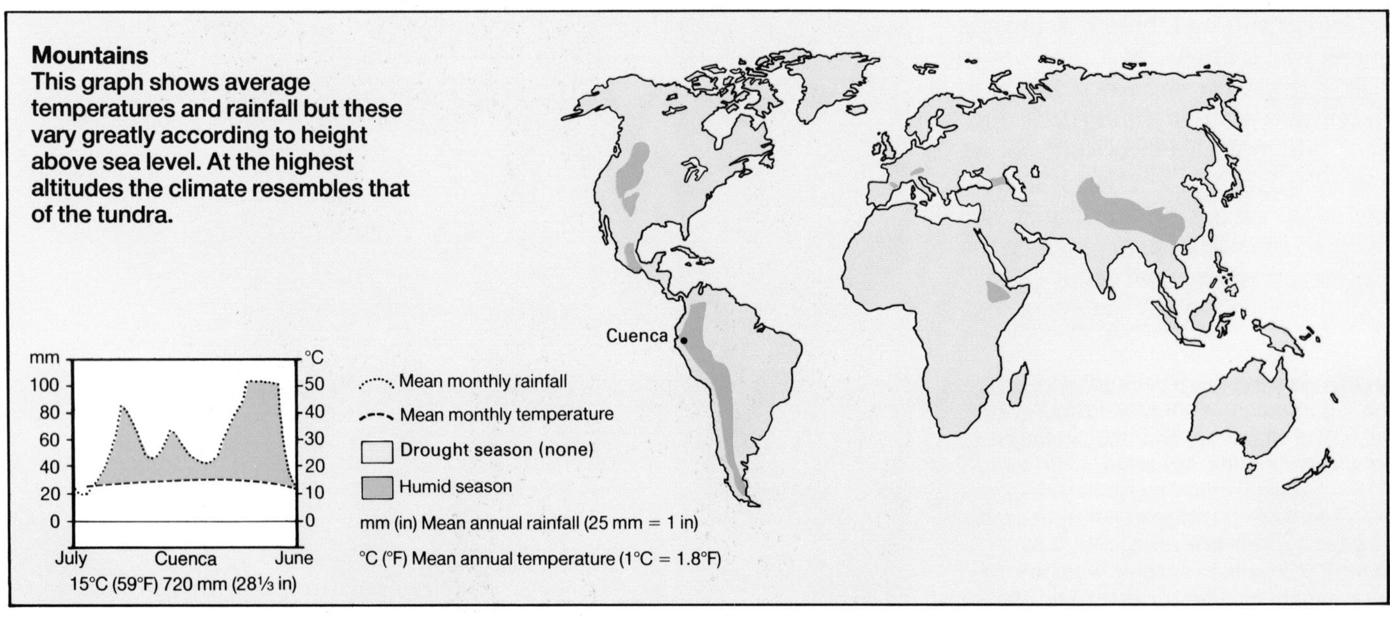

Mountains
This graph shows average temperatures and rainfall but these vary greatly according to height above sea level. At the highest altitudes the climate resembles that of the tundra.

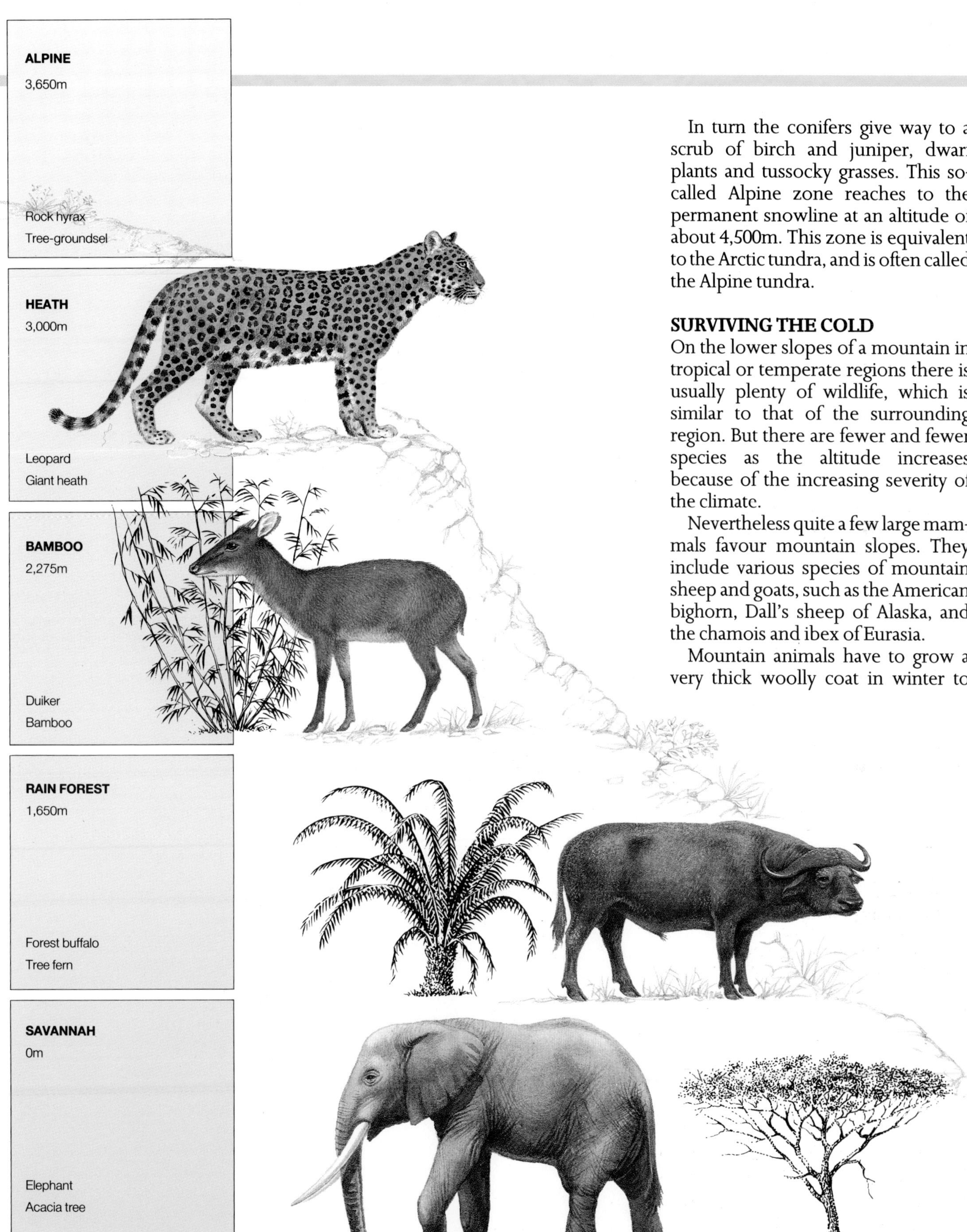

In turn the conifers give way to a scrub of birch and juniper, dwarf plants and tussocky grasses. This so-called Alpine zone reaches to the permanent snowline at an altitude of about 4,500m. This zone is equivalent to the Arctic tundra, and is often called the Alpine tundra.

SURVIVING THE COLD

On the lower slopes of a mountain in tropical or temperate regions there is usually plenty of wildlife, which is similar to that of the surrounding region. But there are fewer and fewer species as the altitude increases because of the increasing severity of the climate.

Nevertheless quite a few large mammals favour mountain slopes. They include various species of mountain sheep and goats, such as the American bighorn, Dall's sheep of Alaska, and the chamois and ibex of Eurasia.

Mountain animals have to grow a very thick woolly coat in winter to keep out the cold. The chinchilla, a rodent, and the camel-like alpaca, both of the Andes, have exceptionally warm coats. So has the Angora goat of Central Asia. All three species are farmed for their coats, the Angora yielding the fibre called mohair.

There are only a few large predators in high mountain regions because of the limited supply of prey. The Rocky Mountains of North America are the haunt of the puma, also called the Mountain lion. In the Himalayas and the highlands of eastern China lives the beautiful Snow leopard, which preys mainly on ibex. Wolves are also found in some mountain regions where they hunt sheep.

▼The vicuña in its high mountain habitat. This camel-like animal lives in the Andes Mountains of South America.

►A group of ibex, which live at high altitudes in Europe and Asia. Ibex have massive horns, up to 1.4m in length.

MIGRATE OR HIBERNATE

Many of the larger mammals and the beasts that prey on them avoid the worst cold of winter by migrating down the mountains into the shelter and higher temperature of the forests.

Many small mammals, on the other hand, hibernate. They include ground squirrels and marmots, which may spend half the year asleep. During the summer, these animals gorge themselves to build up a thick layer of fat, which sustains them through the winter with little or no food.

HIGH WINDS

The high Alpine peaks are buffeted by strong winds much of the time, and birds are few and far between. Only strong fliers can cope with them. They include in the high Andes the condor and in Eurasia the lammergeier. The lammergeier is a scavenger, which feeds on carrion. It sometimes drops bones from a great height to crack them open and get at the marrow they contain. A common bird at lower altitudes is the ptarmigan, which has a white winter plumage for camouflage.

The high winds also discourage winged insects. Most of the native species, such as the grylloblattids of the Rocky Mountains, are wingless. They feed on insects the wind has blown up from lower altitudes.

▼A puma, also called a Mountain lion, pictured in the mixed forest of the Rocky Mountains in the United States.

RIVERS

The water is tumbling swiftly down the mountainside, rushing between the stones that litter the stream bed. On one of these stones is a plump, wren-like bird, which constantly bobs up and down. It is a dipper. It hops down into the water and, walking on the bottom, disappears under the surface. With head down, it walks upstream, probing for insect larvae and crustaceans among the stones. Nearly half a minute later it surfaces, and with larvae wriggling in its bill, it flies back to its nest to feed its five hungry hatchlings.

Although nearly three-quarters of the Earth's surface is covered with water, the dipper's rushing freshwater streams form only a tiny fraction of it. Most of the Earth's water fills the great oceans and is salty. Only about 3 per cent is fresh water, and only about half of this is liquid water flowing in rivers and streams, or trapped in

▲The American dipper lives beside swift-flowing streams from Alaska to Central America. It builds a dome-shaped nest of moss, lined with grass and leaves, usually above running water.

◀Two male Mute swans fighting, because one has intruded into the other's territory. The fight is furious, with much hissing and wing flapping. Almost always the resident wins such a bout.

▶A water spider with its "diving bell". It spins this structure to trap air to breathe so that it can remain underwater for long periods.

lakes and ponds. The rest is frozen as ice or snow in the Arctic and Antarctic and on high mountains.

Fresh and salty water provide quite different conditions for living things and, as a result, contain quite different plant and animal life. Only a few species spend their lives, or part of their lives, in both fresh and saline (salty) waters. They include fish such as the salmon and the freshwater eel.

FEEDING THE FISH

As with other habitats, every body of water has a food chain. At the bottom of the chain is plant material. This may come from the outside in the form of dead leaves. Or it may come from simple plants that grow in the water and make their food by photosynthesis. These plants include single-celled plants such as algae.

In turn simple plants are "grazed" by tiny creatures called zooplankton and by crustaceans, creatures like *Cyclops*. Then higher creatures such as fish eat the zooplankton and crustaceans, and may in turn be eaten by bigger fish.

Water life is not as plentiful in rivers as in the still waters of ponds and lakes. In rivers the current, which is swiftest in the higher upper reaches of a river, sweeps the food supplies downstream.

SUCKERS AND BARBELS

The main creatures that live in the swift-flowing water are invertebrates that keep to the river bed – insect larvae, leeches, and molluscs such as water snails. The larvae of mayflies and caddisflies are specially adapted for life in fast currents. They have little suckers or hooks on their bodies to anchor themselves to the stones.

As the river flows down into the lowlands, it becomes deeper, wider and slower. As it becomes slower, more plant material and dirt particles can settle out, producing a muddy sediment on the bottom. Also, as the river slows, more vegetation grows along its banks providing food and shelter for a wide variety of wildlife.

The sediment on the river bed becomes the home of burrowing creatures, including various worms, and molluscs such as clams and mussels. Insect larvae still abound in the upper layers of sediment, as do crustaceans like the freshwater shrimp. The typical fish of the lower

▼A pair of damselflies mating on a reed. The blue male holds the head of the female in special pincers, while she receives sperm from his body. Then she will lay eggs from her egg-laying tube, or ovipositor. She uses this to pierce the reed and lay eggs inside it.

reaches of the river is the barbel, named for the barbels, or fleshy feelers, on its lower jaw.

DIPPERS, DIVERS AND BATHERS

Among the birds that live around the fast-flowing upper reaches are the dipper and, in the Andes Mountains, the well-named Torrent duck. This duck is well adapted for its habitat, having a streamlined shape and sharp claws for gripping slippery boulders. Many other species of ducks and swans are to be found on the lower reaches of most rivers. Moorhens and coots are also very common, as are kingfishers and herons.

The water is not the natural home of many mammals, but several do spend much of their time in it. They include the water vole, which lives in the river bank, and the otter, one of the finest swimmers of the animal world. In rivers in tropical Africa hippopotamuses ("river horses") spend the day in the river to keep cool.

Manatees are truly aquatic mammals. They live in estuaries and rivers in South America and the southern United States. River dolphins are also aquatic. They live in the estuaries of great rivers such as the Ganges and Indus in India and the Amazon in South America.

▼Manatees playing in the Crystal River, Florida. They have a streamlined body, rather like a seal's, but are stockier and have a blunt head. Unlike seals too they are herbivores, feeding on aquatic plants such as water weeds and seagrass.

►A Brown trout swims over a gravel river bed and among water plants in Hampshire, England. Some Brown trout migrate to the sea to feed (and are also called Sea or Salmon trout), others spend their lives in lakes.

PONDS AND LAKES

The six fluffy black moorhen chicks have recently hatched. With their parents, they are searching for food among the lily pads and weeds that grow in the lake. Some are walking on the leaves, others are swimming in the water. All is calm. Suddenly there is an ominous swirl in the water and one chick disappears. The others scatter in panic. Underwater a pike has the chick clamped in its razor- sharp teeth. The chick struggles, but in vain. There is no escape from such a vicious predator.

The still waters of ponds and lakes provide a favourable environment not only for waterfowl, but for a great variety of plant and animal life. Free-floating microscopic plants such as algae provide the main source of food.

In a river this resource is carried away by the current, but in still water it remains and builds up. The microscopic plants multiply in the water as they undergo photosynthesis. Such plants, known as phytoplankton, undergo an explosion of growth in the spring, when the waters are said to "bloom". Dead leaves and other organic debris, or detritus, are another food resource that builds up on the bottom as a muddy sediment.

TOO MUCH OF A GOOD THING

The abundance and variety of life in a lake depend to a large extent on the nature of the local soils and rocks. The most productive lakes are rich in dissolved mineral matter such as calcium, together with nitrogen and other elements essential for plant growth. Molluscs, worms, flatworms and crustaceans thrive in such water.

Because of the abundance of the plant life, especially plankton, in such lakes, the water is usually green and opaque. And there is usually lush growth of vegetation, such as reeds and water lilies at the water's edge. Such lakes are termed eutrophic.

In many ponds and lakes in farming areas, serious problems are being caused by the run-off of nitrates from the fertilizers applied to the surrounding land. This leads to eutrophication – very rapid plant growth and the build-up of thick layers of dead material on the bottom. As this decomposes, it takes much of the oxygen from the water, which reduces the numbers of fish and other animals that depend on dissolved oxygen to breathe.

▲Some animals that live in and around a European lake In the swampy area of the reed bed are a Sedge warbler (*Acrocephalus schoenobaenus*) (1) and European water vole (*Arvicola terrestris*) (2). In the shallows among aquatic plants are the Common frog (*Rana temporaria*) (3), the Grey moorhen (*Gallinula chloropus*) (4) and the mayfly and its larva (5). In deeper water, which has submerged plants rooted at the bottom, are the Water boatman (*Notoneta glauca*) (6), Great pond snail (*Limnea stagnalis*) (7), Tufted duck (*Aythya fuligula*) (8), flatworm (*Planaria* species) (9) and perch (*Perca fluviatilis*) (10).

Lakes in regions of acid-rich soils, such as peat moors, are quite different. They have brown water due to the presence of acids and suspended plant material. Their life is limited to a few insect species. The clear water of lakes in hard-rock areas are rich in oxygen, but lacking in plankton. And life is limited there too.

►A Roseate spoonbill probes into the muddy bottom of a lake searching for creatures to eat. Because the water is muddy, it finds its prey by touch. It probes with its bill open, and snaps it shut if it feels something moving.

5

4

8

9

3

6

7

10

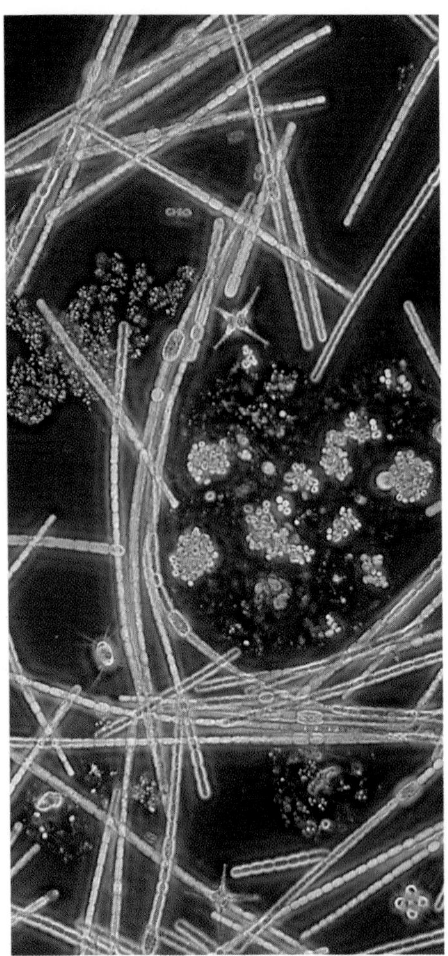

▲Microscopic algae like this are found in lakes and ponds. They are the main food source for animal life, being at the bottom of the food chain.

▼Among the animals that graze on pond plants is the Great pond snail. This one has just laid a "rope" of eggs, which are now attached to its shell.

LAKE ANIMALS

At the lowest level of animal life in ponds and lakes are the tiny creatures that feed on the phytoplankton in the water. They are called zooplankton. They include the single-celled microscopic protozoans; rotifers, which can just about be seen with the naked eye; and crustaceans such as *Daphnia*, a few millimetres long.

The zooplankton, in turn, are a food source for other animals. The larvae of many insects including mosquito, caddisfly and mayfly, feed on them. So do some fish, including the stickleback. Other fish, and amphibians such as frogs and newts, feed on the larvae. Then these animals may be eaten by higher predators, including top carnivore fish such as pike, and waterbirds such as kingfishers and herons.

The fish and other free-swimming creatures of the lakes make up what is called the nekton. This contrasts with the plankton, made up of organisms that merely float.

ON THE BOTTOM

The lake bottom, where organic matter has settled out, is also usually a rich source of food. This detritus provides nourishment for molluscs such as water snails, various worms, and crustaceans – creatures with jointed limbs and shells, such as shrimps. Bacteria also break down the detritus, and are a further food source.

The lake plants themselves are also grazed by fish, ducks, larvae and molluscs. The larger plants are not so useful as food, but provide shelter from predators. They also play a vital role in the life-cycle of species. Insects like dragonflies and damselflies use plant stems to enter the water and deposit their eggs. Later the stems provide the means for the insect larvae or nymphs to leave the water. They eventually metamorphose into adults, ready to take flight.

Insects and the other animals that live at the bottom are called benthos.

Food web in a temperate lake

First trophic level (primary producers)
Second trophic level (herbivores)
Third trophic level
Fourth trophic level
Fifth trophic level
Sixth trophic level

Frog/tadpole
Duck
Leech
Caddisfly larva
Bitterling

▲The food web in a lake in temperate regions A food web links organisms by their feeding habits. Feeding takes place at various levels, called trophic levels. Plants are the primary producers and form the first trophic level. Creatures that eat plants form the second level; animals that eat those creatures form the third trophic level; and so on. In the picture the animals at the various trophic levels are drawn with a coded colour background. The eating habits of each animal are shown by the arrows.

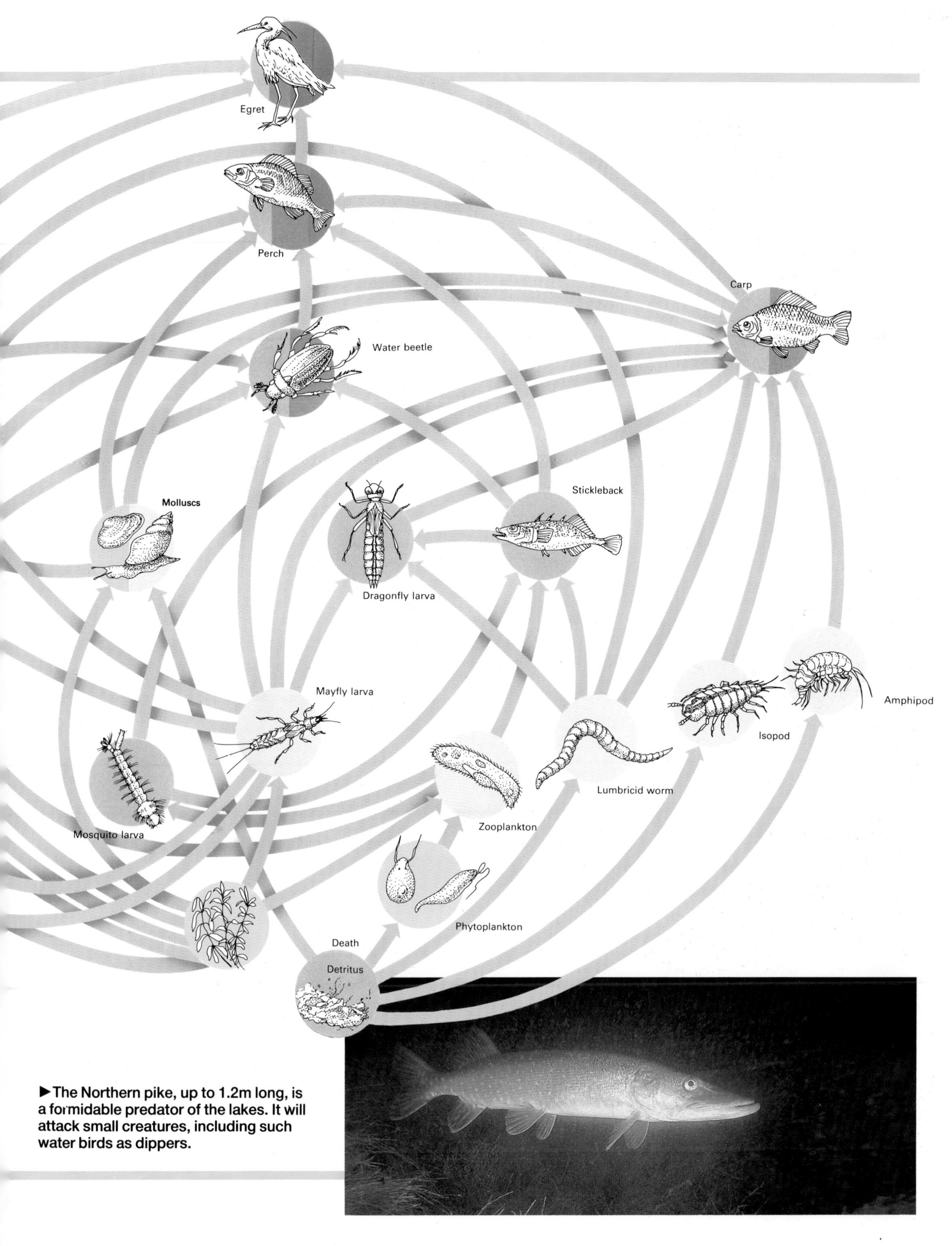

►The Northern pike, up to 1.2m long, is a formidable predator of the lakes. It will attack small creatures, including such water birds as dippers.

FRESHWATER WETLAND

A group of capybaras, the world's largest rodents, are resting at the water's edge in a South American swamp. Some are dozing, but a few are still alert. One spots a caiman, a kind of alligator, swimming nearby and lets out a loud bark. In a flash the others stand alert ready to flee if there is immediate danger. This time there isn't, for the caiman has recently eaten its fill.

Not only in South America but throughout the world there are low-lying regions where fresh water stays on the surface instead of draining away into the ground or into rivers. These areas are called swamps or marshes, or, generally, wetlands. The term swamp refers to a wetland of trees; and a marsh to a wetland of grasses and other low plants.

Vast swamp and marsh areas are found on the flood plains and deltas (river mouths with many channels) of many of the world's great rivers; for example, the Amazon in South America, the Nile in Egypt and the Mekong in Vietnam. In Europe the Coto de Doñana of south-western Spain and the Carmargue region of the Rhône delta in France are notable marsh areas.

In the United States there is a vast swamp and marsh region in North Carolina and Virginia, called the Great Dismal Swamp. In Florida are the great Cypress Swamp and the Everglades. The Everglades region is like a slow-moving river about 15cm deep. It covers an area of 10,000 sq km.

REEDS AND GRASSES

The main plants that grow in swamps and marshes are grasses and reeds, or rushes. Bulrushes, also called cattails and reedmaces, are found in many

▲Toads are common in freshwater wetlands. They spend more time on land than frogs, only returning to the water each spring to spawn. Their eggs are laid in long strings, unlike frogspawn.

▲An American alligator moves through the Everglades, looking for turtles, birds and small mammals to eat. Fully grown adults are up to 5.5m in length.

◀A group of lechwe chasing through the water of the flood plain in Botswana. Lechwe usually graze in shallow water, but occasionally venture shoulder-high in search of food.

parts of the world. So are various species of the common water reed which grow up to about 2.5m tall. The reed-like papyrus is common in tropical and subtropical Africa, where it grows up to 6m tall.

MAMMALS IN MUDDY WATERS

In general, wetlands are not a suitable habitat for large mammals because of the difficulty of moving around. The hippopotamus of the African papyrus swamps is an exception. It can weigh up to 2.5 tonnes and spends most of its time wallowing in the muddy waters. Its faeces, or dung, adds many nutrients to the water, so helping the growth of plant life.

Among other mammals of these swamps are the sitatunga and lechwe. The hooves of these antelopes are specially adapted for their life in the swamps. They splay out widely to distribute the animal's weight and prevent it sinking in the mud.

The swamps of North America are inhabited by smaller mammals, especially the muskrat, a large water vole. It eats vegetation as well as molluscs and crustaceans. An interesting animal is the Swamp rabbit, which does not jump like most other rabbits, but is a good swimmer. These two mammals are preyed on by the American mink, which is an excellent swimmer and also eats fish, frogs, snakes and waterbirds.

AMPHIBIANS AND ALLIGATORS

Marshlands are rich in amphibians and reptiles. The most familiar amphibians are frogs and toads, of which in all there are over three thousand species. Most of them are found in wetlands, as are species of the other amphibians, the newts and salamanders. Amphibians feed on insects, molluscs, spiders and other invertebrates. They are preyed upon by many birds, reptiles and mammals.

The largest reptiles are the alligators and crocodiles. Of these reptiles, the American alligator of the southern United States is found in the largest numbers. Elsewhere most alligator and crocodile species are threatened by overhunting and habitat destruction. They are formidable predators, able to kill animals as big as cattle.

Snakes are also found widely. They move easily through the swampy vegetation and many are good swimmers. They feed on lizards, amphibians, nestlings and small mammals.

BIRD LIFE

Many open wetlands support a rich variety of bird life. The Everglades in Florida is the home of both tropical and temperate species. These include flamingos, Roseate spoonbills, Bald eagles and ospreys.

The many different bird species are each suited for a particular feeding niche. Long-legged birds like the flamingo are able to feed on fauna living in deep water. Shorter-legged species feed in the shallows. Some stab at prey with sharp bills; others sift the muddy water with their spoon-shaped bills.

►Some birds of the Coto de Doñana wetlands in Spain Among the waterfowl are the Marbled teal (*Marmaronetta angustirostris*) **(1)** and the Ruddy shelduck (*Tadorna ferruginea*) **(2)**. The Marsh harrier (*Circus aeruginosus*) **(3)** is the main bird of prey. The Whiskered tern (*Chlidonias hybrida*) **(4)** and Greater flamingo (*Phoenicopterus ruber*) **(5)** nest in number. The Cattle egret (*Bubulcus ibis*) **(6)** is a small heron. The feet of the Purple swamp hen (*Porphyrio porphyrio*) **(7)** are specially adapted for walking on floating vegetation. The Black-crowned night heron (*Nycticorax nycticorax*) **(8)** feeds at night but also by day. The Great reed warbler (*Acrocephalus arundinaceus*) **(9)** nests among the reeds.

BOGS

Bogs are wetlands with organic or peaty soil. They occur in northern temperate regions where the decomposition of plant material takes place very slowly. They also occur in the tundra regions of North America, Europe and Asia. The main vegetation is sphagnum moss. The moss absorbs nearly all the nourishment from the water and makes it acid.

Compared with the other wetlands, the bogs support little animal life. The water is too acid and lacks oxygen. There are no molluscs, such as snails, because these creatures require alkaline, calcium-rich waters to make their shells. The most abundant species are insects, particularly mosquitoes.

The temperature of the northern bogs is usually too cold for reptiles and some amphibians. Frogs are found widely, however, except in the far north. They provide the chief source of food for the main bird predator, the crane.

Mammals are scarce in bog regions. In northern Canada, for example, only two species are plentiful, the beaver and the muskrat.

SALTMARSH

It is late October on the saltmarshes of East Anglia in eastern England. And the dark Brent geese are flying in to their winter feeding grounds. They come in low over the sea in long straggly lines and descend on the wetland recently flooded by the tide. They will remain here, feeding on the lush eel-grass, until the spring. Then they will fly north, back to their Arctic breeding grounds.

Marshes occur near the sea coasts in East Anglia and in many other parts of the world. They become extensive in shallow river deltas, where the rivers have deposited fertile sediment, but, as they are regularly flooded by seawater, only plant species that can tolerate salt can survive. In tropical regions the salty tidal swamps are thickly populated by mangrove trees and form mangrove swamps (see pages 214–15). In temperate regions where grasses are the main kind of vegetation they are called saltmarshes.

In some saltmarshes there are varieties of reeds and bulrushes similar to those found in freshwater wetlands. In others the main plants are grasses, such as eel-grass, chord grass and salt hay. Other plants that tolerate salt may also be found. They include glasswort, so called because it was once used in glassmaking, Sea lavender and Sea purslane. Plants that can live in salty conditions are known as halophytes. Many contain special glands for getting rid of excess salt in their tissues.

LIFE IN THE MARSHES

Few mammals inhabit the saltmarshes because of the nature of the ground. Occasionally small mammals such as rabbits may feed on the plants when the tide goes out. Invertebrates such as worms, crustaceans and insects are the chief land animals of the marshes. They provide food for a wide variety of bird life, particularly wading birds.

THE WADERS

The common wading birds found on the marshes include the redshank, curlew, dunlin, godwit and oyster-catcher. Among the most distinctive feature of the birds is their bill. Most waders have a relatively longer bill than most other birds and they use it to probe into the mud for prey.

The curlew has the longest bill (up to 20cm) and it curves downwards. Curlews also have long legs, so they can feed in deeper waters than most other waders. Touch-sensitive regions near the tip of their bills help them to locate their prey. Birds with a short bill, like the stint, feed at the surface, locating prey by sight.

MIGRANTS

Waders congregate on the salt-marshes and estuaries in the greatest numbers in winter. They are joined there by other birds that live inland for most of the year.

Great flocks of migrants also fly in from their breeding grounds in the far north to escape the severe cold of the Arctic winter. Some of these migrants fly very long distances. The Sharp-tailed sandpiper, for example, breeds in Siberia, but migrates as far south as Australasia for the winter.

◀A river carries large quantities of suspended mineral and organic matter. When it reaches the sea this matter is deposited as muddy silt. Extensive mud flats and marshes build up in river estuaries.

The saltmarshes are also the wintering grounds for many species of geese, which breed on the Arctic tundra. They include the small dark-coloured Brent goose and the larger deep-brown Bean goose. The preferred food of the Brent goose is eel-grass, while that of the Bean goose is the roots of Sea club rush.

►A Marbled godwit probes for worms in the soft mud as the tide goes out. It breeds in northern Canada and winters along coasts as far south as Peru.

▼Brent geese feed on eel-grasses on a saltmarsh in eastern England. Each winter the geese migrate south from the Arctic to saltmarshes all along North Sea coasts.

MANGROVES

A fly settles on a leaf about a metre above the water in a mangrove swamp in Java. Its eyes keep watch for danger from above. But danger lurks below in the water, where an Archer fish is swimming by. The fish comes to the surface and "spits" drops of water into the air. Its aim is good, and the drops knock the fly into the water.

When rivers reach the sea coast, the sediment they carry settles out to form muddy wetlands. In tropical regions, such as Java in South-east Asia, the wetlands soon become colonized by mangrove trees.

There are several kinds of mangroves, but they all have a similar life style. They send down roots from their trunks and branches into the mud below. New trunks grow up from where the roots reach the ground, making a dense thicket.

For much of the time the roots of the mangroves are underneath the salty water. This would kill the roots of ordinary trees because they would not be able to breathe. Mangroves survive because their roots can take in air directly through their aerial roots, which are called pneumatophores.

MANGROVE LIFE

In most mangrove swamps fresh mud is continually being deposited by the river. This provides nourishment for

many invertebrates, such as worms, molluscs and crustaceans, such as crabs. Fiddler crabs scavenge on the exposed mud. They are often territorial and use their over-sized claw to gesticulate at their neighbours.

Invertebrates provide food for a variety of birds, such as the Scarlet ibis. The waters lapping the mangrove roots teem with fish, which are food for birds like the darter. Darters are also known as snakebirds because they often swim with just their long snake-like neck showing above water.

The strangest fish of the mangroves is the mudskipper. It often climbs out of the water at low tide and clings to mangrove roots. Unusually for a fish, it can breathe in the air.

Mammals are generally absent from the ground in mangrove swamps. But in some areas monkeys live in the leafy canopy. The biggest animal at sea level is the crocodile, a fierce predator that will attack any animal that comes within reach.

◄▼Animals of mangrove swamps from different parts of the world Mangrove winkle (*Littorina scabra*) **(1)** from the Seychelle Islands. Soldier crab (*Dotilla mictyroides*) **(2)** and Archer fish (*Toxotes jaculator*) **(3)** from South-east Asia. Proboscis monkey (*Nasalis larvatus*) **(4)** from Borneo. Great egret (*Egretta alba*) **(5)**, common in all mangrove swamps. American darter or anhinga (*Anhinga anhinga*) **(6)** and the Scarlet ibis (*Eudocimus ruber*) **(7)** from the Americas. Saltwater crocodile (*Crocodylus porosus*) **(8)** from South-east Asia and northern Australia. The mudskipper (*Periophthalmus* species) **(9)** from South-east Asia.

SHORELINES

The starfish "smells" there is a meal nearby. It is a mussel, which has snapped the two halves of its shell tightly shut. But this is no defence against the starfish. It climbs over the mussel and uses the suckers on its feet to pull the two halves of the shell apart. Then it thrusts in its stomach tissue and begins to feed.

Starfish and mussels live in one of the most difficult habitats for living things – the intertidal region. This is the part of the seashore over which the tide ebbs and flows twice a day. Organisms that live in this region must be able to live underwater for some of the time, and in the air for the rest. They must also be able to stand up to the pounding of the waves. It might be thought that few species could survive in such a seemingly hostile environment, but in fact the seashore is often remarkably rich in life.

No land-based animals can survive underwater for an extended period, so most of the life in the intertidal region is marine. The main problem then for these marine species is to avoid drying out in the air.

PLANTS ON ROCKY SHORES

Rocky shores and sandy or muddy shores support different kinds of

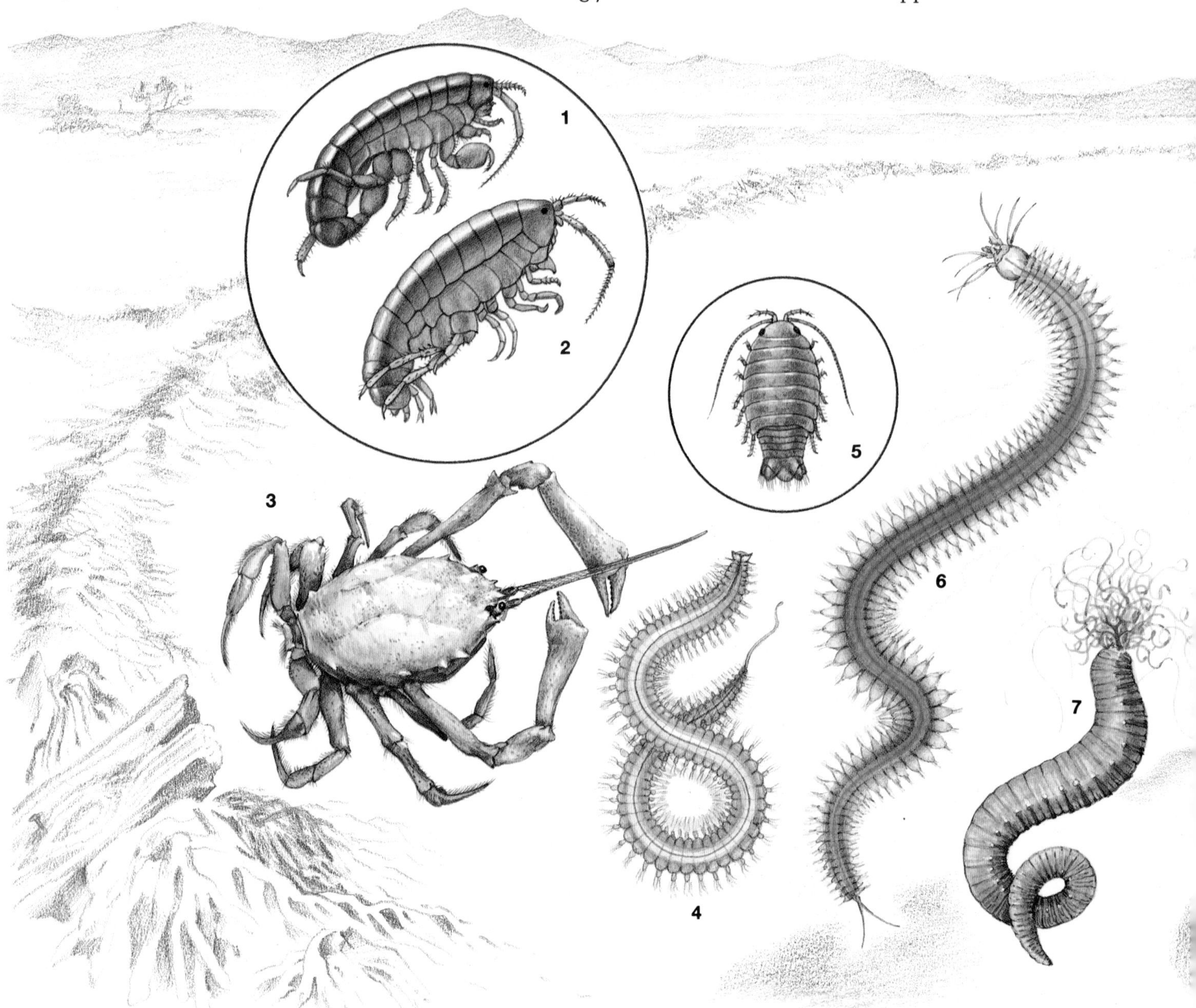

plants and animals. A major feature of rocky shores is the seaweed growing on the seabed and rocks. Seaweeds are simple plants called algae. Most of those in cool and temperate waters are brown. Those in warm tropical waters are usually red or green.

Among the common seaweeds are the kelps and wracks. The kelps are large plants that grow mainly at or below the low-tide level, in the sub-littoral zone. The wracks are found higher up in the mid-shore, or eulittoral zone. Their rubbery leaves do not dry out as quickly as those of the kelp. Some wracks grow even beyond the ordinary high-tide level in the littoral zone.

LIVING IN A SHELL

The commonest kind of animals on rocky shores are molluscs, whose shells help to prevent their bodies drying when the tide goes out. They

◄▼Animals that live on sandy shores in north-western Europe Sandhoppers (e.g. *Orchestia gammarella, Talitrus saltator*) **(1, 2)**. At the high-tide level: on the upper shore: the Masked crab (*Corystes cassivelaunus*) **(3)**, polychaete worms (*Nephtys caeca*) **(4)** and isopods (*Eurydice pulchra*) **(5)**. On the mid-shore: the ragworm (*Nereis diversicolor*) **(6)**, another polychaete worm (*Amphitrite johnstoni*) **(7)**, the Sand mason (*Lanice conchilega*) **(8)** and the Peacock worm (*Sabella pavonina*) **(9)**. On the lower shore: the Sea potato (*Echinocardium cordatum*) **(10)**, the Common otter shell (*Lutraria lutraria*) **(11)**, the Pod razor shell (*Ensis siliqua*) **(12)**, and tellins (e.g. *Tellina tenuis, Tellina fabula*) **(13, 14)**.

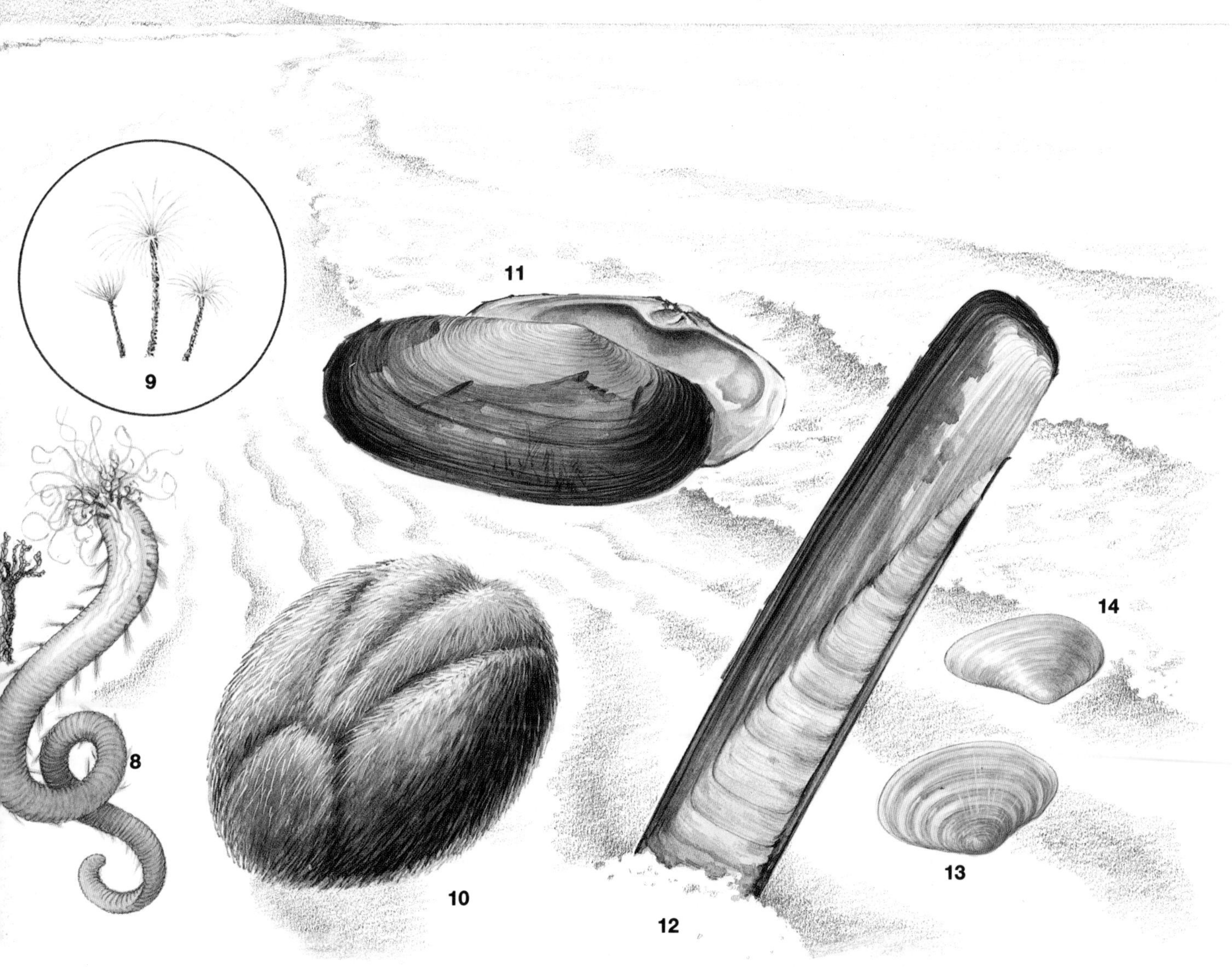

◀Sea anemones are found in many rock pools. The incoming tide brings in a fresh supply of food twice a day.

either close their shells tightly shut or they clamp them to a rock. Typical are limpets, winkles, mussels and whelks. Barnacles are also common on rocky shores. They look like molluscs, but are in fact crustaceans.

Many molluscs, like the limpet, feed on the tiny algae that coat the rocks and often the large seaweeds. Barnacles feed in a different way. They are filter-feeders, which extend long "legs" to catch plankton and minute animals floating in the water. Mussels are also filter-feeders. They take water inside their shells through siphon tubes. Food particles are then filtered out by gills, which the molluscs also use for breathing.

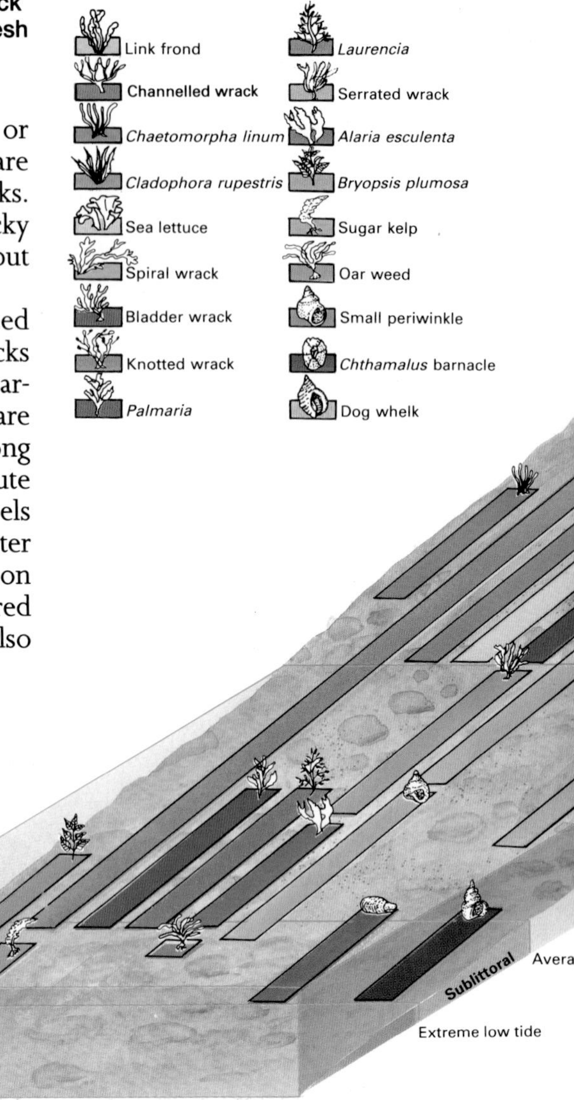

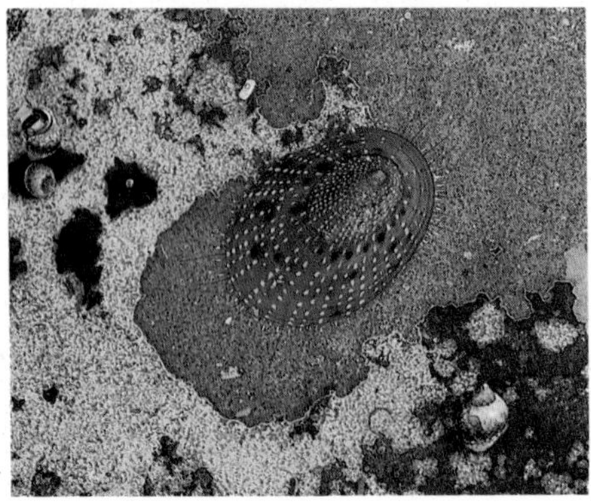

▼Molluscs such as limpets use their rasp-like tongue to graze on the algae that coat the rocks in the tidal region.

Whelks are carnivores that prey on other molluscs. To help them find their prey they have a siphon that directs water over their taste cells. Dog whelks are mobile and prey mainly on molluscs or barnacles that are sedentary, or fixed. The Dog whelk is able to bore through the shells of molluscs to get at their flesh.

ROCK POOLS

Animals that cannot live for long out of water shelter under boulders, or they find crevices and damp overhangs in the rocks, or they inhabit the tidal pools on rocky shores. They include sea anemones, crabs, sea urchins, shrimps and starfishes.

ON SANDY AND MUDDY SHORES

These shores support quite different forms of life. The shifting nature of the shorebed means that seaweeds cannot gain a footing. Animals that graze on plants are therefore absent. The basic food sources for shoreline creatures are tiny algae that cling to grains of sand, and plankton that come in with the tide. The tide also brings in a variety of other edible matter, such as seaweed and dead fish and other creatures. On muddy

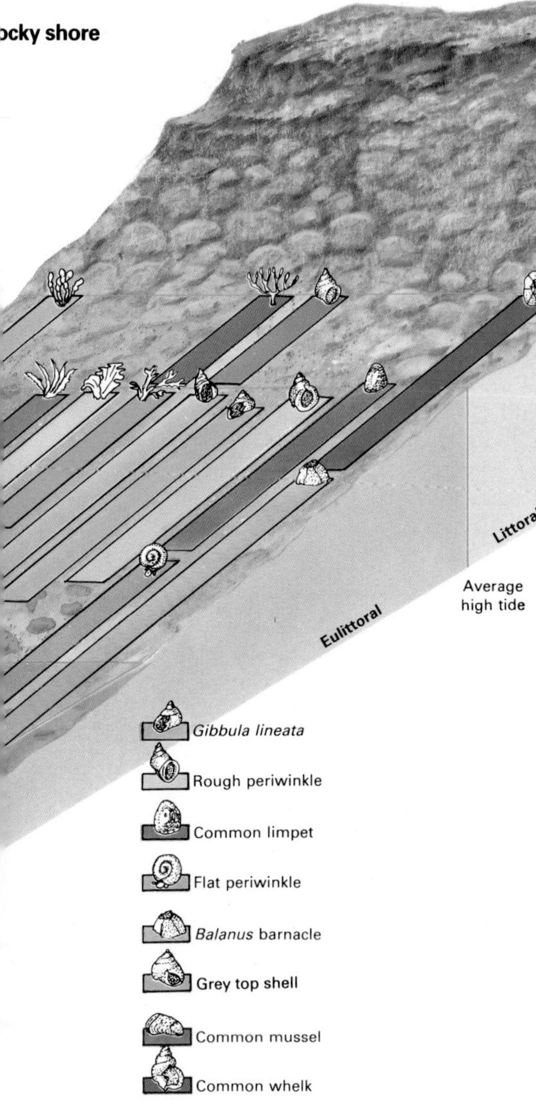

◀Some of the plants and animals that inhabit a rocky shore. Each species is found in certain regions, or zones. The littoral zone is the upper shore around high-tide level. The eulittoral zone is the middle shore between high and low tides. And the sublittoral zone is the lower shore at and below normal low-tide level.

shores around estuaries an additional supply of food is deposited by the outflowing river.

The main life on sandy and muddy shores lives under the surface. This includes a wide variety of marine worms, called polychaetes, such as lugworms and ragworms. These feed on minute plant and animal matter in the sand. The polychaetes known as fan worms have a fan-like crown of filaments on the head. They use the crown for breathing and filtering food from the water. Various molluscs, including clams, are able to burrow into the shorebed.

Crustaceans such as sandhoppers and crabs are active on the surface throughout the tidal region. So are many species of wading birds, from the tiny sandpipers to the large curlews and avocets.

▼Many kinds of crabs scavenge for food on the seashore, feeding on detritus and the remains of dead sea creatures.

▼A jellyfish lies stranded on the shore when the tide goes out. Before the tide comes in again, it will be dead.

OCEANS

A clownfish is swimming in the shallow waters off the Australian coast. It is keeping close to the seabed, which is covered with large sea anemones, whose colourful tentacles wave about in the current. And it never strays far from one particular anenome. The clownfish is only about 5cm long, and is easy prey for larger fish. When one comes near, it dashes into the tentacles of the anenome. With many fish, this would mean death as the tentacles carry stinging cells. But this clownfish is unharmed because it has an association with this particular anenome.

►These small crustaceans are called krill; they provide food for many species of fish and the great baleen whales.

▼The underside of a Common or Moon jellyfish, which is found in large numbers in the North Atlantic.

Life began in the oceans and is still found there in greatest variety. It is richest in the warmer, shallower waters of the continental shelves which surround Australia and the other great land masses. Yet it can still be found even in the ocean deeps, where daylight never reaches and the pressure is enormous. The oceans cover more than two-thirds of the world's surface to an average depth of over 3km. In places there are chasms 11km deep.

The basic food source is the minute plant life called phytoplankton. This consists of single-celled algae, which live in the top 100m or so of the sea, where there is plenty of light. The plankton need the light to make their food by photosynthesis. Many kinds of multi-celled algae, or seaweed, are a source of food for marine life.

MICROSCOPIC PREY

The phytoplankton provide food for a wide variety of tiny "grazing" animals, the zooplankton. The most abundant of these are primitive crustaceans called copepods and the larger krill. The larvae of other marine life – worms, molluscs and fish – also make up the zooplankton.

The copepods and krill in turn provide food for ocean carnivores, small and large. Among these are jellyfishes, found in most oceans. They use stinging tentacles to immobilize their prey, which can also include small fish. Small squid feed on copepods and krill. So do many fish, including herring and mackerel and

►A close-up photo of a sea anemone on the Great Barrier Reef in Australia, showing the tentacles and mouth area.

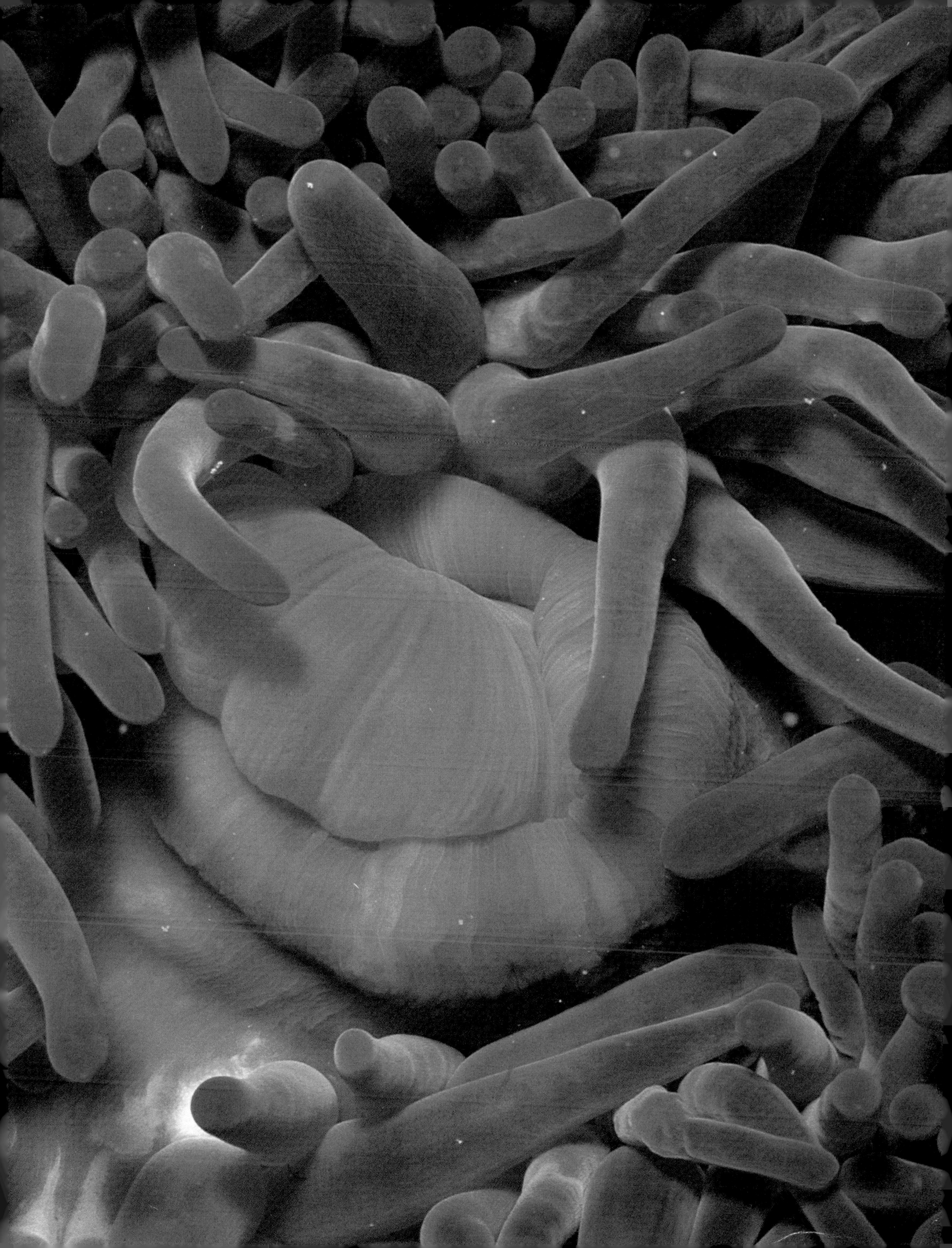

the large manta rays and basking sharks. The huge baleen whales also have a similar diet.

THE NOTORIOUS SHARK

Among the larger marine predators sharks are the best known. Many feed on small fish but others eat almost anything living that comes their way. The notorious Great white shark is one of the most deadly. It is also sometimes called the maneater because it does occasionally attack humans. But its usual diet is sea mammals, such as porpoises and seals. It grows to a length of over 7m, somewhat larger than another fierce predator, the Tiger shark.

ILLUMINATING THE ABYSS

Some of the most curious fish in the oceans exist at great depths, 2,000m or more, in the so-called abyssal zone. At such depths no light penetrates, so it is always dark. Some fish, such as the deep-sea anglers, carry luminous lures on the head to attract prey to them. Most have vicious-looking inward-curving teeth, which allow prey to enter easily, but prevent them coming out again. This is just one adaptation to make sure they hold on to prey, which are scarce in the ocean depths.

▲Life on a coral reef is rich and varied, from exquisitely coloured sea slugs and butterfly fish to this fierce Great white shark. The reefs are formed from the chalky skeletons of corals. Corals are primitive filter-feeding animals closely related to sea anemones.

▼Two butterfly fish flit around a coral reef. Their banded colouring provides camouflage while the black eye band and false eye spot on the dorsal fin helps to confuse would-be predators. Coral reefs are found in warm, shallow tropical seas such as the Red Sea.

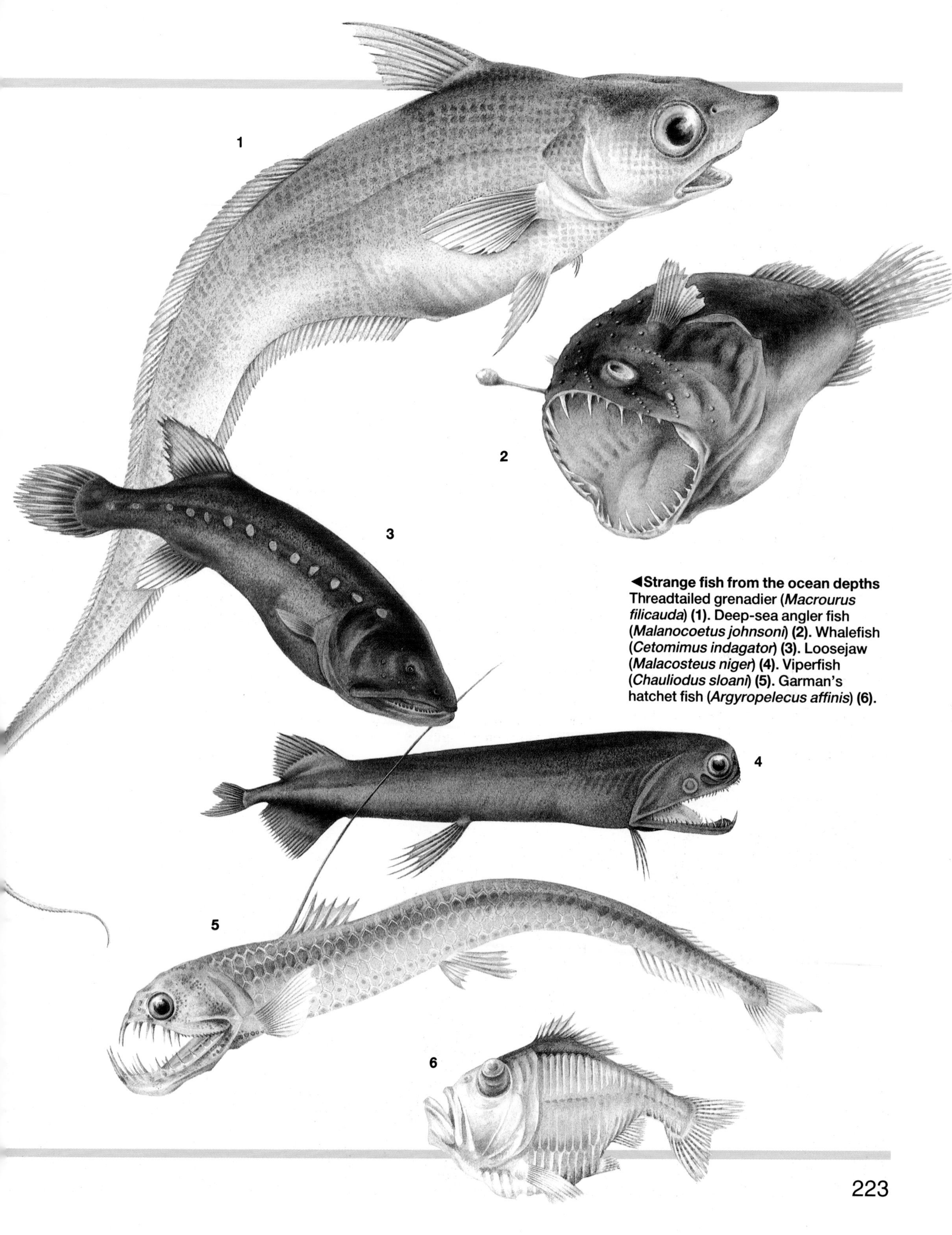

◀Strange fish from the ocean depths Threadtailed grenadier (*Macrourus filicauda*) **(1)**. Deep-sea angler fish (*Malanocoetus johnsoni*) **(2)**. Whalefish (*Cetomimus indagator*) **(3)**. Loosejaw (*Malacosteus niger*) **(4)**. Viperfish (*Chauliodus sloani*) **(5)**. Garman's hatchet fish (*Argyropelecus affinis*) **(6)**.

►▼**Typical features of seals and the walrus** The Harbour seal (*Phoca vitulina*) **(1a)**, a hair seal, has sleek hair and no ear flaps. It is cumbersome on land **(1b)**. The Cape fur seal (*Arcocephalus pusillus*) **(2a)** is a typical eared seal, with ear flaps and thick fur. On land it supports itself on its flippers **(2b)**. The walrus (*Odobenus rosmarus*) **(3a)** has long tusks. It stands and walks on land on all four limbs **(3b)**.

LOW LIFE

A fascinating variety of animals live on or near the seabed. Among the lowly life there are filter-feeders like barnacles and sponges, which prefer to live on rocky seabeds. On sandy seabeds, animals that feed on detritus, or organic matter falling from above, often dominate. They include numerous polychaete worms, molluscs and crustaceans.

Many kinds of fish prey on the invertebrates, including flatfish such as plaice. The plaice, like other flatfish, is totally adapted to life on the seabed. It has a flattened body with both eyes on the same side of its head.

One of the largest predators is a mollusc, the octopus, named after its eight tentacles. It spends most time in rock crevices, emerging only to chase prey that comes near. Another crevice-dweller is the Moray eel, which has blunt, rounded teeth to crush the crabs that form the main part of its diet.

OCEAN MAMMALS

The largest animals found in the sea are whales. Unlike fish and most other marine life, they are warm-blooded. They are mammals, and like land mammals they breathe air into their lungs. The females give birth to live young, which suckle their milk.

Whales are not the only marine mammals. Dolphins, porpoises, seals, walruses and sea lions are mammals too. Whales, dolphins and porpoises spend all of their time in the water. Seals, walruses and sea lions usually feed in the water, but spend some of their time on land, mainly to breed.

The diet of the sea mammals varies from species to species. The largest whales, such as the 27m-long Blue whale, are filter-feeders, straining plankton and krill from the water with the comb-like plates of baleen in their mouth. Other whales, for instance the Sperm whale, feed on fish, squid and crustaceans. The Killer whale attacks penguins, seals and other whales.

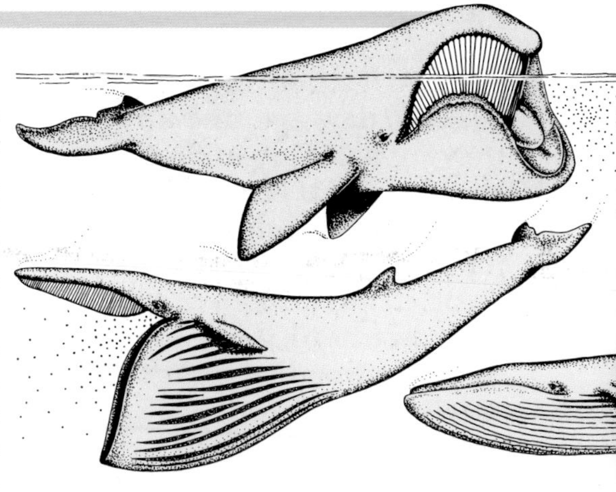

▲Baleen whales use different techniques to filter food through their baleen plates. Right whales (top) filter food by swimming forwards with their mouths open. Rorquals (like the Blue whale) take a mouthful of water and then force it out through the baleen.

▼A Humpback whale feeding at the surface. It is taking a mouthful of water and is about to close its mouth. Then it will expel the water through the comb-like baleen on its upper jaw, leaving any food inside its mouth.

ISLANDS

The two leathery eggs were laid about 10 days ago, and now they are hatching underneath an animal that is neither a reptile nor a bird. It has a fur-covered body rather like an otter, but instead of an otter-like head, it has a broad flat bill rather like a duck. The newly hatched young are tiny, pink and naked. They crawl slowly through the fur on their mother's belly up to glands that soon start to ooze milk. They begin to suckle. This animal is a platypus, a mammal that lays eggs.

▼A rugged coral island, near Tahiti in the South Pacific Ocean. Isolated islands often have distinct species of animals.

The platypus is one of the unique forms of life that developed in Australia. It is a primitive kind of mammal, which might have been expected to die out when more advanced mammals evolved. The main reason it did not die out was that Australia is an island. Many islands have species that have uniquely survived from earlier times. Exactly which species they are depends on when the island separated from the mainland.

Australia became an island some 45 million years ago, when it split away from what is now Antarctica. It contained no advanced mammals at that time, and the surrounding sea then prevented advanced mammals migrating to it. With no competition for its river habitat, the platypus survived.

Australia's other unique animal species – kangaroos, koalas and other marsupials – survived for the same reason. They are also primitive mammals, which raise their young in pouches. They would not have thrived in competition with placental mammals, whose offspring are born more fully developed.

MARSUPIAL NICHES

Marsupials probably originated in South America, and many species are still found there today. But they are different from the Australian species because they have had to face competition from advanced mammals coming from North America.

For example, the introduction of fierce big cats like jaguars led to the extinction of large carnivorous marsupials in South America. Most of the marsupials remaining, such as the Common and mouse opossums, are

omnivores, feeding on fruit, insects, worms and various small animals.

In Australia various species of marsupials have evolved in parallel with placental mammals elsewhere to fill similar ecological niches. Thus, the carnivorous Tasmanian wolf evolved with a similar physical form to the placental wolf on other continents. And the Marsupial mole developed the same body form as the placental mole, and both have the same burrowing habit. This kind of parallel development is called convergent evolution.

►Male kangaroos fighting over a female on heat. Kangaroos are just one of Australia's many unique species.

▼Giant tortoises on the Galapagos Islands. With no enemies, they grew to great size, with only a thin shell.

▲Two rare animals peculiar to the island of Madagascar. The falanouc (top) has an elongated snout and body and feeds on worms and other invertebrates. The fanaloka (bottom) is more fox-like and eats lizards, frogs and rodents.

ON MADAGASCAR

The island of Madagascar lies in the Indian Ocean off the coast of East Africa. The main mammal species on the island are the lemurs, which are found nowhere else. These animals are called prosimians, which means they evolved before the simians – the monkeys and apes. Their ancestors lived in mainland Africa when Madagascar separated about 50 million years ago.

On the mainland these ancestors were eventually replaced by the more advanced monkeys and apes. But on Madagascar no monkeys or apes evolved or could reach the island from outside so the lemur ancestors filled the kinds of niches monkeys and apes fill elsewhere.

ON THE GALAPAGOS ISLANDS

The Galapagos Islands are located near the equator about 1,000km off Ecuador, the country to which they belong. Two distinct forms of animal life have evolved on these isolated islands. Among the largest creatures are the land and marine iguanas and the giant tortoises. Even on separate islands within the Galapagos group the tortoises have developed differences, for example in the pattern of their shell.

The islands are populated by a variety of finches. These evolved from finches that were somehow blown to the islands from the mainland. On the mainland the finches occupied a seed-eating niche among the native birds.

On the islands, however, there was no competition from other birds, so the finches were able to exploit the other food sources. Eventually they evolved different bills to cope with the different foods. For example, some finches have a short, slim bill like a flycatcher's, for eating insects. Others have a thick bill like a parrot's, for cracking nuts.

FLIGHTLESS ISLAND BIRDS

The water around islands is no barrier to birds, which can fly across it, but it is a barrier to larger animals. The result is that the birds often find they have no predators. With no need to escape from predators, some birds lose their ability to fly.

The takahe and kiwi of New Zealand are examples of flightless island birds that still survive. Some have not been so fortunate. They include the moa, also from New Zealand, and the famous dodo, which came from Mauritius. Both these birds were hunted to extinction by those most deadly predators – people.

◄The takahe of New Zealand, a flightless bird of the rail group. The bird is now in danger of extinction because of predators introduced by people.

►A Ring-tailed lemur leaps into the air, with tail outstretched to steady itself. It also uses its tail, smeared with scent, to signal to other lemurs.

FARMLAND

A tiny furry acrobat is using her feet and tail to climb the stiff stalks of ripening wheat. She twists her tail around the stalks to save herself should she fall. This hungry female Harvest mouse spots a weevil and chews that up before it starts on the swollen ears of grain. Then, with her hunger satisfied, she scuttles into the tall grass at the edge of the field. Here she climbs up to her neat spherical nest woven around the grass stems. Inside are six hairless young. They come to life as their mother settles down, blindly search for and find, a teat on her belly and start to suckle.

▲A crop of oil-seed rape in flower. Growing the same kind of plant over vast areas all but eliminates native plant species and the varied animal life that depend on them.

▼**Some animals that have thrived on farming** The Red kangaroo (*Macropus rufus*) **(1)** in Australian grasslands. The Virginia opossum (*Didelphis virginiana*) **(2)** in North America. The Asian white-backed vulture (*Gyps bengalensis*) **(3)**. The Harvest mouse (*Micromys minutus*) **(4)** and Red-legged partridge (*Alectoris rufa*) **(5)** in European wheatfields. The Paddyfield warbler (*Acrocephalus agricola*) **(6)** and Chinese pond heron (*Ardeola bacchus*) **(7)** in South-east Asia. The Cane rat (*Thryonomys gregorianus*) **(8)** in Africa.

2

1

3

Harvest mice now thrive on farm crops, but before about 10,000 years ago, humans had little effect on the environment. They gathered fruits, nuts and roots to eat, like many other animals. They also hunted for meat as do many animal predators.

But around 8,000 BC things began to change. People started to live a more settled life, growing crops and herding sheep and goats so they did not have to hunt so often for meat.

To grow crops well, the new farmers often had to clear forest land and scrub by cutting (slashing) and burning. They changed their environment, and thus began to upset the natural communities of plants and animals. This process has been going on ever since.

GRAIN LOVERS

This man-made biome is often called the agricultural biome, or agribiome. It is a simple biome because farmers grow a limited number of crops in a given area. By concentrating on just a few crops, particularly cereals, farmers create a very particular type of habitat, which can support only limited wildlife. Certain species, however, thrive in agribiomes. It has been so since the days when farming began and rats and mice were attracted to the first great grain stores in the Middle East.

AGRICULTURAL POISONS

To make sure that their crops grow well, farmers feed the soil with fertilizers, and spray the crops with herbicides and pesticides. The herbicides kill off plants that compete with the crop. The pesticides kill pests and diseases that reduce the crop yield. However, these chemicals may harm beneficial creatures as well as pests, and may make their way into the wildlife food chain. For example, birds are killed by the pesticides consumed by the mice they prey on.

Modern chemical farming methods pose a risk to the environment, and so too does the ages-old method of slash and burn. This is now being practised over vast areas of the rain forests where it is destroying the habitats of many of the world's most exotic and unique flora and fauna.

CITY AND TOWN

It is long past midnight in the suburbs of an English town. A terrible scream rings out, but it is not a person screaming. It is a Red fox vixen calling to her mate. This pair of foxes have taken up residence in the area, making a den under an old shed in a neglected garden. They are foraging for food. One is nosing among the scraps on a compost heap in a nearby garden. The other is playing tug of war with a large worm that has come to the surface of the lawn.

Foxes are perhaps not the kind of wildlife one would expect to see in towns. But they are becoming increasingly common, particularly in Britain. They not only feed in suburban gardens, they also breed there. Many other animals have also learned to take advantage of the man-made environment of the city, which is often called the urban biome.

The city provides a habitat quite unlike anything else found in nature. Most of the ground is covered with concrete, tarmac or buildings. This all acts as a heat store, warming the local climate by several degrees. The city is also very noisy, and is full of dust and fumes from thousands of vehicles. And, of course, it is full of people.

The urban biome would thus not appear to be attractive to any wildlife at all! But it turns out in practice to be remarkably rich in species that have learned to live with people in this environment.

LOADS OF RUBBISH

The main thing that attracts many species of animals to cities and the surrounding areas is the waste human beings create. This is thrown into the streets, stuffed into dustbins which are easily knocked over, and dumped on rubbish tips. It provides a plentiful food supply for wildlife.

Raccoons, jackals, coyotes, foxes and opossums are some of the animals that venture into the streets in different parts of the world to raid discarded waste and dustbins. Rats are common everywhere, often living in the drains and sewers beneath the streets and in buildings.

The large rubbish tips on the edge of many towns attract an equally varied range of animals. In some areas

◀The Red fox has taken up residence in many cities and thrives there. Its main diet consists of food scavenged from compost heaps and dustbins.

in North America Brown bears are now common visitors, while in Arctic towns Polar bears have appeared. Sometimes the bears stray into town, bringing them into conflict with the human population.

Many kinds of birds also scavenge on the rubbish tips. In many parts of Europe large flocks of gulls descend on them, particularly Herring gulls and Black-headed gulls. Rubbish scavengers in other parts of the world include the Polar bear in the Arctic, and Black vulture in the Americas and the Marabou stork in Africa.

CITY BIRDS

Buildings in the city provide nesting and roosting sites for many birds. Feral pigeons are perhaps the most common. They are varieties of Rock dove that have descended from once-domesticated birds. They nest on ledges among the buildings, which are

◀A Common kestrel perches on a motorway bridge. The green verges of motorways are a haven for small animals, good prey for the kestrel.

▼The Grey squirrel has so successfully adapted to urban life that it has become a pest in many areas. It will drive away other wildlife and eat their food supply.

a good substitute for their ancestral nesting sites in rocks and cliffs.

Similar sites are chosen by the occasional birds of prey in the city, such as kestrels. These birds prey mainly on another common city bird, the House sparrow. The sparrow, originally a grain-eater, was first attracted to city streets in the days when horses were common, feeding on the grain from their nosebags.

UNWELCOME GUESTS

Many smaller creatures live inside buildings. House mice are common, as are their larger cousins, rats. Rats in particular do enormous damage, gnawing through packaging, cables and wooden structures, and leaving droppings that are a source of disease.

Among insects, cockroaches are perhaps the most unwelcome residents. They are often termed the rats and mice of the insect world, for they have thrived in association with man. They are found particularly in food shops, stores and kitchens. Three species have become widespread pests, the American, German and Oriental cockroaches. They are mainly nocturnal, long-lived, wary and difficult to get rid of.

OPEN SPACES

Most cities usually have areas of open ground, such as formal gardens and parks, often with ponds. The flora will usually include trees, together with a wide variety of flowering shrubs and plants. These plants will attract and support all kinds of insects, which in turn will attract birds and other wildlife. Weed plants colonize waste ground wherever it occurs.

Rivers, canals, reservoirs and lakes provide homes for many kinds of aquatic species. Ducks, coots, gulls and the moorhen all fly in to join pelicans and other imported birds in city parks.

In the suburbs the patchwork of gardens provides a rich habitat for wildlife of every description – foxes and hedgehogs, voles and moles, squirrels and beetles, and birds and butterflies of every hue. Gardens can be a haven for many animals. More species of butterfly are to be found in West African gardens than in nearby tropical rain forests.

▼**Various animals attracted by city waste** The Common raccoon (*Procyon lotor*) (1). The House mouse (*Mus musculus*) (2). The Norway rat (*Rattus norvegicus*) (3). The Herring gull (*Larus argentatus*) (4) and Black-headed gull (*L. ridibundus*) (5).

▲▼**Urban birds and insects** The Feral pigeon (*Columba livia*) **(1)** and House sparrow (*Passer domesticus*) **(2)** roost on city buildings and scavenge on the streets. The Common starling (*Sturnus vulgaris*) **(3)** often flies in to roost at night. Waste-ground plants attract butterflies like the Small white (*Pieris rapae*) **(4)**. The Oriental cockroach (*Blatta orientalis*) **(5)** is an unwelcome insect pest.

▼This Song thrush has built its nest in a storeroom. When natural habitats are lacking, animals have to improvize.

INDEX

Species in *italic* are scientific names. **Bold numbers** refer to illustrations.

PICTURE CREDITS

Key: l left, r right, c centre, t top, b bottom.

Abbreviations: A Ardea. AN Agence Nature. ANT Australasian Nature Transparencies. BA Biophoto Associates. BCL Bruce Coleman Ltd. FL Frank Lane Agency. NHPA Natural History Photographic Agency. NSP Natural Science Photos. OI Ltd Oxford Illustrators Ltd. OSF Oxford Scientific Films. P Prema Photos. PEP Planet Earth Pictures. SAL Survival Anglia Ltd. SPL Science Photo Library.

10t NHPA/M. Walker. 10b NHPA/A. Bannister. 11t Mick Saunders. 11bl, bc BA. 11br SPL/Dr D. Fawcett. 11cr BA. 12tl SPL/E. Gravé. 12tr SPL/Dr Mia Tegner. 12c BCL/G. Cox. 12bl SPL/M. Abbey. 12br SPL/E. Gravé. 12 OI Ltd. 13t BA. 13b BCL/Christian Zuber. 14 OI Ltd. 15 OI Ltd. 16–17 Richard Lewington. 17t Mick Loates. 17b BCL/H. Reinhard. 18 AN/H. Chaumeton. 19cl OSF/P. Parks. 19cr, br, bl OI Ltd. 19bc NHPA/S. Dalton. 20, 21t OI Ltd. 21cl Simon Driver. 21bl OI Ltd. 21br Natural Imagery, William Ervin. 22cl SPL/M. Abbey. 22tr FL/K. Wheeler. 22bl OI Ltd. 22br PEP/K. Vaughan. 23t OI Ltd. 23r John Vissert. 24t (inset) BA. 24t OSF/G. Thompson. 24b SD. 25tl OI Ltd. 25tr SPL/M. Sklar. 26 OSF/Peter Parks. 271 SPL. 27r PEP/N. Greaves. 28 SPL. 28cr Hayward Art Group. 28b, 29 OI Ltd. 30t SPL/K.R. Porter. 30b SPL/Manfred Kage. 31r Mick Saunders. 321 PEP/N. Sefton. 32cr PEP/C. Roessler. 32br OSF/G.I. Bernard. 33 AN/Grospas. 34t SPL/Sinclair Stammers. 34, 35 OI Ltd. 36–37 BCL/J. & D. Bartlett. 37tl BCL/K. Taylor. 37tr NSP/D. MacCaskill. 38 Peter Veit. 39t G. Frame. 39b ANT/G. Fyfe. 40b BL/C.B. Frith. 40–41 OSF/G. Bernard. 41 PEP/K. Lucas. 42 PEP/Richard Coomber. 43t C. Janson. 43b Hayward Art Group. 44 PEP/Peter David. 44–45 PEP/A.P. Barnes. 46 OI Ltd. 46 BA. 47 A. 48tl Dwight R. Kuhn. 49t SAL/J. & D. Bartlett. 49b P. Morris. 50 G. Mazza. 51 Premaphotos Wildlife/K. Preston Mafham. 52t NHPA/S. Dalton. 52b OI Ltd. 53 PEP/J. Hudnall. 54 Mick Saunders. 55tl NHPA/Bill Wood. 55tr BL/H. Reinhard. 55cl & r OI Ltd. 56bl OI Ltd. 56br Hayward Art Group. 57tl BL/C.B. Frith. 57tr PEP/N. Greaves. 57b Michael Fogden. 58 OSF. 60–61t PEP/K. Ammann. 60–61b Ad Cameron. 62–63 Richard Lewington. 63 AN/Chaumeton–Lanceau. 64tl OI Ltd. 64tr, b Simon Driver. 65 OI Ltd. 66–67 Ken Adwick. 68 OAD/G.I. Bernard. 68–69 Kevin Maddison. 70–71 OI Ltd. 72 Denys Ovenden. 73 Premaphotos Wildlife/K. Preston Mafham. 75 NHPA/P. Johnson. 76–77 Hayward Art Group. 77 SPL/Dr G. Murti. 79 Andromeda Oxford Ltd. 80 Paul Brierly. 81 Andromeda Oxford Ltd. 82 Dr G. Mazza. 83t BCL/J. & D. Bartlett. 83b Ardea/P. Morris. 84 OI Ltd. 85t & b Dr J. Cohen. 85c OI Ltd. 86tl OSF/G.I. Bernard. 86–87 Mick Saunders. 88 NHPA/B. Hawkes. 89 SAL/J. Foott. 90t Swift Picture Library/M. Read. 90b Simon Driver. 90–91 Richard Lewington. 92–93 PEP/P. Scoones. 94 AN. 94–95 Denys Ovenden. 97 P. 98–99 OSF/M. Fogden. 100c Priscilla Barrett. 100b, 101 Denys Ovenden. 102t Priscilla Barrett. 102b Simon Driver. 103 PEP/J. Scott. 104 NHPA/A. Bannister. 104–105 Jacana. 106 Priscilla Barrett. 107t PEP. 107b PEP/K. Lucas. 108 Ian Willis. 109t, c Simon Driver. 109b NHPA/A. Bannister. 109 inset J.C. Dickens. 110 PEP/E. Neal. 110–111 Priscilla Barrett. 112t G. Frame. 112b Robert Gillmor. 113b Premaphotos Wildlife/K. G. Preston-Mafham. 114 BCL. 115t N. Bonner. 115b Priscilla Barrett. 116–117 Nature Photographers. 117 Dwight R. Kuhn. 118–119 Denys Ovenden. 120t BCL/Charlie Ott. 120b, 121 Robert Gillmor. 122 NHPA/Peter Johnson. 123 David Dennis. 124cl Simon Driver. 124bl Richard Lewington. 124br William Ervin. 125 Ardea. 126t PEP. 126b Robert Gillmor. 127 NHPA. 128 Ardea. 128–129, 130 Priscilla Barrett. 131 P. Veit. 1321 NHPA/S. Dalton. 132r Jacana. 133t PEP. 133b Priscilla Barrett. 134 PEP/P. Scoones. 134–135, 135t Priscilla Barrett. 135cr Frans Lanting. 136t SAL/J. van Gruisen. 136b Premaphotos Wildlife/K. Preston-Mafham. 137bl. OSF/D. Macdonald. 137r Priscilla Barrett. 138t J. Kaufmann. 138bl Priscilla Barrett. 138br Simon Driver. 139 Premaphotos Wildlife/K. Preston Mafham. 140 P. Hillyard. 141t BCL. 141b NHPA. 142–143 PEP/A. Mounter. 144 SAL/J. Root. 145cr Simon Driver. 145b SAL/J. Bennett. 146cr Simon Driver. 146b Ian Willis. 147t BCL/J. Foott. 147c Ian Willis. 147bl Simon Driver. 147br Biofotos/Heather Angel. 148 Susan Griggs/J. Blair. 149t Mick Loates. 149b, 150t Simon Driver. 150b NHPA/P. Johnson. 151t Hayward Art Group. 151b SAL/C. Buxton & A. Price. 152–153 Denys Ovenden. 153 F.E. Beaton. 154 Hayward Art Group. 155 Andrew Laurie. 156tr Hayward Art Group. 156b Wayne Ford. 157 George Frame. 158 PEP/R. Salm. 159 Hayward Art Group. 160t Biofotos/S. Summerhays. 160b Hayward Art Group. 161 Michael Fogden. 162 Graham Allen. 163 Auscape International/G. Threlfo. 164b Hayward Art Group. 164–165 Denys Ovenden. 165 Ardea. 166 Hayward Art Group. 166–167 Ardea/ 167t OSF. 167b P. 168bl David Hosking. 168br Jacana/F. Winner. 169t BCL/A.J. Deane. 169b Ardea/F. Gohier. 170t J. Kaufmann. 170b Hayward Art Group. 1711 Aquila. 171r Ardea/S. Roberts. 172–173 Denys Ovenden. 174t OSF. 174b Hayward Art Group. 175 Denys Ovenden. 177 ANT/T. and P. Gardner. 178t PEP/Sean Avery. 178b Hayward Art Group. 179tl Natural Science Photos/Dick Brown. 179tr Agence Nature. 179b BL. 1801 NHPA/S. Dalton. 180–181 Denys Ovenden. 181t OSF. 182 C.A. Henley. 184t Jacana/Arthus-Bertrand. 184b Hayward Art Group. 185t OSF/Kathy Tyrrell. 185b SAL/Alan Root. 186 Michael Fogden. 1871 Denys Ovenden. 187r P/K. Preston-Mafham. 188t SAL/Jeff Foott. 189t BL. 189b, 190–191 W. Ervin, Natural Imagery. 192t NHPA/S. Kraseman. 192b Priscilla Barrett. 193t Hayward Art Group. 193b Jacana. 194 OSF/M. Carlisle. 195t Fred Bruemmer. 195b Jacana. 196b Hayward Art Group. 196–197 Hayward Art Group. 198t Frank Lane Picture Agency/Silvestris. 198 BCL/R. Peterson. 199 NHPA/S. Kraseman. 200tr SAL. 200bl NHPA/M. 200br OSF/J.A.L. Cooke. 201 PEP/N. Downer. 202 Sirenia Project, DWRC Florida. 203 Biofotos/Heather Angel. 204–205 Denys Ovenden. 205 BCL. 206t NHPA/M. Walker. 206b Biofotos/H. Angel. 206–207 Mick Saunders. 207b PEP/K. Cullimore. 208t Biofotos/H. Angel. 208–209 A. Bannister. 209 Frank Lane Picture Agency/Fritz Polking. 210–211 Denys Ovenden. 212 G.R. Roberts. 212–213 Swift Picture Library/Mike Read. 213 Ardea. 214–215 Mick Loates. 216–217 Roger Gorringe. 218t E. & D. Hosking/D.P. Wilson. 218 A. Bannister. 218–219 Mick Saunders. 219 Biofotos/H. Angel. 220t NHPA/P. Johnson. 220b OSF/F. Ehrenstrom. 221 PEP/Bill Wood. 222t PEP/Marty Snyderman. 222b BCL/A. Power. 223 Mick Loates. 224 Priscilla Barrett. 225t OI Ltd. 225b Ardea/F. Gohier. 226 Zefa/E. Christian. 227t ANT/Tony Howard.227bl FL/F. Polking. 227br Priscilla Barrett. 228 ANT/M.F. Soper. 228–229 BCL. 230t A. Bannister. 230–231 Denys Ovenden. 232 D.W. Macdonald. 232–233 NHPA/M. Leach. 233 OSF. 234–235 Denys Ovenden. 235 FL/A.R. Hamblin